G000254993

CHURCH
HYMNAL

CHURCH HYMNAL

FIFTH EDITION

Melody Edition

Christ Church
Parish Of Primacy
Bangor

OXFORD
UNIVERSITY PRESS

OXFORD
UNIVERSITY PRESS

Great Clarendon Street, Oxford OX2 6DP, England

Oxford University Press is a department of the University of Oxford.
It furthers the University's objective of excellence in research, scholarship,
and education by publishing worldwide in

Oxford New York

Athens Auckland Bangkok Bogotá Buenos Aires Calcutta
Cape Town Chennai Dar es Salaam Delhi Florence Hong Kong Istanbul
Karachi Kuala Lumpur Madrid Melbourne Mexico City Mumbai
Nairobi Paris São Paulo Shanghai Singapore Taipei Tokyo Toronto Warsaw

and associated companies in Berlin Ibadan

Oxford is a registered trade mark of Oxford University Press
in the UK and in certain other countries

First published 2000

3 5 7 9 10 8 6 4 2

ISBN 0-19-147835-0

Music and text origination by
Barnes Music Engraving Ltd., East Sussex
Printed in Great Britain on acid-free paper by
Clays Ltd., St Ives PLC
Bungay, Suffolk

A music edition is also available

CONTENTS

CONTENTS

B. THE LIFE OF FAITH

C. LITURGICAL MATERIAL

GENERAL PREFACE

HISTORICAL BACKGROUND

Hymn singing has occupied a treasured position in the worship of the Church of Ireland since the first collection 'Hymns for Public Worship' was published in 1856. This book, containing only 180 hymns, had such a wide circulation that there was soon a demand, especially from the clergy, for an extra 100 hymns to be added. As a result, an enlarged book with 280 hymns was published as the first official hymnbook of the Church of Ireland and was given the title *Church Hymnal*, a title that has been retained with every subsequent revision.

Only nine years later, in 1873, the then recently constituted General Synod of the Church of Ireland authorized a second edition of the *Church Hymnal* which was almost twice the size of its predecessor. Some more hymns were added in the form of an appendix in 1891. This enlarged collection, containing 642 hymns in all, remained in use until a third edition of the *Church Hymnal*, containing words only, made its appearance in 1915, the full music version following four years later under the joint editorship of Dr C. H. Kitson and Dr C. G. Marchant. This edition contained 721 hymns, along with 14 Christmas carols in a special section at the back of the book.

Once again, a small appendix was added in the mid-1930s. Following the years of World War Two, with costs of printing and publishing rapidly increasing, the Association for Promoting Christian Knowledge requested the General Synod to consider the possibility of reducing substantially the number of hymns being used in the worship of the Church of Ireland. Although this request was initially given favourable consideration, there were also requests for a limited number of new hymns to be added. The outcome of these somewhat conflicting proposals was the setting up of a committee at the 1952 General Synod to make a further revision of the *Church Hymnal*.

After a lengthy period of preparation, the fourth edition of the *Church Hymnal*, comprising 688 hymns and 31 Christmas carols was published in 1960, the music editor being Dr George H. P. Hewson. An admirable compilation of the best in classical hymnody, it has enriched worship throughout the Church of Ireland over the subsequent period of 40 years. However, its appearance was soon to be followed by what is commonly termed the 'hymn explosion', which saw a rapid growth in new, challenging texts, an ever-increasing diversity of musical styles and a steady stream of new hymnals and worship songbooks, large and small. In preparation for a further revision, therefore, a supplement of over 140 hymns and songs, entitled *Irish Church Praise*, was launched in 1990, to be used in conjunction with the *Church Hymnal* and to meet a growing demand for the use of modern hymns and songs in the Church's worship. Bishop Edward Darling acted as General Editor of this collection, with Dr Anthony Carver and Dr Donald Davison as Music Editors.

While *Irish Church Praise* was widely adopted, its publication was intended only as an interim measure. Indeed, it was only four years later at the 1994 General Synod, held in Cork, that the following Resolution was passed:

> That a Hymnal Revision Committee be established to undertake a revision of the Irish *Church Hymnal* and that the following be elected members of the Hymnal Revision Committee:

Representing the Hymnbook Advisory Committee

Mrs Alison J. Cadden	Canon D. Paul Hoey
Dr W. Donald Davison	Miss Valerie Ireland
Mr David Drinkell	Archdeacon Gordon C. S. Linney*
Mr Mark Duley*	Mrs Nicola Lynas*
The Revd Thomas S. Gordon*	Ms Hilary Pyle*
The Revd Gary L. Hastings	The Revd William J. Stewart*

Representing the Liturgical Advisory Committee

Dr Anthony F. Carver	Bishop Edward F. Darling
Canon Harold C. Miller (*later Bishop of Down & Dromore*)	

Representing the Association for Promoting Christian Knowledge

Canon Michael A. J. Burrows	Dr Kenneth W. Milne
Mr Frederick J. Rankin*	(*co-opted during the project*)
The Revd John W. McKegney	

Representing the General Synod Standing Committee

Dr Edith Newman-Devlin	Mr Martin J. White

(* *denotes those who resigned during the course of revision*)

Mr Cedric Heather, from the staff of Church of Ireland House, was appointed to act as Secretary to the Committee. At a later stage he handed over his task to Miss June Howard, also from the staff of Church of Ireland House.

The Hymnal Revision Committee at its first meeting appointed Bishop Edward Darling to be Chairman of the Committee and to act as General Editor of the proposed hymnal, and Dr Donald Davison, FRCO, to be the Music Editor.

Right from the beginning it became clear that the task facing the Revision Committee, in preparing the fifth edition of the *Church Hymnal*, was going to be much more complex than anything previously undertaken. The vast changes that have taken place in the Christian Church all round the world since 1960 have set a very different and challenging agenda: new forms of worship, new English translations of the Bible, new revised lectionaries, new styles of language, new fashions in music, new emphases in theological interpretation, and a new awareness of, and sensitivity to, the ways that the use of language can either exclude or include. A growth in ecumenical co-operation and the far-reaching influence of the charismatic movement have also had a bearing on the way the revisers would view their appointed task. Signs of a new reformation have become, and are becoming, very apparent throughout the Christian Church; one such sign, presenting perhaps the biggest challenge to the Committee, is the vast number of new hymns and songs that have been written since 1960, many of which have gained widespread popularity throughout the English-speaking world.

The first step taken by the Committee was to contact all the parishes in the Church of Ireland to find out which hymns from the *Church Hymnal* and *Irish Church Praise* were in regular use, which hymns should be deleted, and which new hymns should be included in the revised hymnal. A clear response to 'What do you sing and what do you want to sing?' would certainly be of great value to the Committee as it commenced its work of revision.

We were encouraged by the fact that well over half the parishes of the Church of Ireland responded readily to our questionnaires. All the information received was fed into a computer database, and subsequent analysis yielded much valuable information on the usage of existing hymns and on the relative popularity of new hymns which might be included.

Guided by this extensive survey, we have retained practically all of the great classical hymns which have influenced worshippers down through the years and which are still loved and cherished.

Selecting new hymns, on the other hand, has proved a more difficult task in that we cannot yet be certain which ones will stand the test of time. Nevertheless, we were convinced that a new hymnal must contain a wide-ranging selection of old and new hymns and songs that are compatible when used together in any act of worship. Jesus himself taught us that our involvement in the kingdom of heaven implies our ability to be able to treasure things new and old.

PROBLEMS OF LANGUAGE

As theological understanding, styles of worship and the meaning of language itself have changed over the years, hymnbook compilers have often felt it necessary to alter the wording of certain hymns in order to make them relevant and more meaningful to the average worshipper.

There have been several problem words and phrases which we have debated at length and which have caused us considerable agonising. We cannot claim to have been entirely consistent in the changes we have made: in some cases we found that the original wording could readily be changed, whereas in other cases we were unable to produce something better without marring the poetic quality of the text, and so we allowed the original wording to stand.

There are certain hymns with words and phrases that are rarely understood by those who sing them. We could so easily, for instance, have deleted such phrases as

> 'consubstantial, co-eternal,
> while unending ages run'

and substituted a simpler alternative. We were reluctant, however, to lose that majestic grandeur of language that can still so enrich our worship of God. Often, therefore, we have opted for the retention of such words but have tried to ensure that they are understood by inserting a footnote to indicate their meaning. A 'difficult' hymn, annotated in this way, can be informative and educational and ceases to be regarded as spiritual mumbo-jumbo.

While there is a growing recognition amongst regular worshippers that the language of some of the older hymns should be updated, we deliberately did not adopt a policy of uniformly converting all occurrences of 'thee' and 'thou' to 'you'. Indeed, there are parts of Britain and Ireland today where 'thee', and even 'ye', are still widely used in everyday parlance. Some hymns, of course, can be so modernized without the change of words jarring on the ears of the worshipper. 'Thy kingdom come, O God', for example, can easily be altered to 'Your kingdom come, O God' without any ill effects.

There are some, of course, who believe that one does not have the right to alter a hymn from its original wording; but there are ample precedents for making certain changes, and whenever the Committee has in conscience felt that altering a word or phrase improves a hymn, we make no apology for doing so.

The committee also spent much time ensuring that the language of hymns and songs was as gender-inclusive as possible. Thus, we have avoided, in most cases, the use of such words as 'man', 'sons', 'brothers', etc. whenever the reference is clearly intended to include both male and female persons. We also preferred the use of 'humankind' to 'mankind'. Sometimes, however, poetic style and meaning can be damaged when, with a view to being inclusive, the wording is changed, and, in the few cases where this might have been the case (e.g. 'Dear Lord and Father of mankind'), we have decided that no alterations should be made.

The committee was firmly convinced that we should not remove all gender-specific words when the reference is to God. We felt strongly that we should uphold the historical and theological truth that Jesus Christ came into this world as a man, that God spoke of him 'Thou art my Son', and that he himself frequently referred to God as his father.

The term 'inclusive language' does not only refer to gender. Language can be exclusively damaging if it conveys a racial, ethnic or cultural bias. In this respect, we were concerned that the second verse of the hymn 'Lo! he comes with clouds descending' could nowadays be interpreted as being anti-Semitic and we have altered the wording accordingly.

The committee also spent some time considering how inclusive is the use of militaristic language in certain hymns. Some people are gravely unhappy singing hymns which make mention of armour, battle or warfare. On the other hand, we were conscious that there are those for whom the rousing rendering of 'Onward, Christian soldiers' can be spiritually uplifting and that the battle referred to in such a hymn is entirely compatible with scripture, for, both as individuals and as a Church, we are called to combat sinfulness and evil in this world. Therefore, the committee has retained some of these well-loved hymns, but would express the strong hope that worshippers do not sing them in a spirit of triumphalism, but rather in the knowledge that it is the love of God that conquers all. The triumph of the Christian must be the triumph of the love that 'is not envious or boastful or arrogant or rude' (1 Corinthians 13: 4).

CAROLS

A feature which was common to the past two editions of the Church Hymnal was a special Christmas Carols section at the end of the book. The Committee decided, however, that it would be more appropriate if all Christmas hymns and carols appeared in the one section of the book which focuses on our Lord's Incarnation. Conscious of the many collections of carols that are nowadays published for use with choirs, we have, therefore, removed the separate Christmas Carols section from this edition of the Church Hymnal.

INDEXES

The Committee has provided a number of indexes at the back of the book to help those who plan the worship in our churches to select hymns and songs with both creativity and sensitivity. Among these indexes is a list of topics and subjects which suggest appropriate hymns for different occasions. There is also an index showing hymns that are based on specific biblical passages. This makes it possible for hymns to be chosen at appropriate points in the liturgy to complement the readings of the lectionary that is used.

CHILDREN'S HYMNS

The Committee felt strongly that children should be regarded as full members of the worshipping community, and that there should not, therefore, be a special section in the book entitled 'For Children'. There is a danger that placing certain hymns under such a heading might imply that they are inappropriate for adults or that other hymns are inappropriate for children. There is, however, a suggested list of suitable children's hymns in the index of subjects and topics, and planners of worship might well give serious consideration to regular inclusion of such hymns with congregations where children are active participants.

IRISH HYMNS

When the proposed contents of *Irish Church Praise* were presented to the General Synod for approval in 1989, there was an overwhelming request that the book should include some hymns written in the Irish language. Accordingly, four Irish hymns with English singing translations were added prior to its publication. With this in mind, the Committee has increased the number of Irish hymns in this book and, once again, so that no congregation may feel excluded from using them through unfamiliarity with the language, new English singing translations have been provided. We believe that this adds an inclusivity to the *Church Hymnal* which did not exist in previous editions.

In producing this fifth edition of the *Church Hymnal*, it has been the aim of the Committee to provide a greater range of different styles and sources than were to be found in the 1960 edition—old evangelistic mission hymns used afresh, Taizé chants, Iona worship-songs, charismatic choruses, Irish hymns (with English singing translations), canticle substitutes and other liturgical material, etc. In this respect, the book is certainly 'inclusive' in an even wider sense of the word. The Committee has also taken more risks than previous hymnbook compilers—some of our choices may not 'come off'—but is this not appropriate as we learn afresh to be a pilgrim Church? It is our belief that this selection of material for worship does not imply any departure from the official doctrinal position of the Church of Ireland, but rather reflects the widely-expressed desire for greater diversity of worship: this is a book which is so much more flexible and wide-ranging than any that has gone before it. We have been anxious to provide a collection of hymns which will be a treasured resource book for years to come and which expresses the faith of the Church, with words and images of our time, in 'Jesus Christ, the same yesterday, and today, and for ever' (*Hebrews 13: 8*).

✠ EDWARD F. DARLING

MUSICAL PREFACE*

Hymns are for congregations to sing with enjoyment, understanding, and spiritual profit, in the praise and worship of
Almighty God. Hence the primary objective throughout the
lengthy process of compiling the music in this hymnal has been to
promote the wholehearted participation of the people. The fact
that for the first time congregations in our churches will have the
melody before them should be enormously helpful—even, we
believe, to those who have little or no experience of reading musical notation.

NOTATION

It has seemed desirable that the presentation of the music should
conform closely to the usual conventions in other areas of musical
activity. Thus, for example, time signatures have been included at
the start of most tunes: in tunes where the bar length is not uni-
form, double time signatures have usually been employed, for the
sake of simplicity. Again, in common with most recent hymnals,
the fundamental time unit has been taken (with a few exceptions)
as the crotchet and the dotted crotchet in tunes with simple and
compound time signatures respectively.

Commas above the stave, along with occasional light double
bars, are used to indicate the ends of phrases (coinciding with the
ends of lines of text). It is important to emphasise that in this con-
text the comma is not equivalent to a breath mark. Certainly, at a
point where a comma occurs, a breath is *usually* taken, but this is
not invariably the case: in particular, it is desirable to sing on
without any break into the next phrase when there is a run-on
indication at the end of a line of text.

RETURNING TO SOURCES

Many recent hymnals have, quite properly, paid greater attention
to the original versions of older tunes. This has also been done in
the present book, with the result that quite a number of tunes

---

* This is a considerably reduced version of the Musical Preface in the
full Music Edition.

appearing in the previous edition have been modified to some degree. However, our approach has been pragmatic rather than dogmatic: in some cases, later changes have become so familiar and accepted that a return to an earlier version was judged not to be of practical benefit.

RHYTHM: 'SMALL NOTE' NOTATION

The rhythm of many older tunes (especially those of, or derived from, the Genevan tradition) presents a particular challenge to editors. The original rhythmic variety of such tunes has in many cases been 'ironed out' over the years, generally to their detriment: reversion to the original rhythm usually enhances their effect today. The approach taken here is to print what is judged to be the most effective version, but in addition to place small notes above the stave to indicate an alternative rhythm (usually a later, perhaps more familiar, version).

In a number of hymns we have recognised existing divergences of practice and have been anxious to accommodate these differences in the music: we have indicated rhythmic and melodic variants by means of small notes above the stave and music footnotes respectively.

PITCH

Many of the tunes that were included in the previous edition are here given in a lower key. The best key for a given tune depends on many factors, but there is a general consensus that many tunes were previously pitched too high for the average congregation. With one exception (no. 420), no tune in this book goes above E and the great majority do not go above D: those tunes which have E or E flat (D sharp) as their highest note are generally those where the text demands adequate brightness and power, or where the tune is of unusually wide range (as is the case, for example, with many Irish traditional melodies).

ACKNOWLEDGEMENTS

Throughout the lengthy process of selecting tunes and arriving at a final version of each tune, a number of experienced church musicians have been actively and continuously involved. They are

Members of the Music Sub-Committee

Mrs Alison Cadden
Dr Anthony Carver
Mr David Drinkell
Mr Martin White

Music Consultants

Mr David Bedlow
Dr Harry Grindle

All have given a great amount of advice and help, without which this book would have been immeasurably the poorer.

May the music to be found herein resound to the glory of God and serve to build up the Church through the singing of 'psalms, hymns and spiritual songs'.

DONALD DAVISON

EXPLANATORY NOTES

SIGNS

The sign * placed before the number of a verse indicates that the verse can be omitted, if so desired, without injury to the sense of the hymn.

The sign ‿ is placed at the end of a line when the sense of the words suggests that the next line should follow without a break, if practicable. This sign is intended chiefly for the use of choirs.

The sign ‿ when *not* at the end of a line indicates an elision between two words (e.g. the‿eternal) which must be observed if the words are to fit the tune correctly.

ABBREVIATIONS

adpt. = adapted
altd. = altered
attrib. = attributed
b. = born
c. = *circa*
cent. = century
tr. = translated
v(v). = verse(s)

MISCELLANEOUS

Refrains are shown in *italics*.

The word 'blessed' is normally pronounced as one syllable—viz. 'blest': it is pronounced as a two-syllable word only when printed as 'blessèd'.

THE LOVE OF GOD

1

Bless the Lord, my soul

Jacques Berthier (1923–94)
for the Taizé Community

Bless the Lord, my soul, and bless God's ho - ly name.

Bless the Lord, my soul, who leads me in - to life.

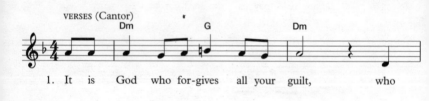

1. It is God who for-gives all your guilt, who

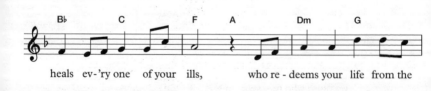

heals ev-'ry one of your ills, who re - deems your life from the

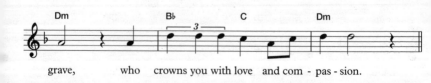

grave, who crowns you with love and com - pas - sion.

The verses are sung by a cantor over the repeated refrain 'Bless the Lord, my soul'.

THE FATHERHOOD OF GOD

2. The Lord is com-pas-sion and love, the Lord is pa-tient and rich in mer-cy. God does not treat us ac-cord-ing to our sins nor re-pay us ac-cord-ing to our faults.

3. As a fa-ther has com-pas-sion on his child-ren, the Lord has mer-cy on those who re-vere him;— for he knows of what we are made, he re-mem-bers that we are dust.

Psalm 103: vv. 1–4, 8, 10, 13–14

3

2

Faithful one

Words and music by Brian Doerksen

Faith - ful one, so un -

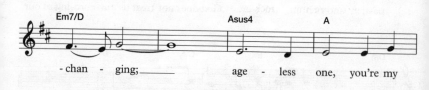

- chan - ging;_____ age - less one, you're my

rock_____ of_____ peace. Lord of all, I de -

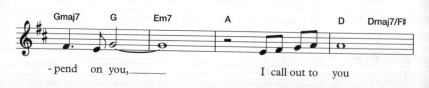

- pend on you,_____ I call out to you

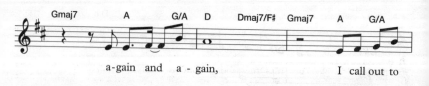

a-gain and a - gain, I call out to

THE FATHERHOOD OF GOD

you   a - gain and a - gain.___

You are my   rock___   in   times___   of   trou - ble,___

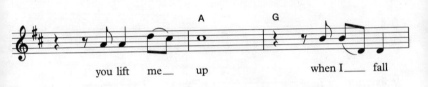

you lift   me___   up   when I___ fall

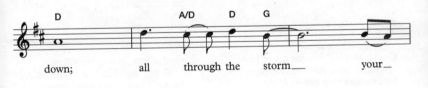

down;   all   through the   storm___   your___

love   is   the___ an -   chor—   my___

hope   is   in___   you___   a - lone.

5

3

Abbot's Leigh   87 87 D

Cyril V. Taylor (1907–91)

1 God is love: let heaven adore him;
    God is love: let earth rejoice;
  let creation sing before him,
    and exalt him with one voice.
  He who laid the earth's foundation,
    he who spread the heavens above,
  he who breathes through all creation,
    he is love, eternal love.

2 God is love, and is enfolding
    all the world in one embrace;
  his unfailing grasp is holding
    every child of every race;
  and when human hearts are breaking
    under sorrow's iron rod,
  then they find that self-same aching
    deep within the heart of God.

3 God is love: and though with blindness
    sin afflicts and clouds the will,
  God's eternal loving-kindness
    holds us fast and guides us still.
  Sin and death and hell shall never
    o'er us final triumph gain;
  God is love, so love for ever
    o'er the universe must reign.

Timothy Rees (1874–1939) altd.
based on 1 John 4: 8

THE FATHERHOOD OF GOD

4

FIRST TUNE

Beechwood   56 64   Josiah Booth (1852–1929)

SECOND TUNE

Sommerlied   56 64   Hermann von Müller [Carey Bonner] (1859–1938)

1 God, who made the earth,
    the air, the sky, the sea,
who gave the light its birth,
    still cares for me.

2 God, who made the grass,
    the flower, the fruit, the tree,
the day and night to pass,
    still cares for me.

3 God, who made the sun,
    the moon, the stars, is he ‿
who, when life's clouds come on,
    still cares for me.

Sarah B. Rhodes (1830–90) altd.

5

Butterfly song

Brian Howard

| D | | | | | | | G | | |

1. If I were a but-ter-fly,— I'd thank you, Lord, for

| D |

giv - ing me wings. And if I were a

ro - bin in a tree, I'd thank you, Lord, that

| A7 | | D |

I could sing. And if I were a fish in the sea,— I'd

| G |

wig - gle my tail— and I'd gig - gle with— glee, but

| A | | | | | | D | G |

I just thank you, Fa-ther, for mak-ing me 'me'._____

| D |

— *For you gave me a heart and you gave me a smile. You*

THE FATHERHOOD OF GOD

gave me Je-sus and you made me your child. And
I just thank you, Fa-ther, for mak-ing me 'me'.

1 If I were a butterfly,
   I'd thank you, Lord, for giving me wings.
   And if I were a robin in a tree,
   I'd thank you, Lord, that I could sing.
   And if I were a fish in the sea,
   I'd wiggle my tail and I'd giggle with glee,
   but I just thank you, Father, for making me 'me'.

   For you gave me a heart
   and you gave me a smile.
   You gave me Jesus
   and you made me your child.
   And I just thank you, Father, for making me 'me'.

2 If I were an elephant,
   I'd thank you, Lord, by raising my trunk.
   And if I were a kangaroo,
   you know I'd hop right up to you.
   And if I were an octopus,
   I'd thank you, Lord, for my fine looks,
   but I just thank you, Father, for making me 'me'.

3 If I were a wiggly worm,
   I'd thank you, Lord, that I could squirm.
   And if I were a crocodile,
   I'd thank you, Lord, for my big smile.
   And if I were a fuzzy-wuzzy bear,
   I'd thank you, Lord, for my fuzzy-wuzzy hair,
   but I just thank you, Father, for making me 'me'.

Brian Howard

6

St Denio   11 11 11 11

Welsh hymn melody (1839)
founded on a folk tune

1 Immortal, invisible, God only wise,
  in light inaccessible hid from our eyes,
      most blessèd, most glorious, the Ancient of Days,
      almighty, victorious, thy great name we praise.

2 Unresting, unhasting, and silent as light,
  nor wanting, nor wasting, thou rulest in might;
      thy justice, like mountains high soaring above
      thy clouds, which are fountains of goodness and love.

3 To all, life thou givest, to both great and small;
  in all life thou livest, the true life of all;
      we blossom and flourish as leaves on the tree,
      and wither and perish; but nought changeth thee.

4 Great Father of glory, pure Father of light,
  thine angels adore thee, all veiling their sight;
      all laud we would render: O help us to see
      'tis only the splendour of light hideth thee.

W. Chalmers Smith (1824–1908)
based on 1 Timothy 1: 17; Psalm 36: 6

THE FATHERHOOD OF GOD

7

Westminster   86 86 (CM)   James Turle (1802–82)

1 My God, how wonderful thou art,
    thy majesty how bright,
  how beautiful thy mercy-seat,
    in depths of burning light!

2 How wonderful, how beautiful,
    the sight of thee must be,
  thine endless wisdom, boundless power,
    and aweful[1] purity!

3 O how I fear thee, living God,
    with deepest, tenderest fears,
  and worship thee with trembling hope,
    and penitential tears!

4 Yet I may love thee too, O Lord,
    almighty as thou art,
  for thou hast stooped to ask of me
    the love of my poor heart.

5 No earthly father loves like thee;
    no mother half so mild
  bears and forbears as thou hast done
    with me, thy sinful child.

6 Father of Jesus, love's reward,
    what rapture will it be
  to fall and worship at thy throne
    and gaze and gaze on thee.

Frederick W. Faber (1814–63) altd.

[1] aweful = inspiring awe

8

Church triumphant   88 88 (LM)   James William Elliott (1833–1915)

1 The Lord is king! Lift up your voice,
O earth, and all you heavens, rejoice;
  from world to world the song shall ring:
  'The Lord omnipotent is king!'

2 The Lord is king! Who then shall dare
resist his will, distrust his care,
  or murmur at his wise decrees,
  or doubt his royal promises?

3 The Lord is king! Child of the dust,
the judge of all the earth is just;
  holy and true are all his ways –
  let every creature sing his praise!

4 God reigns! He reigns with glory crowned:
let Christians make a joyful sound!
  And Christ is seated at his side:
  the Man of love, the crucified.

*5 Come, make your needs, your burdens known:
he will present them at the throne;
  and angel hosts are waiting there
  his messages of love to bear.

6 One Lord one kingdom all secures:
he reigns, and life and death are yours;
  through earth and heav'n one song shall ring:
  'The Lord omnipotent is king!'

Josiah Conder (1789–1855) altd.
based on Psalm 97

THE FATHERHOOD OF GOD

9

Cross of Jesus 87 87

John Stainer (1840–1901)
from *The Crucifixion*

Amplitudo 87 87

Donald Davison (b. 1937)

Alternative tune: 320 HALTON HOLGATE

1 There's a wideness in God's mercy
   like the wideness of the sea;
   there's a kindness in his justice
   which is more than liberty.

2 There is no place where earth's sorrows
   are more keenly felt than heaven;
   there is no place where earth's failings
   have such gracious judgement given.

3 There is plentiful redemption
   through the blood that Christ
      has shed;
   there is joy for all the members
   in the sorrows of the Head.

4 For the love of God is broader
   than the measure of our mind,
   and the heart of the Eternal
   is most wonderfully kind.

5 But we make his love too narrow
   by false limits of our own;
   and we magnify his strictness
   with a zeal he will not own.

6 If our love were but more simple,
   we should take him at his word,
   and our lives would fill with gladness
   in the presence of the Lord.

Frederick W. Faber (1814–63) altd.

GOD THE FATHER, CREATOR

10

FIRST TUNE

Michael   87 87 337

Herbert Howells (1892–1983)

SECOND TUNE

Groeswen   87 87 337

John Ambrose Lloyd (1815–74)

Meine Hoffnung stehet feste

1 All my hope on God is founded;
      he doth still my trust renew.
   Me through change and chance he guideth,
      only good and only true.
            God unknown,
            he alone ⌣
            calls my heart to be his own.

2 Human pride and earthly glory,
      sword and crown betray our trust;
   what with care and toil is builded,
      tower and temple, fall to dust.
            But God's power
            hour by hour
            is my temple and my tower.

3 God's great goodness aye endureth,
      deep his wisdom, passing thought;
   splendour, light and life attend him,
      beauty springeth out of naught.
            Evermore
            from his store
            new-born worlds rise and adore.

4 Daily doth the ⌣ almighty giver
      bounteous gifts on us bestow;
   his desire our soul delighteth,
      pleasure leads us where we go.
            Love doth stand ⌣
            at his hand;
            joy doth wait on his command.

5 Still from earth to God eternal
      sacrifice of praise be done,
   high above all praises praising
      for the gift of Christ his Son.
            Christ doth call ⌣
            one and all;
            ye who follow shall not fall.

Robert Bridges (1844–1930) altd.
based on *Joachim Neander* (1650–80)

11

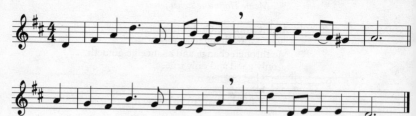

FIRST TUNE

Epworth   86 86 (CM)

Adpt. from a melody by
Charles Wesley the younger (1757–1834)

SECOND TUNE

Haresfield   86 86 (CM)

John Dykes Bower (1905–81)

1 Can we by searching find out God
    or formulate his ways?
  Can numbers measure what he is
    or words contain his praise?

2 Although his being is too bright
    for human eyes to scan,
  his meaning lights our shadowed world
    through Christ, the Son of Man.

3 Our boastfulness is turned to shame,
    our profit counts as loss,
  when earthly values stand beside
    the manger and the cross.

4 We there may recognise his light,
    may kindle in its rays,
  find there the source of penitence,
    the starting-point for praise.

5 There God breaks in upon our search,
    makes birth and death his own:
  he speaks to us in human terms
    to make his glory known.

Elizabeth Cosnett (b. 1936)
based on Job 11: 7

12

Dambusters' March 77 75 77 11

Eric Coates (1886–1958)

1 God is our strength and refuge,
  our present help in trouble;
  and we therefore will not fear,
  though the earth should change!
  Though mountains shake and tremble,
  though swirling floods are raging,
  God the Lord of hosts is with us evermore!

2 There is a flowing river,
  within God's holy city;
  God is in the midst of her—
  she shall not be moved!
  God's help is swiftly given,
  thrones vanish at his presence—
  God the Lord of hosts is with us evermore!

3 Come, see the works of our maker,
  learn of his deeds all-powerful;
  wars will cease across the world
  when he shatters the spear!
  Be still and know your creator,
  uplift him in the nations—
  God the Lord of hosts is with us evermore!

Richard Bewes (b. 1934)
based on Psalm 46

13

London New   86 86 (CM)

Melody from the *Scottish Psalter* (Edinburgh, 1635)
adpt. in Playford's *Psalmes* (London, 1671)

For an explanation of the small notes above the stave, see the Musical Preface.

1 God moves in a mysterious way
    his wonders to perform;
he plants his footsteps in the sea,
    and rides upon the storm.

2 Deep in unfathomable mines
    of never-failing skill
he treasures up his bright designs,
    and works his sovereign will.

3 Ye fearful saints, fresh courage take;
    the clouds ye so much dread
are big with mercy, and shall break
    in blessings on your head.

4 Judge not the Lord by feeble sense,
    but trust him for his grace;
behind a frowning providence
    he hides a smiling face.

5 His purposes will ripen fast,
    unfolding every hour;
the bud may have a bitter taste,
    but sweet will be the flower.

6 Blind unbelief is sure to err,
    and scan his work in vain;
God is his own interpreter,
    and he will make it plain.

William Cowper (1731–1800)

14

Davos 98 457

Michael Baughen (b. 1930)
and Elizabeth Crocker

1 I lift my eyes to the quiet hills
  in the press of a busy day;
      as green hills stand
      in a dusty land
  so God is my strength and stay.

2 I lift my eyes to the quiet hills
  to a calm that is mine to share;
      secure and still
      in the Father's will
  and kept by the Father's care.

3 I lift my eyes to the quiet hills
  with a prayer as I turn to sleep;
      by day, by night,
      through the dark and light
  my Shepherd will guard his sheep.

4 I lift my eyes to the quiet hills
  and my heart to the Father's throne;
      in all my ways
      to the end of days
  the Lord will preserve his own.

Timothy Dudley-Smith (b. 1926)
based on Psalm 121

GOD THE FATHER, CREATOR

15

FIRST TUNE

Neumark   98 98 88

Georg Neumark (1621–81)

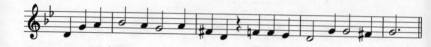

SECOND TUNE

Guidance   98 98 88

Donald Davison (b. 1937)

Wer nur den lieben Gott lässt walten

1 If thou but suffer God to guide thee,
      and hope in him through all thy ways,
  he'll give thee strength whate'er betide thee,
      and bear thee through the evil days;
  who trusts in God's unchanging love
  builds on the rock that nought can move.

*2 What can these anxious cares avail thee,
      these never-ceasing moans and sighs?
  What can it help, if thou bewail thee
      o'er each dark moment as it flies?
  Our cross and trials do but press ⌣
  the heavier for our bitterness.

3 Only be still, and wait his leisure
      in cheerful hope, with heart content ⌣
  to take whate'er thy Father's pleasure,
      his all-discerning love, hath sent;
  nor doubt our inmost wants are known
  to him who chose us for his own.

4 Sing, pray, and keep his ways unswerving;
      so do thine own part faithfully,
  and trust his word: though undeserving,
      thou yet shalt find it true for thee;
  God never yet forsook at need
  the soul that trusted him indeed.

Georg Neumark (1621–81)
tr. *Catherine Winkworth* (1827–78) altd.

16

Old Yeavering 88 87

Noël Tredinnick (b. 1949)

Alternative tune: 180 QUEM PASTORES

1 Like a mighty river flowing,
   like a flower in beauty growing,
   far beyond all human knowing
      is the perfect peace of God.

2 Like the hills serene and even,
   like the coursing clouds of heaven,
   like the heart that's been forgiven
      is the perfect peace of God.

3 Like the summer breezes playing,
   like the tall trees softly swaying,
   like the lips of silent praying
      is the perfect peace of God.

4 Like the morning sun ascended,
   like the scents of evening blended,
   like a friendship never ended
      is the perfect peace of God.

5 Like the azure ocean swelling,
   like the jewel all-excelling,
   far beyond our human telling
      is the perfect peace of God.

Michael Perry (1942–96)

17

Lead me, Lord

From an anthem by S. S. Wesley (1810–76)

Lead me, Lord, lead me in thy right-eous-ness,—
Treor - aigh   mé,   treor-aigh mé,   a   Thiar - na,   go

make thy way plain be - fore my__ face.   face.
siúl - ad ar bhó - thar fir - éan-tach-ta Dé.   Dé:

For it is thou, Lord,__ thou, Lord, on - ly, that
foil - sigh an tslí romham, óir nil__ ann, a Thiar - na, ach

mak - est me dwell in_____ safe - ty.   - ty.
tu - sa a - mháin a choim-eád-ann slán__ mé.   mé.

* Ornament optional, and second time only

This may be sung in two ways:
(i) without repeats, as a short congregational hymn;
(ii) with repeats, each half being first sung by a soloist (or by e.g. Choir Sopranos) and repeated by all.

Lead me, Lord, lead me in thy righteousness,
make thy way plain before my face.
For it is thou Lord, thou, Lord, only,
that makest me dwell in safety.

Psalm 5: 8 and 4: 8

Treoraigh mé, treoraigh mé, a Thiarna,
go siúlad ar bhóthar fíréantachta Dé:
foilsigh an tslí romham, óir níl ann, a Thiarna,
ach tusa amháin a choimeádann slán mé.

tr. *Eibhlín Nic Phairais*

18

Lord, I come before your throne

Words and music by
Robert and Dawn Critchley

1. Lord, I come be-fore your throne of grace; I find rest in your pre-sence, and full-ness of joy. In the wor - ship and won-der I be - hold your face, sing-ing what a faith - ful God have I.

2. Lord of mer-cy, you have heard my cry; through the storm you're the bea-con, my song in the night. In the shel-ter of your wings hear my heart's re - ply, sing-ing what a faith - ful God have I.

REFRAIN

What a faith - ful God have I, what a faith - ful God, what a faith - ful God have I,

GOD'S GUIDANCE AND GRACE

faith-ful_ in ev-'ry way.

3. Lord all sov-'reign, grant-ing peace from heav'n, let me com-fort those who suf-fer with the com-fort you have giv'n. I will tell of your great love for as long as I live, sing-ing what a faith-ful God have I.

REFRAIN

What a faith-ful God have I,_____ what a faith-ful__ __ God,___ what a faith-ful God have I, __

faith-ful_ in ev-'ry way.

GOD THE FATHER, CREATOR

19

Newbury   86 86 (CM)   English traditional melody

Alternative tunes: 372 WILTSHIRE   439i ALBANO

1 There is no moment of my life,
   no place where I may go,
no action which God does not see,
   no thought he does not know.

2 Before I speak, my words are known,
   and all that I decide.
To come or go: God knows my choice,
   and makes himself my guide.

3 If I should close my eyes to him,
   he comes to give me sight;
if I should go where all is dark,
   he makes my darkness light.

4 He knew my days before all days,
   before I came to be;
he keeps me, loves me, in my ways;
   no lover such as he.

Brian Foley (b. 1919)
based on Psalm 139

20

Dominus regit me   87 87   John Bacchus Dykes (1823–76)

St Columba (1)   87 87   Irish traditional melody

1 The King of love my shepherd is,
   whose goodness faileth never;
 I nothing lack if I am his,
   and he is mine for ever.

2 Where streams of living water flow
   my ransomed soul he leadeth,
 and where the verdant pastures grow
   with food celestial feedeth.

3 Perverse and foolish oft I strayed,
   but yet in love he sought me,
 and on his shoulder gently laid,
   and home, rejoicing, brought me.

4 In death's dark vale I fear no ill
   with thee, dear Lord, beside me;
 thy rod and staff my comfort still,
   thy cross before to guide me.

5 Thou spread'st a table in my sight,
   thy unction grace bestoweth,
 and O, what transport of delight
   from thy pure chalice floweth!

6 And so through all the length of days
   thy goodness faileth never;
 Good Shepherd, may I sing thy praise
   within thy house for ever.

Henry Williams Baker (1821–77)
metrical version of Psalm 23

27

21

FIRST TUNE

Melody ascribed to Jessie Seymour Irvine (1836–87)
but more probably by David Grant (1833–93)

Crimond   86 86 (CM)

SECOND TUNE

James Leith MacBeth Bain
(1840–1925)

Brother James' Air   86 86 (CM) extended

When this tune is used, the last two lines of each verse are repeated.

Alternative tune: 206 KILMARNOCK

1 The Lord's my shepherd, I'll not want,
    he makes me down to lie
in pastures green; he leadeth me
    the quiet waters by.

2 My soul he doth restore again
    and me to walk doth make
within the paths of righteousness,
    e'en for his own name's sake.

3 Yea, though I walk in death's dark vale,
    yet will I fear none ill;
for thou art with me, and thy rod
    and staff me comfort still.

4 My table thou hast furnishèd
    in presence of my foes;
my head thou dost with oil anoint,
    and my cup overflows.

5 Goodness and mercy all my life
    shall surely follow me;
and in God's house for evermore
    my dwelling-place shall be.

William Whittingham (1524–79) altd.
Old Scottish metrical version of Psalm 23

22

You shall cross the barren desert

Words and music by Bob Dufford
Words (altd.) based on Isaiah 43: 2–3;
Matthew 5: 3–4; Luke 6: 20–21

GOD'S GUIDANCE AND GRACE

2. If you pass through ra-ging wa - ters,____ you shall not be drowned. If you walk a-mid the burn-ing flames, you shall not be harmed. If you stand be-fore the pow'r of hell and death is at your side, *D.S. (Refrain)* know that I am with you___ through it all.____

3. Bless-ed are your poor, for the king-dom shall be theirs. Bless-ed are you that weep and mourn, for one day you shall laugh. And if wick-ed tongues in - sult and hate you *D.S. (Refrain)* all be-cause of me, bless-ed,___ bless-ed___ are you!____

31

23

Álainn farraige

Scots Gaelic traditional melody

1. Ál - ainn farr - ai - ge spéir - ghlas, ál - ainn uis - cea - cha ciúin',_
2. Tóg - fad suas_ mo chroí - se, tóg - fad suas_ mo ghlór,_

ál - ainn tait - neamh na gréin - e ar na tonn - ta tá fúinn;
mol - fad eis - ean a - choí - che fá gach ion - tas mór;

faoil - eáin 'g eit - eal 'sna spéar - tha, teas le héi - rí an lae;
ar - daigh feas - ta mo smaoin - te mar na sléibh - te san aer,

Ó! nach ál - ainn an saol!__ Ó! nach ál - ainn, a Dhé!
ciún - aigh feas - ta mo chroí - se mar an t-uisc - e soil - éir;

Siúd uait amh - arc na sléibh - te barr' á bhfol - ach fá cheo,_
éist lem ach(ai) - ní, a Thiar - na, tar is có - naigh im chléibh,

caoir - igh ciúin' ar a dtaobh - a, síth is son - as is só.
réit - igh m'an - am; 's im in - tinn déan - sa t'ár - as, a Dhé.

Douglas Hyde (An Craoibhín) (1860–1949)

GOD'S WORLD

1. Beau - ti - ful__ the green - blue sea and the qui - et wa - ters,
2. I will lift up my heart to God, I will lift up my voice,__

beau - ti - ful__ the shin - ing sun on the waves be - low;
I will praise him ev - er - more for his won - der - ful world;

sea - gulls fly - ing a - bove as warmth re - turns with the day;
* like the wa - ter clear my heart will now__ be calm,

O, how love - ly the world is! O, how love - ly, O God!
like the hills in the air my thoughts will now__ a - rise,

See the hills__ be - yond, their sum - mits cov - ered in mist, and
hear my prayer, O Lord, O come, with - in__ me dwell, pre -

qui - et sheep on their sides, O peace, con - tent - ment and joy!
- pare my soul,__ O God, and make your home in my mind.

tr. Anon.
adpt. Donald Davison (b. 1937)

* At this point the line order differs from that in the original.

33

24

Lasst uns erfreuen (Easter Song)
88 44 88 with Alleluias

Melody from Geistliche Kirchengesäng
(Cologne, 1623)

O___ praise him, O___ praise him, al - le - lu - ia, al - le - lu - ia, al - le - lu - ia!

Laudato sia Dio mio Signore

1 All creatures of our God and king,
lift up your voice and with us sing
alleluia, alleluia!
Thou burning sun with golden beam,
thou silver moon with softer gleam:

O praise him, O praise him,
alleluia, alleluia, alleluia!

2 Thou rushing wind that art so strong,
  ye clouds that sail in heaven along,
      O praise him, alleluia!
  Thou rising morn, in praise rejoice,
  ye lights of evening, find a voice:

3 Thou flowing water, pure and clear,
  make music for thy Lord to hear,
      alleluia, alleluia!
  Thou fire so masterful and bright,
  that givest us both warmth and light:

4 Dear mother earth, who day by day
  unfoldest blessings on our way,
      O praise him, alleluia!
  The flowers and fruits that in thee grow,
  let them his glory also show:

5 All ye that are of tender heart,
  forgiving others, take your part,
      O sing ye, alleluia!
  Ye who long pain and sorrow bear,
  praise God and on him cast your care:

*6 And thou, most kind and gentle death,
  waiting to hush our latest breath,
      O praise him, alleluia!
  Thou leadest home the child of God,
  and Christ our Lord the way has trod:

7 Let all things their creator bless,
  and worship him in humbleness,
      O praise him, alleluia!
  Praise, praise the Father, praise the Son,
  and praise the Spirit, Three-in-One:

William Henry Draper (1855–1933) altd.
based on The Canticle of the Sun
by *St. Francis of Assisi* (1182–1226)

25

Royal Oak   76 76 with Refrain

17th-century English traditional melody

All things bright and beau-ti-ful, all crea-tures great and small,

(Fine)

all things wise and won-der-ful, the Lord God made them all.

D.C.

All things bright   76 76 with Refrain

William Henry Monk (1823–1889)

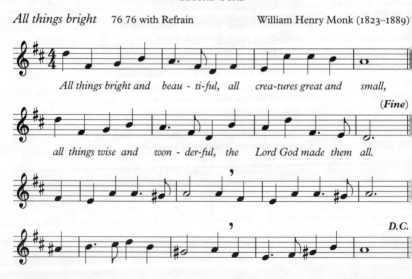

All things bright and beau-ti-ful, all crea-tures great and small,

(Fine)

all things wise and won-der-ful, the Lord God made them all.

D.C.

GOD'S WORLD

All things bright and beautiful,
  all creatures great and small,
all things wise and wonderful,
  the Lord God made them all.

1 Each little flower that opens,
    each little bird that sings,
  he made their glowing colours,
    he made their tiny wings:

2 The purple-headed mountain,
    the river running by,
  the sunset, and the morning
    that brightens up the sky:

3 The cold wind in the winter,
    the pleasant summer sun,
  the ripe fruits in the garden,
    he made them every one:

4 He gave us eyes to see them,
    and lips that we might tell ⌣
  how great is God almighty,
    who has made all things well.

Cecil Frances (Fanny) Alexander (1818–95)

26

Cairnburn   77 77 77

Harry Grindle (b. 1935)

1 God sends us refreshing rain,
  washing street and window pane.
    Scented flowers will catch the fall,
    growing wild on factory wall.
  See, when all the rain has stopped,
  a rainbow over chimney pots.

2 Thank you, Lord, for city lights,
  helping us to see at nights,
    gifts of laughter, friends and fun,
    green parks where we safely run,
  window-boxes, garden plots,
  and rainbows over chimney pots.

3 Jesus walks with young and old
  on the pavements, through the crowd.
    All our prayers and all our fears
    Jesus knows and Jesus hears,
  promises his love and lots
  of rainbows over chimney pots.

4 Birds are flying in the skies,
  high above the traffic noise.
    Swallows swoop when day is done;
    Jesus knows them every one.
  See them fly to tall rooftops,
  to rainbows over chimney pots.

Meta Whittaker (b. 1933)

27

Holy manna 87 87 D

North American folk hymn melody

1 God, who stretched the spangled heavens,
   infinite in time and place,
 flung the suns in burning radiance
   through the silent fields of space;
 we your children, in your likeness,
   share inventive powers with you.
 Great Creator, still creating,
   show us what we yet may do.

2 Proudly rise our modern cities,
   stately buildings, row on row;
 yet their windows, blank, unfeeling,
   stare on canyoned streets below,
 where the lonely drift unnoticed
   in the city's ebb and flow,
 lost to purpose and to meaning,
   scarcely caring where they go.

3 We have ventured worlds undreamed of
   since the childhood of our race;
 known the ecstasy of winging
   through untravelled realms of space;
 probed the secrets of the atom,
   yielding unimagined power,
 facing us with life's destruction
   at our most triumphant hour.

4 As each far horizon beckons,
   may it challenge us anew,
 children of creative purpose,
   serving others, honouring you.
 May our dreams prove rich with promise,
   each endeavour, well begun.
 Great Creator, give us guidance
   till our goals and yours are one.

Catherine Cameron (b. 1927)

28

FIRST TUNE

Solomon   86 86 (CM)

Adapted from an aria in
G. F. Handel's *Solomon* (1749)

SECOND TUNE

Montrose   86 86 (CM)

Melody from Gilmour's
The Psalm-Singer's Assistant (Paisley, 1790)

* Alternative: G

1 I sing the almighty power of God
  that made the mountains rise,
 that spread the flowing seas abroad,
  and built the lofty skies.

2 I sing the wisdom that ordained
  the sun to rule the day;
 the moon shines full at his command,
  and all the stars obey.

3 I sing the goodness of the Lord,
  that filled the earth with food;
 he formed the creatures with his word,
  and then pronounced them good.

4 Lord, how thy wonders are displayed
  where'er I turn mine eye;
 if I survey the ground I tread,
  or gaze upon the sky.

5 There's not a plant or flower below
  but makes thy glories known;
 and clouds arise, and tempests blow,
  by order from thy throne.

6 All creatures, numerous as they be,
  are subject to thy care;
 there's not a place where we can flee
  but God is present there.

7 His hand is my perpetual guard;
  he keeps me with his eye:
 why should I then forget the Lord,
  who is for ever nigh?

Isaac Watts (1674–1748) altd.
based on Psalm 136: 5–9; James 1: 17

29

Rhuddlan   87 87 87

Welsh traditional melody from E. Jones'
Musical Relics of the Welsh Bards (1800)

1 Lord of beauty, thine the splendour
    shown in earth and sky and sea,
 burning sun and moonlight tender,
    hill and river, flower and tree:
 lest we fail our praise to render
    touch our eyes that they may see.

2 Lord of wisdom, whom obeying
    mighty waters ebb and flow,
 while unhasting, undelaying,
    planets on their courses go:
 in thy laws thyself displaying
    teach our minds thy truth to know.

3 Lord of life, alone sustaining
    all below and all above,
 Lord of love, by whose ordaining
    sun and stars sublimely move:
 in our earthly spirits reigning,
    lift our hearts that we may love.

4 Lord of beauty, bid us own thee,
    Lord of truth, our footsteps guide,
 till as Love our hearts enthrone thee,
    and, with vision purified,
 Lord of all, when all have known thee,
    thou in all art glorified.

Cyril A. Alington (1872–1955)

30

Monkland 77 77

John Antes (1740–1811)

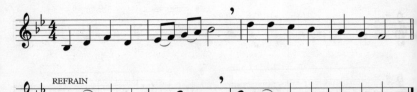

for his_ mer-cies still en-dure, ev - er_ faith-ful, ev - er sure.

1 Let us, with a gladsome mind,
 praise the Lord, for he is kind:

> *for his mercies still endure,*
> *ever faithful, ever sure.*

2 Let us blaze his name abroad,
 for of gods he is the God:

3 He, with all-commanding might,
 filled the new-made world with light:

4 He the golden-tressèd sun
 caused all day his course to run:

5 And the silver moon by night
 'mid her spangled sisters bright:

6 He his chosen race did bless
 in the wasteful[1] wilderness:

7 All things living he doth feed,
 his full hand supplies their need:

8 Let us, then, with gladsome mind,
 praise the Lord, for he is kind:

John Milton (1608–74) altd.
based on Psalm 136

[1] wasteful = uninhabited

31

San Rocco   86 86 (CM)   Derek Williams (b. 1945)

Alternative tune: 13 LONDON NEW

1 Lord of the boundless curves of space
        and time's deep mystery,
    to your creative might we trace ⌣
        all nature's energy.

2 Your mind conceived the galaxy,
        each atom's secret planned,
    and every age of history
        your purpose, Lord, has spanned.

3 Your Spirit gave the living cell ⌣
        its hidden, vital force;
    the instincts which all life impel
        derive from you, their source.

4 Yours is the image humans bear,
        though marred by human sin;
    and yours the liberating care
        again our souls to win.

5 Science explores your reason's ways,
        and faith can this impart
    that in the face of Christ our gaze ⌣
        looks deep within your heart.

6 In Christ the human race has heard ⌣
        your strong compassion plead:
    he is your wisdom's perfect word,
        your mercy's crowning deed.

Albert Frederick Bayly (1901–84)
and others

43

32

O Lord my God   11 10 11 10 with Refrain

Swedish folk melody

REFRAIN

Then sings my soul, my Sav-iour God, to thee, How great thou

art! How great thou art! Then sings my soul, my Sav-iour God, to

thee, How great thou art! How great thou art!

* Alternative: E♭

GOD'S WORLD

O Store Gud

1 O Lord my God! When I in awesome wonder
    consider all the works thy hand hath made,
I see the stars, I hear the mighty thunder,
    thy pow'r throughout the universe displayed:

> *Then sings my soul, my Saviour God, to thee,*
> *How great thou art! How great thou art!*
> *Then sings my soul, my Saviour God, to thee,*
> *How great thou art! How great thou art!*

2 When through the woods and forest glades I wander,
    and hear the birds sing sweetly in the trees;
when I look down from lofty mountain grandeur,
    and hear the brook, and feel the gentle breeze:

3 And when I think that God, his Son not sparing,
    sent him to die—I scarce can take it in,
that on the cross, my burden gladly bearing,
    he bled and died to take away my sin:

4 When Christ shall come with shout of acclamation
    and take me home—what joy shall fill my heart!
Then I shall bow in humble adoration
    and there proclaim, my God, how great thou art!

Swedish hymn (pub. 1891) by *Carl Boberg* (1859–1940)
tr. 1949 (from the Russian) by *Stuart K. Hine* (1899–1989)
based on Psalm 8; Romans 5: 9–11;
1 Thessalonians 4: 16–17

33

Kerrington   11 10 11 10   Donald Davison (b. 1937)

Alternative tune: 127 or 157 HIGHWOOD

1 O Lord of every shining constellation
    that wheels in splendour through the midnight sky:
  grant us your Spirit's true illumination
    to read the secrets of your work on high,

2 You, Lord, have made the atom's hidden forces;
    your laws its mighty energies fulfil:
  teach us, to whom you give such rich resources,
    in all we use, to serve your holy will.

3 O Life, awaking life in cell and tissue;
    from flower to bird, from beast to brain of man:
  help us to trace, from birth to final issue,
    the sure unfolding of your ageless plan.

4 You, Lord, have stamped your image on your creatures
    and, though they mar that image, love them still:
  lift up our eyes to Christ, that in his features
    we may discern the beauty of your will.

5 Great Lord of nature, shaping and renewing,
    you made us more than nature's progeny;
  you help us tread, with grace our souls enduing,
    the road to life and immortality.

Albert Frederick Bayly (1901–84)

34

Hanover   10 10 11 11

From *A Supplement to the New Version* (1708)
probably by William Croft (1678–1727)

1 O worship the King all-glorious above;
   O gratefully sing his power and his love;
      our shield and defender, the Ancient of days,
      pavilioned in splendour, and girded with praise.

2 O tell of his might, O sing of his grace,
   whose robe is the light, whose canopy space;
      his chariots of wrath the deep thunder-clouds form,
      and dark is his path on the wings of the storm.

3 The earth with its store of wonders untold,
   Almighty, thy power hath founded of old,
      hath stablished it fast by a changeless decree,
      and round it hath cast, like a mantle, the sea.

4 Thy bountiful care what tongue can recite?
   It breathes in the air, it shines in the light;
      it streams from the hills, it descends to the plain,
      and sweetly distils in the dew and the rain.

5 Frail children of dust, and feeble as frail,
   in thee do we trust, nor find thee to fail;
      thy mercies how tender, how firm to the end,
      our maker, defender, Redeemer and friend.

6 O measureless might, ineffable love,
   while angels delight to hymn thee above,
      thy ransomed creation, though feeble their lays,
      with true adoration shall sing to thy praise.

Robert Grant (1779–1838)
based on Psalm 104

35

London (Addison's) 88 88 D (DLM) extended John Sheeles (1688–176

1 The spacious firmament on high,
with all the blue ethereal sky,
  and spangled heavens, a shining
    frame,
  their great Original proclaim.
The unwearied sun, from day to day,
does his Creator's power display,
  and publishes to every land
  the work of an almighty hand.

2 Soon as the evening shades prevail,
the moon takes up the wondrous tale
  and nightly to the listening earth
  repeats the story of her birth;
while all the stars that round her burn
and all the planets in their turn,
  confirm the tidings, as they roll,
  and spread the truth from pole
    to pole.

3 What though in solemn silence all
  move round the dark terrestrial ball;
    what though nor re-al voice nor sound
    amid their radiant orbs be found;
  in reason's ear they all rejoice,
  and utter forth a glorious voice;
    for ever singing as they shine,
    'The hand that made us is divine.'

Joseph Addison (1672–171
based on Psalm 19: 1–

36

Tyrol   76 76 D

Tyrolese carol melody

v. I

1 We thank you, God our Father,
    for all your loving care;
  we thank you that you made the world
    so very bright and fair.
  We thank you for the sunshine,
    and for the pleasant showers;
  and we thank you, God our Father,
    we thank you for the flowers.

2 Out in the sunny meadows,
    and in the woodlands cool,
  and under every hedgerow,
    and by each reedy pool,
  and on the lonely moorland,
    and by the broad highway—
  with colours bright, so pure and fresh,
    they spring up every day.

3 And in the dusty city,
    where busy crowds pass by;
  and where the tall dark houses
    stand up and hide the sky,
  and where through lanes and alleys
    no pleasant breezes blow,
  dear God our Father, even there
    you make the flowers grow.

4 And whether in the city
    or in the fields they dwell,
  always the same sweet message
    the sweet young flowers tell.
  For they are all so wonderful,
    they show your power abroad;
  and they are all so beautiful,
    they tell your love, O God.

Catherine MacSorley (1848–1929) altd.

49

37

St George's, Windsor   77 77 D

George J. Elvey (1816–93)

1 Come, ye thankful people, come,
   raise the song of harvest-home;
      all is safely gathered in
      ere the winter storms begin;
   God our Maker doth provide
   for our wants to be supplied;
      come to God's own temple, come,
      raise the song of harvest-home.

2 All the world is God's own field,
   fruit unto his praise to yield;
      wheat and tares together sown,
      unto joy or sorrow grown;
   first the blade, and then the ear,
   then the full corn shall appear;
      Lord of harvest, grant that we
      wholesome grain and pure may be.

3 For the Lord our God shall come,
   and shall take his harvest home;
      from his field shall in that day
      all offences purge away;
   give his angels charge at last
   in the fire the tares to cast;
      but the fruitful ears to store
      in his garner evermore.

4 Even so, Lord, quickly come,
   to thy final harvest-home;
      gather thou thy people in,
      free from sorrow, free from sin;
   there for ever purified
   in thy presence to abide:
      come, with all thine angels, come,
      raise the glorious harvest-home.

Henry Alford (1810–71) altd.

38

Abbot's Leigh   87 87 D

Cyril V. Taylor (1907–91)

1 Father, blessing every seed-time,
   and refreshing all the soil,
ripening the gracious harvest
   for which all thy servants toil:
O thou source of every blessing
   showered daily from above,
hearken to our lips confessing
   our thanksgiving for thy love.

2 Here we bless thy hand that gave us
   thought and feeling, life and limb;
bless thy Son, who died to save us,
   in our glad and joyous hymn;
bless thy Spirit, who doth make us
   fit to worship as we ought;
Father, leave not nor forsake us,
   till into thy garner brought.

3 With thy dews and sunshine tend us
   through life's long and changeful year;
from the enemy defend us,
   lest the tares of sin appear:
let thine eye and hand the keepers
   of our souls for ever be,
till thine angel harvest-reapers
   sheaves of glory bind for thee.

John S. B. Monsell (1811–75)

39

East Acklam 84 84 888 4 Francis Jackson (b. 1917)

Alternative tune: 67 AR HYD Y NOS

1 For the fruits of his creation,
    thanks be to God!
  For his gifts to every nation,
    thanks be to God!
  For the ploughing, sowing, reaping,
  silent growth while we are sleeping;
  future needs in earth's safe keeping,
    thanks be to God!

2 In the just reward of labour,
    God's will is done;
  in the help we give our neighbour,
    God's will is done;
  in our world-wide task of caring
  for the hungry and despairing;
  in the harvests we are sharing,
    God's will is done.

3 For the harvests of the Spirit,
    thanks be to God!
  For the good we all inherit,
    thanks be to God!
  For the wonders that astound us,
  for the truths that still confound us;
  most of all, that love has found us,
    thanks be to God!

F. Pratt Green (b. 1903)

53

40

University 86 86 (CM)

Melody from John Randall's
Psalms and Hymn Tunes (Cambridge, 1794)
probably by Charles Collignon (1725–85)

1 Father of mercies, God of love,
   whose gifts all creatures share,
the rolling seasons as they move
   proclaim thy constant care.

2 When in the bosom of the earth
   the sower hid the grain,
thy goodness marked its secret birth,
   and sent the early rain.

3 The spring's sweet influence, Lord, was thine,
   the seasons know thy call;
thou mad'st the summer sun to shine,
   the summer dews to fall.

4 Thy gifts of mercy from above
   matured the swelling grain;
and now the harvest crowns thy love,
   and plenty fills the plain.

5 O ne'er may our forgetful hearts
   o'erlook thy bounteous care,
but what our Father's hand imparts
   still own in praise and prayer.

6 To Father, Son, and Holy Ghost,
   the God whom we adore,
be glory, as it was, is now,
   and shall be evermore.

Alice Flowerdew (1759–1830)

41

English traditional melody
collected by Lucy Broadwood (1858–1929)

Shipston 87 87

Alternative tune: 385 SUSSEX

1 God, whose farm is all creation,
    take the gratitude we give;
 take the finest of our harvest,
    crops we grow that all may live.

2 Take our ploughing, seeding, reaping,
    hopes and fears of sun and rain,
 all our thinking, planning, waiting,
    ripened in this fruit and grain.

3 All our labour, all our watching,
    all our calendar of care,
 in these crops of your creation,
    take, O God: they are our prayer.

John Arlott (1914–91) altd.

42

Bishopthorpe   86 86 (CM)

Melody from Gardner's
Select Portions of the Psalms (London, *c*.1786)
ascribed to Jeremiah Clarke (*c*.1673–1707)

First line as given in 1960 edition:

1 Good is the Lord, our heavenly King,
   who makes the earth his care;
   visits the pastures every spring,
   and bids the grain appear.

2 Good is the Lord, whose liberal hand
   is daily opened wide,
   to scatter plenty through the land,
   that all may be supplied.

3 Good is the Lord, it is his love
   which makes the earth to yield;
   his clouds drop fatness from above,
   he whitens every field.

4 Good is the Lord, his love should raise
   a joyful harvest song:
   say 'He is good!' and let his praise
   be heard from every tongue.

5 Good is the Lord, he gives us bread;
   he gives his people more,
   by him their souls with grace are fed,
   a rich, a boundless store.

Isaac Watts (1674–1748)
based on Psalms 65: 8–11; 78: 23–24;
104: 28, 30; & 145: 16

43

Whorlton 65 65 D

John Bacchus Dykes (1823–76)

1 Holy is the seed-time, when the buried grain
   sinks to sleep in darkness, but to wake again.
     Holy is the spring-time, when the living corn
     bursting from its prison rises like the morn.

2 Holy is the harvest, when each ripened ear
   bends before the blade and crowns the golden year.
     Store them in our garners; winnow them with care;
     give to God the glory in our praise and prayer.

3 Holy seed our Master sows throughout his field;
   be the harvest holy which our hearts shall yield;
     quickened by his Spirit, strengthened by his grace,
     till in risen splendour we behold his face.

4 Glory to the Father, who has seen our need;
   glory to the Saviour, who has sown the seed;
     glory to the Spirit, giving the increase;
     glory, as it has been, is, and shall not cease!

Margaret A. Headlam 1862 altd.

44

Bunessan   55 54 D   Scots Gaelic traditional melody

For this tune with guitar chords, see no. 58.
Alternative tune: 611i ADDINGTON

1 Praise and thanksgiving,
    Father, we offer,
  for all things living⌣
    you have made good;
  harvest of sown fields,
    fruits of the orchard,
  hay from the mown fields,
    blossom and wood.

2 Lord, bless the labour⌣
    we bring to serve you,
  that with our neighbour⌣
    we may be fed.
  Sowing or tilling,
    we would work with you;
  harvesting, milling,
    for daily bread.

3 Father, providing⌣
    food for your children,
  your wisdom guiding
    teaches us share
  one with another,
    so that, rejoicing,
  sister and brother⌣
    may know your care.

4 Then will your blessing⌣
    reach every people;
  each one confessing⌣
    your gracious hand:
  when you are reigning
    no one will hunger,
  your love sustaining
    fruitful the land.

Albert Frederick Bayly (1901–84) altd.

45

Vienna (St Boniface) 77 77

Melody from
Justin Heinrich Knecht (1752–1817)

for his mer-cies still en-dure, ev - er faith-ful, ev - er sure.

Alternative tune: 30 MONKLAND

1 Praise, O praise our God and king:
hymns of adoration sing:

    for his mercies still endure,
    ever faithful, ever sure.

2 Praise him that he made the sun
day by day his course to run:

3 And the silver moon by night,
shining with her gentle light:

4 Praise him that he gave the rain
to mature the swelling grain:

5 And has bid the fruitful field
crops of precious increase yield:

6 Praise him for our harvest-store;
he has filled the garner-floor;

7 And for richer food than this,
pledge of everlasting bliss:

8 Glory to our bounteous king;
glory let creation sing:

    glory to the Father, Son,
    and blessed Spirit, Three-in-One.

Henry Williams Baker (1821–77)
based on Psalm 136

46

Tā an fómhar

Irish traditional melody

The slurs refer to the English text; metrical irregularities in the Irish text are not indicated, but are easily accommodated.

HARVEST

1 Tá an fómhar seo go haerach, céad buíochas le hÍosa,
   tá eorna ina slaoda is caomhchruithneacht tíortha;
   tá cnó buí ar na craobha, is sméar ar an bhfíordhris,
   is céad glóire don AonMhac le déantar gach ní acu.

2 Ógfhlaith breá, tréitheach, is léannta 's is líofa,
   is cumhachtaí 's is tréine, is féile, is fíre;
   tá ceol ag na héanlaith, gan traochadh dá hinsint
   gur lem' stórsa is breith' buíochas don tsaol uile timpeall.

3 Sé 'sheolann na réalta, teacht gréine is taoide,
   beir néalta na spéire, an ghaoth agus na síonta,
   éin bhinne an aeir uile, is éisc insan míonmhuir,
   is fós 'chuireann féar glas chun tréada na dtíortha.

Micheál Óg Ó Longáin (d. 1801)

1 *The harvest is bright, all thanks be to Jesus,*
   with barley in swathes and wheat safe gathered;
   yellow nuts on the branches and berries on the brambles,
   and glory to God's Son by whom each were fashioned.

2 *Most able fine Prince, most learnèd and fluent,*
   most powerful and strong, most true and generous;
   with music unceasing, the birds are now singing
   that to my dear Lord the whole world should be thankful.

3 *For he rules the stars, the tides' and sun's rising,*
   gives clouds in the sky, the wind and rain-storms,
   all the birds of the air and the fishes in the water,
   and also plants green grass for all herds to graze on.

tr. *Donald A. R. Caird* (b. 1925)
and *Gary Hastings* (b. 1956)
versified *Donald Davison* (b. 1937)

47

Wir pflügen 76 76 D with Refrain

J. A. P. Schulz (1747–1800)

REFRAIN

All good gifts a - round us are sent from heaven a - bove;

then thank the Lord, O thank the Lord, for all___ his love.

* Alternative:

for all___ his___ love.

HARVEST

Wir pflügen und wir streuen

1 We plough the fields, and scatter
    the good seed on the land,
but it is fed and watered
    by God's almighty hand;
he sends the snow in winter,
    the warmth to swell the grain,
the breezes and the sunshine,
    and soft refreshing rain.

> *All good gifts around us*
>   *are sent from heaven above;*
> *then thank the Lord, O thank the Lord,*
>   *for all his love.*

2 He only is the maker
    of all things near and far;
he paints the wayside flower,
    he lights the evening star;
the winds and waves obey him,
    by him the birds are fed;
much more to us, his children,
    he gives our daily bread.

3 We thank you, then, O Father,
    for all things bright and good,
the seed-time and the harvest,
    our life, our health, our food.
Accept the gifts we offer,
    for all your love imparts,
and that which you most welcome,
    our humble, thankful hearts.

Matthias Claudius (1740–1815)
tr. *Jane Montgomery Campbell* (1817–78) altd.
Refrain based on James 1: 17

48

Stewardship   11 10 11 10   Valerie Ruddle (b. 1932)

Alternative tunes: 190i EPIPHANY   466 O QUANTA QUALIA

1 God in his love for us lent us this planet,
  gave it a purpose in time and in space:
small as a spark from the fire of creation,
  cradle of life and the home of our race.

2 Thanks be to God for its bounty and beauty,
  life that sustains us in body and mind:
plenty for all, if we learn how to share it,
  riches undreamed of to fathom and find.

3 Long have our human wars ruined its harvest;
  long has earth bowed to the terror of force;
long have we wasted what others have need of,
  poisoned the fountain of life at its source.

4 Earth is the Lord's: it is ours to enjoy it,
  ours, as his stewards, to farm and defend.
From its pollution, misuse, and destruction,
  good Lord deliver us, world without end!

F. Pratt Green (b. 1903)

49

Andrew   66 66 88

David McCarthy (b. 1931)

Music: © Stainer & Bell Ltd

SECOND TUNE

St John (*Adoration*)   66 66 88

From *The Parish Choir* (1851)
(with altered rhythms)

CARE FOR THE CREATED ORDER

1 Lord, bring the day to pass
   when forest, rock and hill,
the beasts, the birds, the grass,
   will know your finished will:
when we attain our destiny
   and nature its lost unity.

2 Forgive our careless use ⌣
   of water, ore and soil—
the plenty we abuse
   supplied by others' toil:
save us from making self our creed,
   turn us towards our neighbour's need.

3 Give us, when we release ⌣
   creation's secret powers,
to harness them for peace,
   our children's peace and ours:
teach us the art of mastering,
   which makes life rich and draws death's sting.

4 Creation groans, travails,
   bound in its future plight,
until the hour it hails ⌣
   the new-born of the light,
who enter on their true estate.
   Come, Lord: new heavens and earth create.

Ian M. Fraser (b. 1917)
v. 4 based on Romans 8: 18–25

50

Genesis

Graham Westcott (b. 1947)

1. Think of a world with - out a - ny flow - ers,
2. Think of a world with - out a - ny a - ni - mals,
3. Think of a world with - out a - ny peo - ple,

think of a world with - out a - ny trees,
think of a field with - out a - ny herd,
think of a street with no one liv - ing there,

think of a sky with - out a - ny sun - shine,
think of a stream with - out a - ny fish - es,
think of a town with - out a - ny hous - es,

think of the air with - out a - ny breeze. We
think of a dawn with - out a - ny bird. We
no one to love and no - bo - dy to care. We

thank you, Lord, for flowers and trees and sun - shine.
thank you, Lord, for all your liv - ing crea - tures. We
thank you, Lord, for fa - mi - lies and friend - ships.

CARE FOR THE CREATED ORDER

thank you, Lord, and praise your ho - ly name.

1. Think of a world without any flowers,
    think of a world without any trees,
   think of a sky without any sunshine,
       think of the air without any breeze.
   We thank you, Lord, for flowers and trees and sunshine.
   We thank you, Lord, and praise your holy name.

2. Think of a world without any animals,
    think of a field without any herd,
   think of a stream without any fishes,
       think of a dawn without any bird.
   We thank you, Lord, for all your living creatures.
   We thank you, Lord, and praise your holy name.

3. Think of a world without any people,
    think of a street with no one living there,
   think of a town without any houses,
       no one to love and nobody to care.
   We thank you, Lord, for families and friendships.
   We thank you, Lord, and praise your holy name.

Doreen (Bunty) Newport (b. 1927)

51

FIRST TUNE

Morning hymn   88 88 (LM)

François H. Barthélémon (1741–1808)

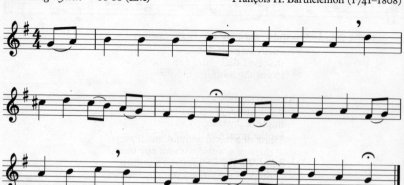

SECOND TUNE

Deus tuorum militum   88 88 (LM)

Melody from *Grenoble Antiphoner* (1753)

1 Awake, my soul, and with the sun
  thy daily stage of duty run;
    shake off dull sloth, and joyful rise,
    to pay thy morning sacrifice.

2 Redeem thy mis-spent time that's past,
  and live this day as if thy last;
    improve thy talent with due care;
    for the great day thyself prepare.

3 Let all thy converse be sincere,
  thy conscience as the noon-day clear;
    think how all-seeing God thy ways
    and all thy secret thoughts surveys.

4 Wake, and lift up thyself, my heart,
  and with the angels bear thy part,
    who all night long unwearied sing
    high praise to the eternal King.

5 O Lord, direct, control, this day,
  all I design, or do, or say;
    that all my powers, with all their might,
    in thy sole glory may unite.

6 Praise God, from whom all blessings flow;
  praise him, all creatures here below;
    praise him above, ye heavenly host;
    praise Father, Son, and Holy Ghost.

Thomas Ken (1637–1711) altd.

52

FIRST TUNE

Ratisbon   77 77 77

Melody from J. G. Werner's
Choralbuch (Leipzig, 1815)

SECOND TUNE

England's Lane   77 77 77

Adapted from an English folk-song melody
by Geoffrey Shaw (1879–1943)

TIME: MORNING

1 Christ, whose glory fills the skies,
    Christ, the true, the only Light,
Sun of Righteousness, arise;
    triumph o'er the shades of night:
Day-spring from on high, be near;
    Day-spring, in my heart appear.

2 Dark and cheerless is the morn
    unaccompanied by thee;
joyless is the day's return
    till thy mercy's beams I see—
till they inward light impart,
    glad my eyes and warm my heart.

3 Visit then this soul of mine,
    pierce the gloom of sin and grief,
fill me, Radiancy divine,
    scatter all my unbelief:
more and more thyself display,
    shining to the perfect day.

Charles Wesley (1707–88)

53

Christe sanctorum (1)   11 11 11 5   Melody from *Paris Antiphoner* (1681)

A - - men.

Nocte surgentes

1 Father, we praise you, now the night is over,
   active and watchful, stand we all before you;
   singing, we offer prayer and meditation:
       thus we adore you.

2 Monarch of all things, fit us for your mansions;
   banish our weakness, health and wholeness sending;
   bring us to heaven, where your saints united ⌣
       joy without ending.

3 All-holy Father, Son and equal Spirit,
   Trinity blessèd, send us your salvation;
   yours is the glory, gleaming and resounding ⌣
       through all creation. Amen.

Latin, 10th century or earlier
tr. *Percy Dearmer* (1867–1936) altd.

54

St Owen   10 13 10   Sherrell Prebble

1 How beautiful the morning and the day;
  my heart abounds with music, my lips can only say:
  how beautiful the morning and the day.

2 How glorious the morning and the day;
  my heart is still and listens, my soul begins to pray
  to him who is the glory and the day.

3 How beautiful the blessings Jesus brings
  of peace and joy and rapture that make my spirit sing:
  how beautiful the blessings that he brings.

4 How merciful the working of his grace,
  arousing faith and action my soul would never face
  without his matchless mercy and his grace.

5 How barren was my life before he came,
  supplying love and healing; I live now to acclaim
  the majesty and wonder of his name.

Owen Barker altd.

55

North Coates   65 65   Timothy R. Matthews (1826–1910)

1 Let this day be holy;
      Lord, accept my prayer,
   and the thanks I offer ⌣
      for a Father's care.

2 Bless the bread you give me
      for my food today:
   for the strength it brings me,
      in your words I pray.

3 Let my work be holy,
      honest work and true,
   done as in your sight, Lord,
      bless the work I do.

4 Let my joy be holy,
      free from taint of sin,
   joy which they have only
      who are pure within.

5 Let my grief be holy,
      comfort me in pain;
   fill my life with hope, Lord,
      heaven's joy to gain.

*6 Let my rest be holy,
      angels watching near;
   send good thoughts, and keep me ⌣
      safe from harm and fear.

                    John Ffolliott (1824–94) altd.

56

Cross Deep   88 88 (LM)

Barry Rose (b. 1934)

Alternative tunes: 59 MELCOMBE   513 DANIEL

1 Lord, as I wake I turn to you,
    yourself the first thought of my day:
  my King, my God, whose help is sure,
    yourself the help for which I pray.

2 There is no blessing, Lord, from you
    for those who make their will their way,
  no praise for those who will not praise,
    no peace for those who will not pray.

3 Your loving gifts of grace to me,
    those favours I could never earn,
  call for my thanks in praise and prayer,
    call me to love you in return.

4 Lord, make my life a life of love,
    keep me from sin in all I do;
  Lord, make your law my only law,
    your will my will, for love of you.

Brian Foley (b. 1919)
based on Psalm 5

57

Providence   84 84

Richard R. Terry (1865–1938)

1 Lord, for tomorrow and its needs
      I do not pray.
   Keep me, my God, from stain of sin
      just for today.

2 Let me both diligently work
      and duly pray.
   Let me be kind in word and deed
      just for today.

3 Let me no wrong or idle word
      unthinking say;
   but set a seal upon my lips
      just for today.

4 And if today my tide of life
      should ebb away,
   give me the grace of peace divine,
      dear Lord, today.

5 So for tomorrow and its needs
      I do not pray;
   but keep me, guide me, love me, Lord,
      just for today.

Sybil Farish Partridge [*Sister M. Xavier*]
            (1856–1917) altd.

58

Bunessan   55 54 D

Scots Gaelic traditional melody

1 Morning has broken
     like the first morning;
  blackbird has spoken
     like the first bird.
  Praise for the singing!
     Praise for the morning!
  Praise for them, springing
     fresh from the Word!

2 Sweet the rain's new fall
     sunlit from heaven,
  like the first dew-fall
     on the first grass.
  Praise for the sweetness
     of the wet garden,
  sprung in completeness
     where his feet pass.

3 Mine is the sunlight!
     Mine is the morning
  born of the one light
     Eden saw play!
  Praise with elation,
     praise every morning,
  God's re-creation
     of the new day!

Eleanor Farjeon (1881–1965)

59

Melcombe   88 88 (LM)

Melody by Samuel Webbe the elder (1740–1816) in his
An Essay on the Church Plain Chant (London, 1782)

1 New every morning is the love
  our wakening and uprising prove;
    through sleep and darkness safely brought,
    restored to life and power and thought.

2 New mercies, each returning day,
  hover around us while we pray;
    new perils past, new sins forgiven,
    new thoughts of God, new hopes of heaven.

3 If, on our daily course, our mind
  be set to hallow all we find,
    new treasures still, of countless price,
    God will provide for sacrifice.

*4 Old friends, old scenes will lovelier be,
  as more of heaven in each we see;
    some softening gleam of love and prayer
    shall dawn on every cross and care.

5 The trivial round, the common task,
  will furnish all we ought to ask,
    room to deny ourselves, a road
    to bring us daily nearer God.

6 Only, O Lord, in your dear love,
  fit us for perfect rest above;
    and help us, this and every day,
    to live more nearly as we pray.

John Keble (1792–1866) altd.
based on Lamentations 3: 22–23

60

Splendor paternae gloriae   88 88 (LM)   Plainsong melody (Sarum form), mode i

A - men.

Herr Jesu Christ, dich zu uns wend
88 88 (LM)

Later version (as given by J. S. Bach)
of melody in *Pensum Sacrum*
(Gorlitz, 1648)

Alternative tune: 59 MELCOMBE (on previous page)

Splendor paternae gloriae

1 O Jesus, Lord of heavenly grace,
 thou brightness of the Father's face,
  thou fountain of eternal light,
  whose beams disperse the shades of night;

2 come, holy Sun of heavenly love,
 pour down thy radiance from above,
  and to our inward hearts convey⌣
  the Holy Spirit's cloudless ray.

3 May he our actions deign to bless,
 and loose the bonds of wickedness;
  from sudden falls our feet defend,
  and guide us safely to the end.

4 May faith, deep rooted in the soul,
 subdue our flesh, our minds control;
  may guile depart, and discord cease,
  and all within be joy and peace.

5 O hallowed thus be every day;
 let meekness be our morning ray,
  and faithful love our noon-day light,
  and hope our sunset calm and bright.

6 O Christ, with each returning morn
 thine image to our hearts is borne;
  O may we ever clearly see⌣
  our Saviour and our God in thee.

St Ambrose (340–97)
tr. *John Chandler* (1806–76)

61

Slithers of gold   11 10 11 10

John L. Bell (b. 1949)
and Graham Maule (b. 1958)

1. To-day I a-wake___ and God is be-fore___ me. At

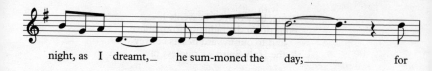

night, as I dreamt,___ he sum-moned the day;___ for

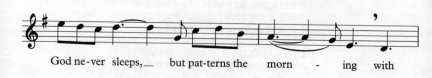

God ne-ver sleeps,___ but pat-terns the morn - ing with

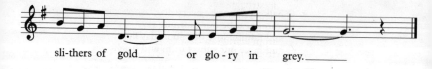

sli-thers of gold___ or glo-ry in grey.___

TIME: MORNING

1 Today I awake
  and God is before me.
  At night, as I dreamt,
  he summoned the day;
  for God never sleeps,
  but patterns the morning
  with slithers of gold
  or glory in grey.

2 Today I arise
  and Christ is beside me.
  He walked through the dark
  to scatter new light.
  Yes, Christ is alive,
  and beckons his people
  to hope and to heal,
  resist and invite.

3 Today I affirm
  the Spirit within me
  at worship and work,
  in struggle and rest.
  The Spirit inspires
  all life which is changing
  from fearing to faith,
  from broken to blessed.

4 Today I enjoy
  the Trinity round me,
  above and beneath,
  before and behind;
  the Maker, the Son,
  the Spirit together—
  they called me to life
  and call me their friend.

John L. Bell (b. 1949)
and *Graham Maule* (b. 1958)

62

Eventide   10 10 10 10

William Henry Monk (1823–89)

1 Abide with me, fast falls the eventide;
   the darkness deepens; Lord, with me abide;
      when other helpers fail and comforts flee,
      help of the helpless, O abide with me.

2 Swift to its close ebbs out life's little day;
   earth's joys grow dim, its glories pass away;
      change and decay in all around I see;
      O thou who changest not, abide with me.

3 I need thy presence every passing hour;
   what but thy grace can foil the tempter's power?
      Who like thyself my guide and stay can be?
      Through cloud and sunshine, O abide with me.

4 I fear no foe with thee at hand to bless;
   ills have no weight, and tears no bitterness.
      Where is death's sting? Where, grave, thy victory?
      I triumph still, if thou abide with me.

5 Hold thou thy cross before my closing eyes;
   shine through the gloom, and point me to the skies;
      heaven's morning breaks, and earth's vain shadows flee;
      in life, in death, O Lord, abide with me.

Henry Francis Lyte (1793–1847)
based on Luke 24: 29; 1 Corinthians 15: 55

63

Tallis's Canon   88 88 (LM)

Melody by Thomas Tallis (*c.*1505–85)
abridged to LM in Thomas Ravenscroft's
Psalmes (London, 1621)

1 All praise to thee, my God, this night,
   for all the blessings of the light;
     keep me, O keep me, King of kings,
     beneath thine own almighty wings.

2 Forgive me, Lord, for thy dear Son,
   the ill that I this day have done,
     that with the world, myself, and thee,
     I, ere I sleep, at peace may be.

3 Teach me to live, that I may dread
   the grave as little as my bed;
     teach me to die, that so I may
     rise glorious at the aweful[1] day.

4 O may my soul on thee repose,
   and may sweet sleep mine eyelids close;
     sleep that shall me more vigorous make
     to serve my God when I awake.

5 When in the night I sleepless lie,
   my soul with heavenly thoughts supply;
     let no ill dreams disturb my rest,
     no powers of darkness me molest.

6 Praise God, from whom all blessings flow;
   praise him, all creatures here below;
     praise him above, ye heavenly host;
     praise Father, Son, and Holy Ghost.

Thomas Ken (1637–1711)

---

[1] 'aweful' is an old spelling for 'awful' and is used here in the poetic sense meaning 'inspiring awe'.

64

Quam dilecta   66 66

Henry L. Jenner (1820–98)

1 And now this holy day
   is drawing to its end;
   once more to you, O Lord,
   our thanks and praise ascend.

2 We thank you for this rest
   from earthly care and strife;
   we thank you for this help
   to higher, holier life.

3 We thank you for your house;
   it is your palace-gate,
   where, seated on your throne
   of mercy, still you wait.

4 We thank you for your word,
   your gospel's joyful sound;
   O may its holy fruits
   within our hearts abound.

5 To God the Father, Son,
   and Spirit, glory be,
   from all in earth and heaven,
   through all eternity.

Edward Harland (1810–90) altd.

65

Angelus   88 88 (LM)

Cantica Spiritualia (Munich, 1847),
adpt. from a melody by Georg Joseph in
Scheffler's *Heiligen Seelen-Lust* (Breslau, 1657)

1 At evening, when the sun had set,
   the sick, O Lord, around you lay:
in what distress and pain they met,
   but with what joy they went away!

2 Once more the evening comes, and we
   oppressed with various ills draw near;
and though your form we cannot see,
   we know and feel that you are here.

3 O Saviour Christ, our fears dispel—
   for some are sick and some are sad,
and some have never loved you well,
   and some have lost the love they had.

*4 And none, O Lord, have perfect rest,
   for none are wholly free from sin;
and those who long to serve you best
   are conscious most of wrong within.

5 O Saviour Christ, the Son of Man,
   you have been troubled, tempted, tried;
your kind but searching glance can scan
   the very wounds that shame would hide.

6 Your touch has still its ancient power;
   no word from you can fruitless fall:
hear in this solemn evening hour
   and in your mercy heal us all.

Henry Twells (1823–1900) altd.
based on Mark 1: 32–34

66

Te lucis ante terminum (A)   88 88 (LM)   Sarum plainsong melody, mode viii

A - men.

Te lucis ante terminum (B)   88 88 (LM)   Sarum plainsong melody, mode viii

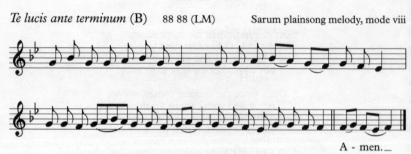

A - men.

The two plainsong melodies are appropriate for Ferial and Festal use respectively.

Te lucis ante terminum

1 Before the ending of the day,
   creator of the world, we pray
      that thou with wonted love wouldst keep
      thy watch around us while we sleep.

2 O let no evil dreams be near,
   or phantoms of the night appear;
      our ghostly enemy restrain,
      lest aught of sin our bodies stain.

Ferial (ordinary) Doxology

3a Almighty Father, hear our cry
    through Jesus Christ our Lord most high,
        who with the Holy Ghost and thee
        doth live and reign eternally. Amen.

Advent Doxology

3b To thee, O Christ, all glory be,
    whose Advent sets thy people free,
        whom, with the Father, we adore,
        and Holy Spirit, evermore. Amen.

Christmas Doxology

3c Lord Jesus, King of heaven and earth,
    we praise thee for thy virgin-birth;
        thou art the Father's only Son,
        with God the Spirit, ever one. Amen.

Epiphany Doxology

3d Thy glory, Christ, is manifest;
    all peoples, Lord, by thee are blessed;
        whom with the Father, we adore,
        and Holy Spirit, evermore. Amen.

Lent Doxology

3e Grant, ever-blessèd Trinity,
    and ever-perfect Unity,
        that this, our fast of forty days,
        may work our profit and thy praise. Amen.

Passiontide Doxology

3f To thee, O saving Three in One,
    let homage due by all be done;
        and grant us, by the cross restored,
        to share the Victor's great reward. Amen.

Easter Doxology

3g All praise be thine, O risen Lord,
    from death to endless life restored;
        whom with the Father, we adore,
        and Holy Spirit, evermore. Amen.

Pentecost Doxology

3h To God the Father, God the Son,
    and God the Spirit praise be done;
        may Christ the Lord upon us pour
        the Spirit's gifts for evermore. Amen.

Verses 1–3 (Ferial) Latin, before 8th Century.
tr. by the Compilers of *Hymns A. & M.*
Seasonal Doxologies from 'Celebrating Common Prayer' altd.

66

THIRD TUNE

Tallis's Canon   88 88 (LM)

Melody by Thomas Tallis (*c.*1505–85)
abridged to LM in Thomas Ravenscroft's
Psalmes (London, 1621)

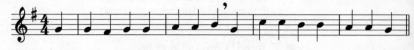

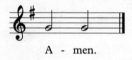

A - men.

Te lucis ante terminum

1 Before the ending of the day,
   creator of the world, we pray
      that thou with wonted love wouldst keep
      thy watch around us while we sleep.

2 O let no evil dreams be near,
   or phantoms of the night appear;
      our ghostly enemy restrain,
      lest aught of sin our bodies stain.

Ferial (ordinary) Doxology

3a Almighty Father, hear our cry
    through Jesus Christ our Lord most high,
       who with the Holy Ghost and thee
       doth live and reign eternally. Amen.

Advent Doxology

3b To thee, O Christ, all glory be,
    whose Advent sets thy people free,
       whom, with the Father, we adore,
       and Holy Spirit, evermore. Amen.

Christmas Doxology

3c Lord Jesus, King of heaven and earth,
    we praise thee for thy virgin-birth;
       thou art the Father's only Son,
       with God the Spirit, ever one. Amen.

Epiphany Doxology

3d Thy glory, Christ, is manifest;
    all peoples, Lord, by thee are blessed;
      whom with the Father, we adore,
      and Holy Spirit, evermore. Amen.

Lent Doxology

3e Grant, ever-blessèd Trinity,
    and ever-perfect Unity,
      that this, our fast of forty days,
      may work our profit and thy praise. Amen.

Passiontide Doxology

3f To thee, O saving Three in One,
    let homage due by all be done;
      and grant us, by the cross restored,
      to share the Victor's great reward. Amen.

Easter Doxology

3g All praise be thine, O risen Lord,
    from death to endless life restored;
      whom with the Father, we adore,
      and Holy Spirit, evermore. Amen.

Pentecost Doxology

3h To God the Father, God the Son,
    and God the Spirit praise be done;
      may Christ the Lord upon us pour
      the Spirit's gifts for evermore. Amen.

Verses 1–3 (Ferial) Latin, before 8th Century.
tr. by the Compilers of *Hymns A. & M.*
Seasonal Doxologies from 'Celebrating Common Prayer' altd.

67

Ar hyd y nos   84 84 888 4

Welsh traditional melody

* Alternative: G

1 God, who made the earth and heaven,
   darkness and light;
  who the day for toil has given,
   for rest the night;
  may your angel-guards defend us,
  slumber sweet your mercy send us,
  holy dreams and hopes attend us,
   this livelong night.

2 Guard us waking, guard us sleeping,
   and when we die,
  may we, in your mighty keeping,
   all peaceful lie.
  When the last dread call shall wake us,
  do not then, our God, forsake us,
  but to reign in glory take us
   with you on high.

Verse 1 by *Reginald Heber* (1783–1826) altd.
Verse 2 by *Richard Whately* (1787–1863) altd.

68

Glenfinlas   65 65   Kenneth George Finlay (1882–1974)

1 Now the day is over,
   night is drawing nigh,
shadows of the evening
   steal across the sky.

2 Now the darkness gathers,
   stars begin to peep,
birds and beasts and flowers
   soon will be asleep.

3 Jesus, give the weary
   calm and sweet repose;
with thy tenderest blessing
   may their eyelids close.

4 Grant to little children
   visions bright of thee;
guard the sailors tossing
   on the deep blue sea.

5 Comfort every sufferer
   watching late in pain;
those who plan some evil
   from their sin restrain.

6 Through the long night watches
   may thine angels spread
their white wings above me,
   watching round my bed.

7 When the morning wakens,
   then may I arise
pure and fresh and blameless
   in thy holy eyes.

Sabine Baring-Gould (1834–1924)

69

St Venantius   88 88 (LM)   Melody from the *Paris Antiphoner* (1681)

A - men.

SECOND TUNE

Christe, qui lux es   88 88 (LM)   Plainsong melody, mode ii

A - men.____

Christe, qui lux es et dies

1 O Christ, who art the Light and Day,
thou drivest darksome night away!
We know thee as the Light of light,
illuminating mortal sight.

2 All-holy Lord, we pray to thee,
keep us tonight from danger free;
grant us, dear Lord, in thee to rest,
so be our sleep in quiet blessed.

3 And while the eyes soft slumber take,
still be the heart to thee awake;
be thy right hand upheld above
thy servants resting in thy love.

4 O strong defender, be thou nigh
to bid the powers of darkness fly;
keep us from sin, and guide for good
thy servants purchased by thy blood.

5 Remember us, dear Lord, we pray
while in this mortal flesh we stay:
'tis thou who dost the soul defend—
be present with us to the end.

6 All praise to God the Father be,
all praise, eternal Son, to thee,
whom with the Spirit we adore,
for ever and for evermore. Amen.

6th-century Latin
tr. *William J. Copeland* (1804–85)
and others

70

Strength and Stay   11 10 11 10

John Bacchus Dykes (1823–76)

Alternative tune: 430 SCHOOL HOUSE

Rerum Deus tenax vigor

1 O Strength and Stay, upholding all creation,
       who ever dost thyself unmoved abide,
   yet day by day the light in due gradation
       from hour to hour through all its changes guide;

2 grant to life's day a calm unclouded ending,
       an eve untouched by shadows of decay;
   the brightness of a holy death-bed blending
       with dawning glories of the eternal day.

3 Hear us, O Father, gracious and forgiving,
       through Jesus Christ, thy co-eternal Word,
   who, with the Holy Ghost, by all things living
       now and to endless ages art adored.

St Ambrose (340–97)
tr. *John Ellerton* (1826–93)
and *F. J. A. Hort* (1828–92)

71

Ellers   10 10 10 10   Edward J. Hopkins (1818–1901)

1 Saviour, again to thy dear name we raise
   with one accord our parting hymn of praise;
      we stand to bless thee ere our worship cease,
      then, lowly kneeling, wait thy word of peace.

2 Grant us thy peace upon our homeward way;
   with thee began, with thee shall end the day;
      guard thou the lips from sin, the hearts from shame,
      that in this house have called upon thy name.

3 Grant us thy peace, Lord, through the coming night,
   turn thou for us its darkness into light;
      from harm and danger keep thy children free,
      for dark and light are both alike to thee.

4 Grant us thy peace throughout our earthly life,
   our balm in sorrow and our stay in strife;
      then, when thy voice shall bid our conflict cease,
      call us, O Lord, to thine eternal peace.

John Ellerton (1826–93)
based on Psalm 139: 11–12; John 14: 27

72

FIRST TUNE

Abends   88 88 (LM)

H. S. Oakeley (1830–1903)
written for the (*Irish*) *Church Hymnal* (1874)

SECOND TUNE

Hesperus   88 88 (LM)

Henry Baker (1835–1910)

TIME: EVENING

1 Sun of my soul, thou Saviour dear,
  it is not night if thou be near;
      O may no earth-born cloud arise
      to hide thee from thy servant's eyes.

2 When the soft dews of kindly sleep
  my wearied eyelids gently steep,
      be my last thought, how sweet to rest
      for ever on my Saviour's breast.

3 Abide with me from morn till eve,
  for without thee I cannot live;
      abide with me when night is nigh,
      for without thee I dare not die.

4 Watch by the sick; enrich the poor
  with blessings from thy boundless store;
      be every mourner's sleep tonight,
      like infant's slumbers, pure and light.

5 Come near and bless us when we wake,
  ere through the world our way we take;
      till in the ocean of thy love
      we lose ourselves in heaven above.

John Keble (1792–1866)

73

St Clement   98 98

Clement C. Scholefield (1839–1904)

1 The day thou gavest, Lord, is ended,
 the darkness falls at thy behest;
to thee our morning hymns ascended,
 thy praise shall sanctify our rest.

2 We thank thee that thy Church unsleeping,
 while earth rolls onward into light,
through all the world her watch is keeping,
 and rests not now by day or night.

3 As o'er each continent and island
 the dawn leads on another day,
the voice of prayer is never silent,
 nor dies the strain of praise away.

4 The sun, that bids us rest, is waking
 thy people 'neath the western sky,
and hour by hour fresh lips are making
 thy wondrous doings heard on high.

5 So be it, Lord; thy throne shall never,
 like earth's proud empires, pass away;
thy kingdom stands, and grows for ever,
 till all thy creatures own thy sway.

John Ellerton (1826–93) altd.

74

Simeon   88 88 (LM)   Samuel Stanley (*c.*1767–1822)

Alternative tunes: 76i DEEP HARMONY   353 WORCESTER (BIRSTAL)

1 First of the week and finest day,
       when God commanded light to shine:
   cast darkness and its works away
       to celebrate with bread and wine.

2 First of the week was Easter morn
       when Christ the Lord from death was raised;
   new life, fresh hope that day was born
       and God in heaven and earth was praised.

3 First of the week the Spirit came
       to fill the Church with grace and power;
   the rushing wind and tongues of flame
       were heralds of that promised hour.

4 First of the week we set aside
       to meet, to learn, to give, to pray;
   to spread Christ's gospel far and wide—
       in truth, this is the Lord's own day!

David Mowbray (b. 1938)

75

Dismissal (Kingstown)   87 87 87   William Letton Viner (1790–1867)

1 Lord, dismiss us with your blessing,
   fill our hearts with joy and peace;
let us each, your love possessing,
   triumph in redeeming grace;
      O refresh us,
      O refresh us,
   travelling through this wilderness.

2 Thanks we give and adoration
   for your gospel's joyful sound;
may the fruits of your salvation
   in our hearts and lives abound;
      may your presence,
      may your presence
   with us evermore be found.

18th cent.
attrib. *John Fawcett* (1740–1817)
based on Luke 2: 29

76

Deep harmony 88 88 (LM) Handel Parker (1854–1928)

Wareham 88 88 (LM) William Knapp (1698–1768)

1 Sweet is the work, my God and King,
  to praise your name, give thanks and sing;
    to show your love by morning light,
    and talk of all your truth at night.

2 Sweet is the day, the first and best,
  on which I share your sacred rest;
    so let my heart in tune be found,
    like David's harp of joyful sound.

3 My heart shall triumph in the Lord
  and bless his works, and bless his word:
    his works of grace, how bright they shine—
    how deep his counsels, how divine!

4 Soon shall I see and hear and know
  what mortals cannot reach below,
    and all my powers for God employ
    in that eternal world of joy.

Isaac Watts (1674–1748) altd.
based on Psalm 92

77

Wareham   88 88 (LM)

William Knapp (1698–1768)

1 This day, at God's creating word,
    first o'er the earth the light was poured;
      O Lord, this day upon us shine,
      and fill our souls with light divine.

2 This day the Lord, for sinners slain,
    in might victorious rose again;
      O Jesus, may we raisèd be
      from death of sin to life in thee.

3 This day the Holy Spirit came
    with fiery tongues of cloven flame:
      O Spirit, fill our hearts today
      with grace to hear and grace to pray.

4 O day of light, and life, and grace,
    from earthly toils sweet resting place,
      these hallowed hours, best gift of love,
      give we again to God above.

W. Walsham How (1823–97) altd.

78

This is the day

Fiji Island folk melody

1 This is the day that the Lord has made.
  We will rejoice and be glad in it.

2 This is the day when he rose again.
  We will rejoice and be glad in it.

3 This is the day when the Spirit came.
  We will rejoice and be glad in it.

based on Psalm 118: 24

79

Orientis partibus (1)   77 77

French medieval melody from the Office of
Pierre de Corbeil (d. 1222)

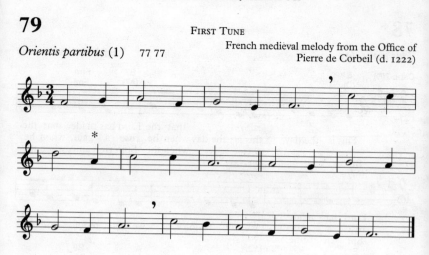

* This note is sometimes sung as B flat.

Carne (*Keine Schönheit*)   77 77

Melody from Scheffler's
Heilige Seelen-Lust (Breslau, 1657)

Alternative tune: 655 BUCKLAND

1 Advent tells us Christ is near;
  Christmas tells us Christ is here;
      then we learn what life can be
      in our Lord's Epiphany.

2 Forty days we keep in Lent,
  praying, fasting, penitent,
      give our lives to Christ anew
      and to him be always true.

3 Holy Week begins with palms—
  crowds with branches, singing psalms;
      on Good Friday they will cry
      'Nail him on a cross to die.'

4 We rejoice on Easter Day;
  'Christ is risen indeed', we say;
      in the bread and wine he's shown,
      and his risen power is known.

5 Christ ascends to heaven again,
  glorious now as King to reign;
      and we give him special praise
      through those joyful fifty days.

6 Pentecost—it is the birth
  of the Church in all the earth,
      when the Holy Spirit came
      in sure signs of wind and flame.

7 So to God through all our days
  we will gladly sing our praise:
      'Glory to the One in Three,
      God the Holy Trinity.'

Edward F. Darling (b. 1933)
and *Harold Miller* (b. 1950)
based on a hymn by
Katherine Hankey (1834–1911)

80

Faithfulness   11 10 11 10 with Refrain   W. M. Runyan (1870–1957)

REFRAIN

Great is thy faith-ful-ness, great is thy faith-ful-ness,

morn-ing by morn-ing new mer-cies I see;

all I have need-ed thy hand hath pro-vi-ded,

great is thy faith-ful-ness, Lord, un-to me!

1 Great is thy faithfulness, O God my Father,
    there is no shadow of turning with thee;
thou changest not, thy compassions, they fail not,
    as thou hast been thou for ever wilt be.

> *Great is thy faithfulness, great is thy faithfulness,*
> *morning by morning new mercies I see;*
> *all I have needed thy hand hath provided,*
> *great is thy faithfulness, Lord, unto me!*

2 Summer and winter, and spring-time and harvest,
    sun, moon and stars in their courses above,
join with all nature in manifold witness
    to thy great faithfulness, mercy and love.

3 Pardon for sin and a peace that endureth,
    thine own dear presence to cheer and to guide;
strength for today and bright hope for tomorrow,
    blessings all mine, with ten thousand beside!

Thomas O. Chisholm (1866–1960)
based on Lamentations 3: 22–23
and Genesis 8: 22

81

Lord of the years   11 10 11 10   Michael Baughen (b. 1930)

© Michael Baughen/Jubilate Hymns

Marlborough Park   11 10 11 10   Donald Davison (b. 1937)

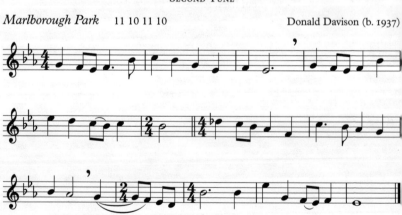

1 Lord, for the years your love has kept and guided,
   urged and inspired us, cheered us on our way,
 sought us and saved us, pardoned and provided,
   Lord of the years, we bring our thanks today.

2 Lord, for that word, the word of life which fires us,
   speaks to our hearts and sets our souls ablaze,
 teaches and trains, rebukes us and inspires us,
   Lord of the word, receive your people's praise.

3 Lord, for our land, in this our generation,
   spirits oppressed by pleasure, wealth and care;
 for young and old, for this and every nation,
   Lord of our land, be pleased to hear our prayer.

4 Lord, for our world, when we disown and doubt him,
   loveless in strength, and comfortless in pain;
 hungry and helpless, lost indeed without him,
   Lord of the world, we pray that Christ may reign.

5 Lord, for ourselves; in living power remake us,
   self on the cross and Christ upon the throne;
 past put behind us, for the future take us,
   Lord of our lives, to live for Christ alone.

Timothy Dudley-Smith (b. 1926)

82

FIRST TUNE

Ruth   65 65 D

Samuel Smith (1821–1917)

SECOND TUNE

Heritage   65 65 D

John Boal (b. 1945)

1 Summer suns are glowing
    over land and sea,
 happy light is flowing
    bountiful and free.
 Every thing rejoices
    in the mellow rays,
 all earth's thousand voices
    swell the psalm of praise.

2 God's free mercy streameth
    over all the world,
 and his banner gleameth
    everywhere unfurled.
 Broad and deep and glorious
    as the heaven above,
 shines in might victorious
    his eternal love.

3 Lord, upon our blindness
    thy pure radiance pour;
 for thy loving-kindness
    makes us love thee more.
 And when clouds are drifting
    dark across our sky,
 then, the veil uplifting,
    Father, be thou nigh.

4 We will never doubt thee,
    though thou veil thy light;
 life is dark without thee:
    death with thee is bright.
 Light of light, shine o'er us
    on our pilgrim way;
 go thou still before us
    to the endless day.

W. Walsham How (1823–97)

83

Irish   86 86 (CM)

Melody from *Hymns and Sacred Poems*
(Dublin, 1749)

AT THE BEGINNING OF A NEW YEAR

Lapsus est annus

1 The year is gone beyond recall,
   with all its hopes and fears,
   with all its bright and gladd'ning smiles,
   with all its mourners' tears.

2 Thy thankful people praise thee, Lord,
   for countless gifts received,
   and pray for grace to keep the faith
   which saints of old believed.

3 To thee we come, O gracious Lord,
   the new-born year to bless;
   defend our land from pestilence,
   give peace and plenteousness.

4 Forgive this nation's many sins,
   the growth of vice restrain,
   and help us all with sin to strive,
   and crowns of life to gain.

5 From evil deeds that stain the past
   we now desire to flee,
   and pray that future years may all
   be spent, good Lord, for thee.

6 O Father, let thy watchful eye
   still look on us in love,
   that we may praise thee, year by year,
   as angels do above.

Francis Pott (1832–1909)

84

Neander (Unser Herrscher) 87 87 87

Melody from Joachim Neander's
Alpha and Omega (Bremen, 1680)

1 Alleluia! raise the anthem,
   let the skies resound with praise;
   sing to him who found the ransom,
   Ancient of eternal Days:
   God from God, the Word incarnate,
   whom the heaven of heaven obeys.

2 Long before he raised the mountains,
   formed the seas or built the sky,
   love eternal, free and boundless,
   moved the Lord of life to die;
   fore-ordained the Prince of princes
   for the throne of Calvary.

3 There, for us and our redemption,
   see him all his life-blood pour;
   there he wins our full salvation,
   dies that we may die no more;
   then, arising, lives for ever,
   reigning where he was before.

*4 Yet this earth he still remembers,
   still by him his flock are fed;
   for he gives them food immortal,
   gives himself, the living Bread;
   leads them where the precious fountain
   from the smitten rock is shed.

5 Laud and honour to the Father,
   laud and honour to the Son,
   laud and honour to the Spirit,
   ever Three and ever One,
   consubstantial[1], co-eternal,
   while unending ages run.

Job Hupton (1762–1849)
and *John Mason Neale* (1818–66) altd.

[1] Father, Son, and Holy Spirit are united in one common substance or nature.

85

Céad míle fáilte romhat   12 9 10 13   Irish traditional melody

1 Céad míle fáilte romhat, a Íosa, a Íosa,
   céad míle fáilte romhat, a Íosa.
   Céad míle fáilte romhat, a Shlánaitheoir,
   céad míle míle fáilte romhat, Íosa, a Íosa.

2 Glóir agus moladh duit, a Íosa, a Íosa,
   glóir agus moladh duit, a Íosa.
   Glóir agus moladh duit, a Shlánaitheoir,
   glóir, moladh agus buíochas duit, Íosa, a Íosa.

Irish Traditional

1 *Gladly I welcome you, O Jesus, O Jesus,*
   gladly I welcome you, O Jesus.
   Gladly I welcome you, Redeemer, Lord,
   a hundred thousand welcomes now, Jesus, O Jesus.

2 *Glory and praise to you, O Jesus, O Jesus,*
   glory and praise to you, O Jesus.
   Glory and praise to you, Redeemer, Lord,
   all glory, praise and thanks to you, Jesus, O Jesus.

English versification by *Donald Davison* (b. 1937)

86

Vulpius (Gelobt sei Gott)   888 with Alleluias   Melody from Melchior Vulpius's
Gesangbuch (Jena, 1609)

Al - le - lu - ia,_____ al - le - lu - ia,_____ al - le - lu - ia!

1 Christ is the King! O friends, rejoice;
brothers and sisters, with one voice
let the world know he is your choice.

Alleluia, alleluia, alleluia!

2 O magnify the Lord, and raise
anthems of joy and holy praise
for Christ's brave saints of ancient days.

3 They with a faith for ever new
followed the King, and round him drew
thousands of faithful servants true.

4 O Christian women, Christian men,
all the world over, seek again
the way disciples followed then.

5 Christ through all ages is the same:
place the same hope in his great name;
with the same faith his word proclaim.

6 Let love's unconquerable might
your scattered companies unite
in service to the Lord of light.

7 So shall God's will on earth be done,
new lamps be lit, new tasks begun,
and the whole Church at last be one.

G. K. A. Bell (1883–1958) altd.

87

Christe sanctorum (2)   10 11 11 6   Melody from *Paris Antiphoner* (1681)

Glo - ry   to   God   on   high.

1 Christ is the world's Light, he and none other;
   born in our darkness, he became our brother.
   If we have seen him, we have seen the Father:
       Glory to God on high!

2 Christ is the world's Peace, he and none other;
   no one can serve him and despise a brother.
   Who else unites us, one in God the Father?
       Glory to God on high!

3 Christ is the world's Life, he and none other;
   sold once for silver, murdered here, our brother—
   he who redeems us, reigns with God the Father:
       Glory to God on high!

4 Give God the glory, God and none other;
   give God the glory, Spirit, Son and Father;
   give God the glory, God in Man my brother:
       Glory to God on high!

F. Pratt Green (b. 1903)

88

Schönster Herr Jesu (Silesian) 569 558

Melody from Hoffman & Richter's
Silesian Folk-Songs (1842)

SECOND TUNE

Schönster Herr Jesu (Münster) 569 558

Melody from the
Münster Gesangbuch (1677)

Schönster Herr Jesu

1 Fairest Lord Jesus,
   Lord of all creation,
Jesus, of God and Mary the Son;
   you will I cherish,
   you will I honour,
you are my soul's delight and crown.

2 Fair are the meadows,
   fairer still the woodlands,
robed in the verdure and bloom of spring.
   Jesus is fairer,
   Jesus is purer,
he makes the saddest heart to sing.

3 Fair is the sunshine,
   fairer still the moonlight
and fair the twinkling starry host.
   Jesus shines brighter,
   Jesus shines clearer
than all the stars that heaven can boast.

4 Fair are the flowers,
   fairer still the children,
in all the freshness of youth arrayed:
   yet is their beauty⌣
   fading and fleeting;
my Jesus, yours will never fade.

5 All fairest beauty,
   heavenly and earthly,
wondrously, Jesus, in you I see;
   none can be nearer,
   fairer or dearer,
than you, my Saviour, are to me.

German (Münster, 1677)
tr. *Lilian Stevenson* (1870–1960) adpt.

89

Personent hodie   66 66 6 with Refrain

Melody from *Piae Cantiones*
(Griefswald, 1582)

Sing a - loud, loud, loud; sing a - loud, loud, loud:

God is good, God is truth, God is beau - ty— praise him!

1 God is love—his the care,
  tending each, everywhere;
  God is love—all is there!
    Jesus came to show him,
    that we all might know him:

    Sing aloud, loud, loud;
    sing aloud, loud, loud:
      God is good,
      God is truth,
      God is beauty—praise him!

2 Jesus shared all our pain,
  lived and died, rose again,
  rules our hearts, now as then—
    for he came to save us
    by the truth he gave us:

3 To our Lord praise we sing—
  light and life, friend and king,
  coming down love to bring,
    pattern for our duty,
    showing God in beauty:

Percy Dearmer (1867–1936) altd.

90

King divine 77 77 with Refrain

Charles Rigby (1901–1962)

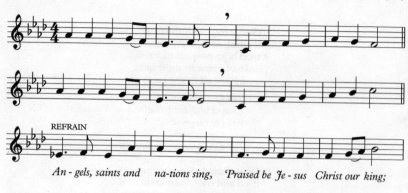

REFRAIN

An - gels, saints and na - tions sing, 'Praised be Je - sus Christ our king;

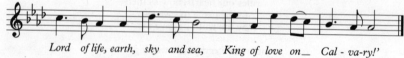

Lord of life, earth, sky and sea, King of love on— Cal - va-ry!'

SECOND TUNE

Rex 77 77 with Refrain

W. H. Grattan Flood (1859–1928)

REFRAIN

An - gels, saints and na - tions sing, 'Praised be Je - sus Christ our king;

Lord of life, earth, sky and sea, King of love on Cal - va - ry!'

1 Hail Redeemer, King divine!
  priest and Lamb, the throne is thine;
    king whose reign shall never cease,
    prince of everlasting peace:

> *Angels, saints and nations sing,*
> *'Praised be Jesus Christ our king;*
> *Lord of life, earth, sky and sea,*
> *King of love on Calvary!'*

2 King, whose name creation thrills,
  rule our minds, our hearts, our wills,
    till in peace each nation rings
    with thy praises, King of kings:

3 King, most holy, king of truth,
  guide the lowly, guide the youth;
    Christ, the king of glory bright,
    be to us eternal light:

Patrick Brennan (1877–1952)

91

He is Lord

Anon.

1 He is Lord, he is Lord;
   he is risen from the dead and he is Lord;
   every knee shall bow, every tongue confess
   that Jesus Christ is Lord.

*2 He is love, he is love;
   he has shown us by his cross that he is love;
   all his people sing with one voice of joy
   that Jesus Christ is love.

*3 He is life, he is life;
   he has died to set us free and he is life;
   and he calls us all to live evermore,
   for Jesus Christ is life.

*4 He is King, he is King;
   he will draw all nations to him, he is King;
   and the time shall be when the world shall sing
   that Jesus Christ is King.

Anon.

The second, third and fourth stanzas (marked for optional use)
are a later addition to the original credal statement of the first
stanza which is based on Philippians 2: 10–11.

92

St Peter 86 86 (CM)   Alexander R. Reinagle (1799–1877)

Alternative tune: 547 STRACATHRO

1 How sweet the name of Jesus sounds
   in a believer's ear!
It soothes our sorrows, heals our wounds,
   and drives away our fear.

2 It makes the wounded spirit whole,
   and calms the troubled breast;
'tis manna to the hungry soul,
   and to the weary rest.

3 Dear Name! the rock on which I build,
   my shield and hiding-place,
my never-failing treasury, filled
   with boundless stores of grace.

4 Jesus, my saviour, shepherd, friend,
   my prophet, priest, and king,
my lord, my life, my way, my end,
   accept the praise I bring.

5 Weak is the effort of my heart,
   and cold my warmest thought;
but when I see thee as thou art,
   I'll praise thee as I ought.

6 Till then I would thy love proclaim
   with every fleeting breath;
and may the music of thy Name
   refresh my soul in death.

John Newton (1725–1807) altd.

93

Lord of the dance

North American Shaker tune
adpt. by Sydney Carter (b. 1915)

1. I danced in the morn-ing when the
2. I danced for the scribe and the
3. I danced on the Sab-bath and I
4. I danced on a Fri - day when the
5. They cut me_ down_ and I

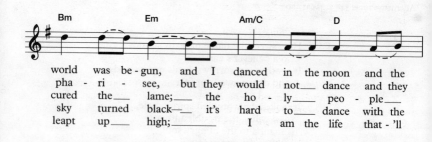

world was be - gun, and I danced in the moon and the
pha - ri - see, but they would not_ dance and they
cured the_ lame;_ the ho - ly_ peo - ple_
sky turned black— it's hard to_ dance with the
leapt up_ high;_____ I am the life that - 'll

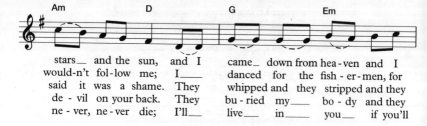

stars_ and the sun, and I came_ down from hea - ven and I
would-n't fol-low me; I____ danced for the fish - er-men, for
said it was a shame. They whipped and they stripped and they
de - vil on your back. They bu - ried my_ bo - dy and they
ne - ver, ne - ver die; I'll_ live_ in_ you_ if you'll

danced on the earth; at Beth-le - hem_ I had my birth.
James and_ John;_ they came with_ me and the Dance went on.
hung me on high, and they left me_ there on a Cross to die.
thought I'd_ gone,_ but I am the Dance and I still go on.
live in_ me——_ I am the Lord of the Dance, said he.

JESUS, SAVIOUR AND LORD

Dance, then, wher-ev-er you may be; I am the Lord of the Dance, said he, and I'll lead you all, wher-ev-er you may be, and I'll lead you all in the Dance, said he.

1 I danced in the morning when the world was begun,
  and I danced in the moon and the stars and the sun,
    and I came down from heaven and I danced on the earth;
    at Bethlehem I had my birth.

> *Dance, then, wherever you may be;*
> *I am the Lord of the Dance, said he,*
> *and I'll lead you all, wherever you may be,*
> *and I'll lead you all in the Dance, said he.*

2 I danced for the scribe and the pharisee,
  but they would not dance and they wouldn't follow me;
    I danced for the fishermen, for James and John;
    they came with me and the Dance went on.

3 I danced on the Sabbath and I cured the lame;
  the holy people said it was a shame.
    They whipped and they stripped and they hung me high,
    and they left me there on a Cross to die.

4 I danced on a Friday when the sky turned black—
  it's hard to dance with the devil on your back.
    They buried my body and they thought I'd gone,
    but I am the Dance and I still go on.

5 They cut me down and I leapt up high;
  I am the life that'll never, never die;
    I'll live in you if you'll live in me—
    I am the Lord of the Dance, said he.

Sydney Carter (b. 1915)

94

FIRST TUNE

Evelyns   65 65 D   William Henry Monk (1823–89)

SECOND TUNE

Camberwell   65 65 D   Michael Brierley (b. 1932)

Fine   *D.C.*

OPTIONAL BRIDGE

1 In the name of Jesus
        every knee shall bow,
    every tongue confess him
        King of glory now;
    'tis the Father's pleasure ‿
        we should call him Lord,
    who from the beginning
        was the mighty Word.

*2 Mighty and mysterious
        in the highest height,
    God from everlasting,
        very Light of Light;
    in the Father's bosom
        with the Spirit blessed,
    Love, in Love eternal,
        rest, in perfect rest.

*3 At his voice creation ‿
        sprang at once to sight,
    all the angel faces,
        all the hosts of light;
    thrones and dominations,
        stars upon their way,
    all the heavenly orders
        in their great array.

4 Humbled for a season,
        to receive a name
    from the lips of sinners
        unto whom he came;
    faithfully he bore it
        spotless to the last,
    brought it back victorious
        when from death he passed.

5 Bore it up triumphant
        with its human light,
    through all ranks of creatures
        to the central height;
    to the eternal Godhead,
        to the Father's throne,
    filled it with the glory ‿
        of his triumph won.

*6 Name him, Christians, name him,
        with love strong as death,
    but with awe and wonder,
        and with bated breath;
    he is God the Saviour,
        he is Christ the Lord,
    ever to be worshipped,
        trusted and adored.

7 In your hearts enthrone him;
        there let him subdue ‿
    all that is not holy,
        all that is not true;
    crown him as your captain
        in temptation's hour,
    let his will enfold you
        in its light and power.

8 With his Father's glory
        Jesus comes again,
    angel hosts attend him
        and announce his reign;
    for all wreaths of empire
        meet upon his brow,
    and our hearts confess him
        King of glory now.

Caroline M. Noel (1817–77) altd.
v. 1 based on Philippians 2: 10–11

95

Jesu, meine Freude 665 D 786

Melody from Johann Crüger's
Praxis Pietatis Melica (Berlin, 1653)
adpt. J. S. Bach (1685–1750)

Jesu, meine Freude

1 Jesu, priceless treasure,
source of purest pleasure,
truest friend to me;
ah, how long I've panted,
and my heart hath fainted,
thirsting, Lord, for thee!
Thine I am, O spotless Lamb,
I will suffer naught to hide thee,
naught I ask beside thee.

*2 In thine arm I rest me,
foes who would molest me
cannot reach me here;
though the earth be shaking,
every heart be quaking,
Jesus calms my fear;
sin and hell in conflict fell
with their bitter storms assail me:
Jesus will not fail me.

3 Hence, all fears and sadness,
for the Lord of gladness,
Jesus, enters in;
those who love the Father,
though the storms may gather,
still have peace within;
yea, whate'er I here must bear,
still in thee lies purest pleasure,
Jesu, priceless treasure!

Johann Franck (1618–77)
tr. *Catherine Winkworth* (1829–78)

96

Jesus is Lord   11 12 11 12 with Refrain

David Mansell (b. 1936)

1 Jesus is Lord! Creation's voice proclaims it,
    for by his power each tree and flower was planned and made.
Jesus is Lord! The universe declares it—
    sun, moon and stars in heaven cry: 'Jesus is Lord!'

Jesus is Lord, Jesus is Lord!
Praise him with alleluias, for Jesus is Lord.

2 Jesus is Lord! Yet from his throne eternal
    in flesh he came to die in pain on Calvary's tree.
Jesus is Lord! From him all life proceeding,
    he gave his life a ransom, thus setting us free.

3 Jesus is Lord! O'er sin the mighty conqueror,
    from death he rose and all his foes shall own his name.
Jesus is Lord! God sends his Holy Spirit,
    showing by works of power that Jesus is Lord.

David Mansell (b. 1936)
based on Mark 10: 45; Romans 10: 9;
1 Corinthians 12: 3

97

Truro   88 88 (LM)

Melody from Thomas Williams'
Psalmodia Evangelica (London, 1789)

SECOND TUNE

Rimington   88 88 (LM)

Francis Duckworth (1862–1941)

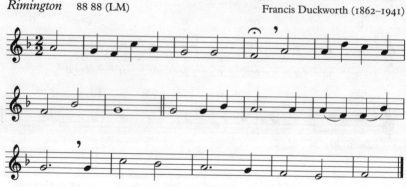

1 Jesus shall reign where'er the sun
   does his successive journeys run;
      his kingdom stretch from shore to shore,
      till moons shall wax and wane no more.

2 To him shall endless prayer be made,
   and praises throng to crown his head;
      his name, like incense, shall arise
      with every morning sacrifice.

3 People and realms of every tongue
   dwell on his love with sweetest song,
      and infant voices shall proclaim
      their early blessings on his name.

4 Blessings abound where'er he reigns;
   the prisoners leap to lose their chains,
      the weary find eternal rest,
      and all who suffer want are blessed.

5 Let all creation rise and bring
   peculiar honours to our King;
      angels descend with songs again,
      and earth repeat the long Amen.

Isaac Watts (1674–1748) altd.
based on Psalm 72: 12–19

98

FIRST VERSION

Harts 77 77

Benjamin Milgrove (1731–1810)

SECOND VERSION
(as given in 1960 edition)

Harts 77 77

Later form of melody
by Benjamin Milgrove (1731–1810)

THE NAMING OF JESUS
JANUARY 1

1 Jesus! Name of wondrous love!
 Name all other names above!
  Unto which must every knee
  bow in deep humility.

2 Jesus! Name by God decreed
 for this child of David's seed,
  which the angel Gabriel
  did the maiden mother tell.

3 Jesus! Name of priceless worth
 to the fallen of the earth,
  for the promise that it gave,
  'Jesus shall his people save'.

4 Jesus! Name of mercy mild,
 given to the holy child
  when the cup of human woe
  first he tasted here below.

5 Jesus! only Name that's given
 to all people under heaven,
  whereby those to sin enslaved
  burst their fetters and are saved.

6 Jesus! Name of wondrous love!
 Human Name of God above!
  Pleading only this, we claim
  our salvation in that name.

W. Walsham How (1823–97) altd.

99

Lydia   86 86 (CM) extended

Pub. anonymously 1844
attrib. Thomas Phillips (1735–1807)

The last line of each verse is repeated.

1 Jesus, the name high over all,
  in hell, or earth, or sky:
angels and mortals prostrate fall,
  and devils fear and fly.

2 Jesus, the name to sinners dear,
  the name to sinners given;
it scatters all their guilty fear,
  it turns their hell to heav'n.

3 Jesus the prisoner's fetters breaks,
  and bruises Satan's head;
power into strengthless souls he speaks,
  and life into the dead.

*4 O that the world might taste and see
  the riches of his grace!
The arms of love that compass me
  would all the world embrace.

*5 His righteousness alone I show,
  his saving grace proclaim:
'tis all my business here below
  to cry 'Behold the Lamb!'

6 Happy, if with my final breath
  I might but gasp his name,
preach him to all, and cry in death
  'Behold, behold the Lamb!'

Charles Wesley (1707–88) altd.

100

Jesus loves me   77 77 with Refrain

Melody (1862) by
William B. Bradbury (1816–88)

Yes, Je - sus loves me! Yes, Je - sus loves me!

Yes, Je - sus loves me! The Bi - ble tells me so.

The small notes indicate the original rhythm.

1 Jesus loves me: this I know,
   for the Bible tells me so;
      little ones to him belong,
      they are weak, but he is strong.

   Yes, Jesus loves me!
   Yes, Jesus loves me!
   Yes, Jesus loves me!
   The Bible tells me so.

2 Jesus loves me: he who died
   heaven's gate to open wide;
      he will help me and will stay
      close beside me all the way.

   Anna B. Warner (1820–1915) altd.

101

St Bernard   86 86 (CM)   Adapted from *Tochter Sion* (Cologne, 1741)

Alternative tunes: 654 GRÄFENBERG (NUN DANKET ALL)   673i METZLER'S REDHEAD (ST MARY MAGDALENE)

Jesu, dulcis memoria

1 Jesus, the very thought of thee
    with sweetness fills the breast;
  but sweeter far thy face to see,
    and in thy presence rest.

2 No voice can sing, no heart can frame,
    nor can the memory find
  a sweeter sound than thy blessed name,
    O Saviour of mankind!

3 O hope of every contrite heart,
    O joy of all the meek,
  to those who ask how kind thou art,
    how good to those who seek!

4 But what to those who find? Ah, this
    nor tongue nor pen can show:
  the love of Jesus, what it is
    none but his loved ones know.

*5 Jesus, thy mercies are untold
    through each returning day;
  thy love exceeds a thousandfold
    whatever we can say.

6 Jesus, our only joy be thou,
    as thou our prize wilt be;
  in thee be all our glory now,
    and through eternity.

                              12th cent.
          tr. *Edward Caswall* (1814–78) altd.

102

Majestas   66 55 66 64   Michael Baughen (b. 1930)

1 Name of all majesty,
   fathomless mystery,
   King of the ages
      by angels adored;
   power and authority,
   splendour and dignity,
   bow to his mastery,
      Jesus is Lord!

2 Child of our destiny,
   God from eternity,
   love of the Father
      on sinners outpoured;
   see now what God has done
   sending his only Son,
   Christ the belovèd one,
      Jesus is Lord!

3 Saviour of Calvary,
   costliest victory,
   darkness defeated
      and Eden restored;
   born as a man to die,
   nailed to a cross on high,
   cold in the grave to lie,
      Jesus is Lord!

4 Source of all sovereignty,
   light, immortality,
   life everlasting
      and heaven assured;
   so with the ransomed, we
   praise him eternally,
   Christ in his majesty,
      Jesus is Lord!

Timothy Dudley-Smith (b. 1926)

103

Londonderry Air (2)   11 10 11 10 11 10 11 12   Irish traditional melody
from Limavady, Co. Londonderry

1 O Christ the same, through all our story's pages,
  our loves and hopes, our failures and our fears;
 eternal Lord, the King of all the ages,
  unchanging still, amid the passing years—
 O living Word, the source of all creation,
  who spread the skies, and set the stars ablaze,
 O Christ the same, who wrought our whole salvation,
  we bring our thanks to you for all our yesterdays.

2 O Christ the same, the friend of sinners sharing
  our inmost thoughts, the secrets none can hide,
 still as of old upon your body bearing
  the marks of love, in triumph glorified—
 O Son of Man, who stooped for us from heaven,
  O Prince of life, in all your saving power,
 O Christ the same, to whom our hearts are given,
  we bring our thanks to you for this the present hour.

3 O Christ the same, secure within whose keeping
  our lives and loves, our days and years remain,
 our work and rest, our waking and our sleeping,
  our calm and storm, our pleasure and our pain—
 O Lord of love, for all our joys and sorrows,
  for all our hopes, when earth shall fade and flee,
 O Christ the same, beyond our brief tomorrows,
  we bring our thanks to you for all that is to be.

Timothy Dudley-Smith (b. 1926)

104

Gladness   86 86 (CM)   George William Torrance (1835–1907)

Lyngham   86 86 (CM) extended   Thomas Jarman (1782–1862)

1 O for a thousand tongues to sing
   my dear Redeemer's praise,
the glories of my God and King,
   the triumphs of his grace!

2 Jesus! the name that charms our fears,
   that bids our sorrows cease;
'tis music in the sinner's ears,
   'tis life, and health, and peace!

3 He breaks the power of cancelled sin,
   he sets the prisoner free;
his blood can make the foulest clean,
   his blood availed for me.

4 He speaks; and, listening to his voice,
   new life the dead receive;
the mournful broken hearts rejoice;
   the humble poor believe.

5 Hear him, ye deaf; his praise, ye dumb,
   your loosened tongues employ;
ye blind, behold your Saviour come,
   and leap, ye lame, for joy.

6 My gracious Master and my God,
   assist me to proclaim,
to spread through all the world abroad,
   the honours of thy Name.

Charles Wesley (1707–88)

105

Ebenezer 87 87 D

From an anthem by Thomas J. Williams (1869–1944)

1 O the deep, deep love of Jesus,
  vast, unmeasured, boundless, free,
rolling as a mighty ocean
  in its fullness over me!
Underneath me, all around me,
  is the current of his love:
leading onward, leading homeward,
  to that glorious rest above.

2 O the deep, deep love of Jesus—
  spread his praise from shore to shore!
He who loves us, ever loves us,
  changes never, nevermore;
he who died to save his loved ones,
  intercedes for them above;
he who called them his own people
  watches over them in love.

3 O the deep, deep love of Jesus,
  love of every love the best;
vast the ocean of his blessing,
  sweet the haven of his rest!
O the deep, deep love of Jesus—
  for my Heaven of heavens is he;
this my everlasting glory—
  Jesus' mighty love for me.

Samuel T. Francis (1834–1925) altd.

106

St Botolph   86 86 (CM)   Gordon Slater (1896–1979)

Jesu, rex admirabilis

1 O Jesus, King most wonderful,
    thou conqueror renowned,
  thou sweetness most ineffable,
    in whom all joys are found!

2 When once thou visitest the heart,
    then truth begins to shine,
  then earthly vanities depart,
    then kindles love divine.

3 Thee, Jesus, may our voices bless,
    thee may we love alone,
  and ever in our lives express
    the image of thine own.

4 Abide with us, and let thy light
    shine, Lord, on every heart;
  dispel the darkness of our night,
    and joy to all impart.

5 Jesus, our love and joy, to thee,
    the Virgin's holy Son,
  all might and praise and glory be
    while endless ages run.

                        12th cent.
            tr. *Edward Caswall* (1814–78) altd.

This hymn was originally the second part of hymn 101.

107

Living, he loved me   11 10 11 10 with Refrain   Charles H. Marsh (1886–1956)

REFRAIN

Liv-ing, he loved me; dy-ing, he saved me; bur-ied, he car - ried my sins far a - way;___ ris-ing, he jus - ti-fied free-ly for ev - er: one day he's com - ing, O glo - ri - ous day!___

JESUS, SAVIOUR AND LORD

1 One day when heaven was filled with his praises,
   one day when sin was as black as could be,
Jesus came forth to be born of a virgin,
   dwelt among us, my example is he!

   Living, he loved me; dying, he saved me;
      buried, he carried my sins far away;
   rising, he justified freely for ever:
      one day he's coming, O glorious day!

2 One day they led him up Calvary's mountain,
   one day they nailed him to die on the tree;
suffering anguish, despised and rejected;
   bearing our sins, my Redeemer is he.

3 One day they left him alone in the garden,
   one day he rested, from suffering free;
angels came down o'er his tomb to keep vigil;
   hope of the hopeless, my Saviour is he.

4 One day the grave could contain him no longer,
   one day the stone rolled away from the door;
then he arose, over death he had conquered,
   now is ascended, my Lord evermore!

5 One day the trumpet will sound for his coming,
   one day the skies with his glory will shine;
wonderful day, my belovèd ones bringing;
   glorious Saviour, this Jesus is mine!

J. Wilbur Chapman (1859–1918)

108

Gerontius   86 86 (CM)   John Bacchus Dykes (1823–76)

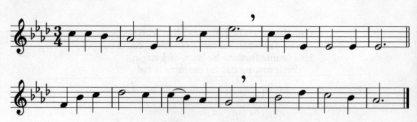

Chorus angelorum   86 86 (CM)   Arthur Somervell (1863–1937)

Billing   86 86 (CM)   Richard R. Terry (1865–1938)

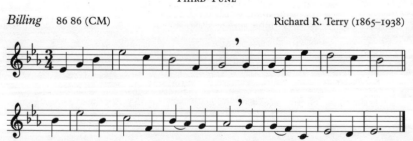

Alternative tune: 349 RICHMOND

1 Praise to the Holiest in the height,
    and in the depth be praise;
in all his words most wonderful,
    most sure in all his ways.

2 O loving wisdom of our God!
    When all was sin and shame,
a second Adam to the fight
    and to the rescue came.

3 O wisest love! that flesh and blood,
    which did in Adam fail,
should strive afresh against the foe,
    should strive and should prevail;

4 and that a higher gift than grace
    should flesh and blood refine,
God's presence, and his very self
    and essence all-divine.

5 O generous love! that he who smote
    in Man, for man, the foe,
the double agony in Man,
    for man, should undergo;

6 and in the garden secretly,
    and on the cross on high,
should teach his brethren, and inspire
    to suffer and to die.

7 Praise to the Holiest in the height,
    and in the depth be praise;
in all his words most wonderful,
    most sure in all his ways.

John Henry Newman (1801–90)
from 'The Dream of Gerontius'

109

Sing alleluia to the Lord

Linda Stassen

JESUS, SAVIOUR AND LORD

1 Sing alleluia to the Lord,
  sing alleluia to the Lord,
  sing alleluia, sing alleluia,
  sing alleluia to the Lord.

2 Jesus is risen from the dead,
  Jesus is risen from the dead,
  Jesus is risen, Jesus is risen,
  Jesus is risen from the dead.

3 Jesus is Lord of heaven and earth,
  Jesus is Lord of heaven and earth,
  Jesus is Lord, Jesus is Lord,
  Jesus is Lord of heaven and earth!

4 Jesus is coming for his own,
  Jesus is coming for his own,
  Jesus is coming, Jesus is coming,
  Jesus is coming for his own.

v. 1 *Linda Stassen*
vv. 2–4 Anon.

110

Stories of Jesus   84 84 54 54

F. A. Challinor (1866–1952)

1 Tell me the stories of Jesus
    I love to hear;
  things I would ask him to tell me
    if he were here;
  scenes by the wayside,
    tales of the sea,
  stories of Jesus,
    tell them to me.

2 First let me hear how the children
    stood round his knee;
  and I shall think of his blessing
    resting on me;
  words full of kindness,
    deeds full of grace,
  while love was shining
    in Jesus' face.

3 Tell me, in words full of wonder,
　　how rolled the sea,
　tossing the boat in a tempest
　　on Galilee;
　how Jesus, doing
　　his Father's will,
　ended the storm with
　　'Peace, peace be still'.

4 Into the city I'd follow
　　the children's band,
　waving a branch of the palm-tree
　　high in my hand;
　worshipping Jesus,
　　yes, I would sing
　loudest hosannas,
　　for he is King!

5 Show me that scene in the garden,
　　of bitter pain;
　and of the cross where my Saviour
　　for me was slain;
　and, through the sadness,
　　help me to see
　how Jesus suffered
　　for love of me.

6 Tell me with joy of his rising
　　up from the grave;
　and how he still lives triumphant,
　　ready to save.
　Wonderful story,
　　Jesus my friend,
　living and loving
　　right to the end.

W. H. Parker (1845–1929) altd.
v. 6 *Ruth Fagg*

111

Evan   86 86 (CM)   William Henry Havergal (1793–1870)

1 There is a name I love to hear,
  I love to sing its worth;
  it sounds like music in mine ear,
  the sweetest name on earth.

2 It tells me of a Saviour's love,
  who died to set me free;
  it tells me of his precious Blood,
  the sinner's perfect plea.

3 It tells me of a Father's smile
  beaming upon his child;
  it cheers me through this 'little while',
  through desert waste and wild.

4 Jesus, the name I love so well,
  the name I love to hear;
  no saint on earth its worth can tell,
  no heart conceive how dear.

5 This name shall shed its fragrance still
  along this thorny road,
  shall sweetly smooth the rugged hill
  that leads me up to God.

6 And there with all the blood-bought throng,
  from sin and sorrow free,
  I'll sing the new eternal song
  of Jesus' love to me.

Frederick Whitfield (1829–1904)

112

There is a Redeemer

Melody Green

1 There is a Redeemer,
Jesus, God's own Son,
precious Lamb of God, Messiah,
Holy One.

Thank you, O my Father,
for giving us your Son,
and leaving your Spirit
till the work on earth is done.

2 Jesus my Redeemer,
name above all names,
precious Lamb of God, Messiah,
O for sinners slain.

3 When I stand in glory
I will see his face,
and there I'll serve my King forever
in that holy place.

Melody Green
based on Isaiah 47: 4; Acts 1: 8;
Philippians 2: 9; Revelation 22: 3–4

113

Battle Hymn   15 15 15 6 with Refrain

William Steffe (*c.*1852)

REFRAIN

Come and sing a-loud your prais - es, come and sing a-loud your prais - es, come and sing a-loud your prais - es, for Je - sus Christ is here.

JESUS, SAVIOUR AND LORD

1 There is singing in the desert, there is laughter in the skies,
  there are wise men filled with wonder, there are shepherds with surprise;
  you can tell the world is dancing by the light that's in their eyes,
      for Jesus Christ is here.

> *Come and sing aloud your praises,*
> *come and sing aloud your praises,*
> *come and sing aloud your praises,*
>   *for Jesus Christ is here.*

2 He hears deaf men by the lakeside, he sees blind men in the streets,
  he goes up to those who cannot walk, he talks to all he meets,
  touching silken robes or tattered clothes, it's everyone he greets,
      for Jesus Christ is here.

Geoffrey Marshall-Taylor (b. 1943)

114

Margaret

Timothy R. Matthews (1826–1910)

O come to my heart, Lord Je - sus; there is room in my heart for thee.

1 Thou didst leave thy throne and thy kingly crown
   when thou camest to earth for me;
   but in Bethlehem's home was there found no room
   for thy holy nativity.

   O come to my heart, Lord Jesus;
   there is room in my heart for thee.

2 Heaven's arches rang when the angels sang,
   to proclaim thy royal degree;
   yet in lowly birth didst thou come to earth,
   and in deepest humility.

*3 Though the fox found rest, and the bird its nest
   in the shade of the cedar tree;
   yet the earth was the bed for thy weary head
   in the desert of Galilee.

4 Though thou camest, Lord, with the living word
   that should set thy people free;
   yet with mocking scorn, and with crown of thorn
   they bore thee to Calvary.

5 When the heav'ns shall ring, and the angels sing,
   at thy coming to victory,
   let thy voice call me home, saying, 'Yet there is room,
   there is room at my side for thee'.

Emily E. S. Elliott (1836–1897) altd.
based on Luke 2: 7; Matthew 8: 20

115

St James   86 86 (CM)   Raphael Courteville (*c.*1676–1772)

1 Thou art the Way: to thee alone
    from sin and death we flee;
  and they who would the Father seek
    must seek him, Lord, by thee.

2 Thou art the Truth: thy word alone
    true wisdom can impart;
  thou only canst inform the mind
    and purify the heart.

3 Thou art the Life: the rending tomb
    proclaims thy conquering arm;
  and those who put their trust in thee
    nor death nor hell shall harm.

4 Thou art the Way, the Truth, the Life:
    grant us that Way to know,
  that Truth to keep, that Life to win,
    whose joys eternal flow.

George W. Doane (1799–1859) altd.
based on John 14: 6

116

Jackson (*Byzantium*)   86 86 (CM)

Thomas Jackson (1715–81)
from *Twelve Psalm Tunes* (1780)

1 To our Redeemer's glorious name,
    awake the sacred song!
O may his love, immortal theme,
    tune every heart and tongue!

2 His love, what mortal thought can reach,
    what mortal tongue display?
Imagination's utmost stretch
    in wonder dies away.

3 The Saviour left his throne on high,
    left the bright realms of bliss,
and came to earth, for us to die;
    was ever love like this?

4 O Lord, while we adoring pay
    our humble thanks to thee,
may every heart with rapture say,
    'The Saviour died for me'.

Anne Steele (1716–78) altd.

117

Melody set to *Pange lingua*
in C. Ett's *Cantica Sacra* (Munich, 1840)

Oriel   87 87 87

Gloriosi Salvatoris nominis praeconia

1 To the name of our salvation
    laud and honour let us pay;
 which for many_a generation
    hid in God's foreknowledge lay,
 but with holy exultation
    we may sing aloud today.

2 Jesus is the name we treasure,
    name beyond what words can tell;
 name of gladness, name of pleasure,
    ear and heart delighting well;
 name of sweetness passing measure,
    saving us from sin and hell.

3 'Tis the name that whoso preaches
    speaks like music to the ear;
 who in prayer this name beseeches
    finds sweet comfort always near;
 who its perfect wisdom reaches
    heavenly joy possesses here.

4 Jesus is the name exalted
    over every other name;
 in this name whene'er assaulted,
    we can put our foes to shame;
 strength to them who else had halted,
    eyes to blind, and feet to lame.

5 Therefore we in love adoring
    this most blessèd name revere,
 Holy Jesus, thee imploring
    so to write it in us here,
 that hereafter, heavenward soaring,
    we may sing with angels there.

15th cent. tr. *John Mason Neale* (1818–66) altd.
based on Philippians 2: 9–11

GOD THE SON, REDEEMER

118

Glasgow   86 86 (CM)

Melody from Thomas Moore's
The Psalm-Singer's Pocket Companion
(Glasgow, *c.* 1756)

1 Behold, the mountain of the Lord
  in latter days shall rise
 on mountain tops, above the hills,
  and draw the wondering eyes.

2 To this the joyful nations round,
  all tribes and tongues, shall flow;
 'up to the hill of God', they'll say,
  'and to his house we'll go.'

3 The beam that shines from Zion hill
  shall lighten every land;
 the king who reigns in Salem's towers
  shall all the world command.

4 Among the nations he shall judge;
  his judgments truth shall guide;
 his sceptre shall protect the just,
  and quell the sinner's pride.

5 No strife shall rage, nor hostile feuds
  disturb those peaceful years;
 to ploughshares all shall beat their swords,
  to pruning-hooks their spears.

6 Come then, O come from every land,
  to worship at his shrine;
 and, walking in the light of God,
  with holy beauties shine.

Scottish Paraphrases (1781) altd.
based on Isaiah 2: 2–6 and Micah 4: 1–5

162

119

FIRST TUNE

John Stainer (1840–1901)
from *The Crucifixion*

Cross of Jesus 87 87

SECOND TUNE

Later form of a melody by William Boyce (1711–79)
as given in S. S. Wesley's *European Psalmist* (1872)

Halton Holgate 87 87

Alternative tunes: 123 STUTTGART 268 HYFRYDOL

1 Come, thou long-expected Jesus,
   born to set thy people free;
   from our fears and sins release us;
   let us find our rest in thee.

2 Israel's strength and consolation,
   hope of all the earth thou art;
   dear desire of every nation,
   joy of every longing heart.

3 Born thy people to deliver,
   born a child and yet a king;
   born to reign in us for ever,
   now thy gracious kingdom bring.

4 By thine own eternal Spirit,
   rule in all our hearts alone:
   by thine all-sufficient merit,
   raise us to thy glorious throne.

Charles Wesley (1707–88)

120

Psalm 42 (Genevan)   87 87 77 88

Melody by Louis Bourgeois (*c.*1510–61)
in the French edition of the
Genevan Psalter (1551)

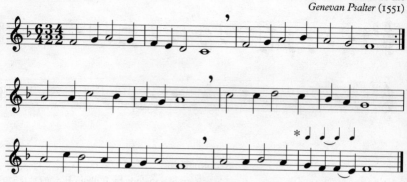

* Original rhythm

Tröstet, tröstet meine Lieben

1 Comfort, comfort ye my people,
   speak ye peace, thus saith our God;
comfort those who sit in darkness
   mourning 'neath their sorrows' load.
Speak ye to Jerusalem
of the peace that waits for them;
   tell her that her sins I cover,
   and her warfare now is over.

*2 Yes, her sins our God will pardon,
   blotting out each dark misdeed;
all that well deserved his anger
   he will no more see nor heed.
She hath suffered many_a day,
now her griefs have passed away,
   God will change her pining sadness
   into ever-springing gladness.

3 Hark, the voice of one that crieth
   in the desert far and near,
calling us to new repentance,
   since the kingdom now is here.
Oh, that warning cry obey!
Now prepare for God a way;
   let the valleys rise to meet him
   and the hills bow down to greet him.

4 Make ye straight what long was crookèd,
   make the rougher places plain;
let your hearts be true and humble,
   as befits his holy reign.
For the glory of the Lord
now o'er earth is shed abroad;
   and all flesh shall see the token
   that the word is never broken.

Johannes Olearius (1611–84)
tr. *Catherine Winkworth* (1827–78) altd.
based on Isaiah 40: 1–5

121

Conditor alme   88 88 (LM)

Plainsong melody, mode iv

A - men.

Soldau   88 88 (LM)

Melody from Johann Walther's
Geystliche Gesangk Buchleyn (Wittenberg, 1524)
as given in Dibdin's *Standard Psalm Book* (1852)

Alternative tune: 567 SONG 34 (ANGELS' SONG)

Conditor alme siderum

1 Creator of the starry height,
   thy people's everlasting light,
   Jesu, redeemer of us all,
   hear thou thy servants when they call.

2 Thou, grieving at the helpless cry
   of all creation doomed to die,
   didst come to save our fallen race
   by healing gifts of heav'nly grace.

3 When earth was near its evening hour,
   thou didst, in love's redeeming pow'r,
   like bridegroom from his chamber,
   come
   forth from a virgin-mother's womb.

4 At thy great name, exalted now,
   all knees in lowly homage bow;
   all things in heav'n and earth adore,
   and own thee King for evermore.

5 To thee, O Holy One, we pray,
   our judge in that tremendous day,
   ward off, while yet we dwell below,
   the weapons of our crafty foe.

6 To God the Father, God the Son
   and God the Spirit, Three in One,
   praise, honour, might and glory be
   from age to age eternally.

7th-century Latin
tr. *John Mason Neale* (1818–66)

165

122

The Advent Prose — 'Rorate caeli desuper'

Rorate caeli

Plainsong: mode i
Words from ancient Advent Liturgies
based on Isaiah 40: 1–2; 43: 11 and 64: 6–11

REFRAIN

Drop down, ye hea-vens, from a-bove, and let the skies pour down right-eous-ness.

VERSES

1. Be not wroth ve — ry sore, O Lord, nei-ther re-mem-ber in-i-qui-ty

for ev — er: thy ho-ly ci-ties are a wil-der-ness, Si-on is___

a wil — der-ness, Je-ru — sa-lem a de — so-la — tion:

our ho-ly and our beau-ti-ful house,___ where our fa - thers praised thee.

2. We have sinned, and are as an un-clean thing, and we all do fade as a leaf:

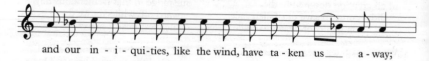

and our in - i - qui-ties, like the wind, have ta-ken us___ a-way;

The refrain is sung at the beginning and after each verse.

Traditionally, each verse is sung by a cantor and the following refrain is sung by all: at the beginning, the first phrase of the refrain is sung by the cantor and the second phrase by all. However, other arrangements are possible; for example, the verses may be sung by part or all of the choir, all present joining in the refrain.

thou hast— hid thy face from— us: and hast con-sumed us,

be - cause— of our———— in - i - qui - ties.

3. Ye are my wit-ness-es, saith the Lord, and my ser-vant whom I have

cho - sen; that ye may know me and be - lieve— me: I, e - ven I,

am the— Lord, and be - side me there is— no Sa - viour:

and there is none that can de - li - ver out—— of my— hand.

4. Com-fort— ye, com-fort ye my peo - ple, my sal-va-tion shall not tar - ry:

I have blot-ted out as— a thick cloud thy trans - gress - ions:

fear not,— for I will save— thee:— for I— am— the Lord thy— God,

the Ho - ly One of Is - ra - el, thy— Re - deem - er.

123

Stuttgart 87 87

Adapted from a melody in C. F. Witt's
Harmonia Sacra (Gotha, 1715)

THE ANNUNCIATION OF OUR LORD
MARCH 25

1 God the Father sends his angel
   from his throne in heav'n above;
when the angel speaks to Mary,
   Mary's heart is full of love.

2 Gabriel says: 'Rejoice, O Mary,
   full of grace: the Lord is near.
You will bear God's Son, O Maiden:
   God has promised, have no fear'.

3 Mary says: 'I am God's servant;
   I will keep his holy Word;
I will gladly be the mother
   of my Saviour and my Lord'.

4 Now the Spirit overshadows
   God the Father's chosen one:
she becomes the maiden-mother
   of the Father's only Son.

5 God the Word, the Father's Wisdom
   comes on earth as Mary's child:
God, our glory, shines among us,
   God with us is reconciled.

6 Praise the Father, fount of blessing,
   praise his Son, whom Mary bore,
praise the Lord of life, the Spirit,
   praise one God for evermore.

James Quinn (b. 1919)
based on Luke 1: 26–38

124

Bristol   86 86 (CM)   From Thomas Ravenscroft's *Psalmes* (1621)

For the significance of the small notes above the stave, see the Musical Preface.
Alternative tune: 285 ST MAGNUS (NOTTINGHAM)

1 Hark the glad sound! the Saviour comes,
   the Saviour promised long:
   let every heart prepare a throne,
   and every voice a song.

2 He comes the prisoners to release,
   in Satan's bondage held;
   the gates of brass before him burst,
   the iron fetters yield.

3 He comes the broken heart to bind,
   the wounded soul to cure;
   and with the treasures of his grace
   to enrich the humble poor.

4 Our glad hosannas, Prince of peace,
   your welcome shall proclaim;
   and heaven's eternal arches ring
   with your belovèd name.

Philip Doddridge (1702–51) altd.
based on Luke 4: 18–19

125

Crüger   76 76 D

adpt. by William Henry Monk (1823–89)
from a chorale by Johann Crüger (1598–1662)
in his *Gesangbuch* (Berlin, 1640)

1 Hail to the Lord's anointed,
   great David's greater Son!
Hail, in the time appointed,
   his reign on earth begun!
he comes to break oppression,
   to set the captive free,
to take away transgression,
   and rule in equity.

*2 He comes with succour speedy
   to those who suffer wrong;
to help the poor and needy
   and bid the weak be strong;
to give them songs for sighing,
   their darkness turn to light,
whose souls, condemned and dying,
   were precious in his sight.

3 He shall come down like showers
   upon the fruitful earth;
and love, joy, hope, like flowers,
   spring in his path to birth:
before him on the mountains
   shall peace, the herald, go;
and righteousness in fountains
   from hill to valley flow.

4 Kings shall fall down before him,
   and gold and incense bring;
all nations shall adore him,
   his praise all people sing:
to him shall prayer unceasing
   and daily vows ascend;
his kingdom still increasing,
   a kingdom without end.

5 O'er every foe victorious,
   he on his throne shall rest,
from age to age more glorious,
   all-blessing and all-blessed:
the tide of time shall never
   his covenant remove;
his name shall stand for ever;
   that name to us is Love.

James Montgomery (1771–1854)
based on Psalm 72

126

Merton   87 87

William Henry Monk (1823–89)

Vox clara ecce intonat

1 Hark! a thrilling voice is sounding,
    'Christ is nigh', it seems to say;
  'Cast away the dreams of darkness,
    O ye children of the day!'

2 Wakened by the solemn warning,
    let the earth-bound soul arise;
  Christ, her Sun, all ill dispelling,
    shines upon the morning skies.

3 Lo! the Lamb, so long expected,
    comes with pardon down from heaven:
  let us haste, with tears of sorrow,
    one and all to be forgiven;

4 that when next he comes in glory,
    and the world is wrapped in fear,
  with his mercy he may shield us,
    and with words of love draw near.

5 Honour, glory, might and blessing
    to the Father and the Son,
  with the everlasting Spirit,
    while eternal ages run.

6th-century Latin
tr. *Edward Caswall* (1814–78)

127

Highwood   11 10 11 10   Richard R. Terry (1865–1938)

1 Hark what a sound, and too divine for hearing,
  stirs on the earth and trembles in the air!
Is it the thunder of the Lord's appearing?
  Is it the music of his people's prayer?

2 Surely he cometh, and a thousand voices
  shout to the saints, and to the deaf are dumb;
surely he cometh, and the earth rejoices,
  glad in his coming who hath sworn, 'I come'.

3 This hath he done, and shall we not adore him?
  This shall he do, and can we still despair?
Come, let us quickly fling ourselves before him,
  cast at his feet the burden of our care.

4 Yea, through life, death, through sorrow and through sinning
  he shall suffice me, for he hath sufficed:
Christ is the end, for Christ was the beginning,
  Christ the beginning, for the end is Christ.

Frederic W. H. Myers (1843–1901)

128

Little Cornard   66 66 88

Martin Shaw (1875–1958)

1 Hills of the north, rejoice,
     river and mountain-spring,
   hark to the advent voice;
     valley and lowland, sing.
   Christ comes in righteousness and love,
   he brings salvation from above.

2 Isles of the southern seas,
     sing to the listening earth;
   carry on every breeze⌣
     hope of the world's new birth:
   in Christ shall all be made anew;
   his word is sure, his promise true.

3 Lands of the east, arise!
     He is your brightest morn;
   greet him with joyous eyes,
     praise shall his path adorn:
   the God whom you have longed to know⌣
   in Christ draws near, and calls you now.

4 Shores of the utmost west,
     lands of the setting sun,
   welcome the heavenly guest
     in whom the dawn has come:
   he brings a never-ending light,
   who triumphed o'er our darkest night.

5 Shout as you journey home;
     songs be in every mouth!
   Lo, from the north they come,
     from east and west and south:
   in Jesus all shall find their rest,
   in him the longing earth be blessed.

Charles E. Oakley (1832–65)
and Editors of English Praise, altd.

GOD THE SON, REDEEMER

129

Our God reigns

Leonard Smith Jnr. (b. 1942)

1. How love-ly on the moun-tains are the feet of him who brings good news,_____ good news, an-noun-cing peace, pro-claim-ing news of hap-pi-ness:__ __ our God reigns,_____ our God reigns!_____

REFRAIN

Our God reigns!_____ Our God reigns!_____ __ Our God reigns!_____ Our God reigns!_____

1 How lovely on the mountains are the feet of him
  who brings good news, good news,
  announcing peace, proclaiming news of happiness:
  our God reigns, our God reigns!

  Our God reigns! (4 times)

2 You watchmen, lift your voices joyfully as one,
  shout for your king, your king!
  See eye to eye the Lord restoring Zion:
  our God reigns, our God reigns!

3 Waste places of Jerusalem, break forth with joy!
  We are redeemed, redeemed.
  The Lord has saved and comforted his people:
  our God reigns, our God reigns!

4 Ends of the earth, see the salvation of our God!
  Jesus is Lord, is Lord!
  Before the nations, he has bared his holy arm:
  our God reigns, our God reigns!

Leonard E. Smith Jnr. (b. 1942)
based on Isaiah 52: 7–10

130

St Thomas   87 87 87

18th-century melody from Samuel Webbe's
Essay on the Church Plain Chant (London, 1782)

1 Jesus came, the heavens adoring,
   came with peace from realms on high;
Jesus came for our redemption,
   lowly came on earth to die;
      alleluia! alleluia!—
   came in deep humility.

2 Jesus comes again in mercy,
   when our hearts are bowed with care;
Jesus comes again in answer
   to an earnest heartfelt prayer;
      alleluia! alleluia!—
   comes to save us from despair.

3 Jesus comes to hearts rejoicing,
   bringing news of sins forgiven;
Jesus comes in sounds of gladness,
   leading souls redeemed to heaven;
      alleluia! alleluia!—
   now the gate of death is riven.

4 Jesus comes on clouds triumphant,
   when the heavens shall pass away;
Jesus comes again in glory;
   let us then our homage pay:
      alleluia! ever singing
   till the dawn of endless day.

Godfrey Thring (1823–1903) altd.

131

Wellington 88 88 (LM)

Michael Fleming (b. 1928)

Alternative tune: 243ii GONFALON ROYAL

Macht hoch die Thür, das Thor macht weit

1 Lift up your heads, you mighty gates;
   behold, the king of glory waits!
       The King of kings is drawing near;
       the Saviour of the world is here.

2 O blessed the land, the city blessed,
   where Christ the ruler is confessed!
       O happy hearts and happy homes
       to whom this King in triumph comes.

3 Fling wide the portals of your heart;
   make it a temple set apart ⌣
       from earthly use for heaven's employ,
       adorned with prayer and love and joy.

4 Redeemer, come, with us abide!
   Our hearts to you we open wide:
       let us your inner presence feel;
       your grace and love in us reveal.

Georg Weissel (1590–1635) based on Psalm 24: 7, 9
tr. *Catherine Winkworth* (1829–78) altd.

132

Helmsley   87 87 47 extended

Later form of a melody in John Wesley's
Select Hymns with Tunes Annext (1765)

* Version given in 1960 edition:

1 Lo! he comes with clouds descending,
    once for favoured sinners slain;
  thousand thousand saints attending
    swell the triumph of his train:
      alleluia!
    God appears on earth to reign.

2 Every eye shall now behold him
    robed in dreadful majesty;
  we who set at nought and sold him,
    pierced, and nailed him to the tree:
      Lord, have mercy,
    let us all thine Advent see.

3 Those dear tokens of his Passion
    still his dazzling body bears,
  cause of endless exultation
    to his ransomed worshippers:
      with what rapture
    gaze we on those glorious scars!

4 Yea, amen, let all adore thee,
    high on thine eternal throne;
  Saviour, take the power and glory;
    claim the kingdom for thine own:
      O come quickly,
    Everlasting God, come down.

John Cennick (1718–55)
and *Charles Wesley* (1707–88) altd.
based on Revelation 1: 7

133

Personent hodie   66 66 6 with Refrain

Melody from *Piae Cantiones*
(Griefswald, 1582)

VERSES

REFRAIN

Ring, bells, ring,   ring,   ring!   Sing, choirs, sing,   sing,   sing!

1–3. When he comes,   when he comes,   who will make him   wel - come?
  4. Je - sus comes!   Je - sus comes!   We will make him   wel - come.

1 Long ago, prophets knew
  Christ would come, born a Jew,
  come to make all things new,
    bear his people's burden,
    freely love and pardon.

  Ring, bells, ring, ring, ring!
  Sing, choirs, sing, sing, sing!
  When he comes, when he comes,
  who will make him welcome?

2 God in time, God in man,
  this is God's timeless plan:
  he will come, as a man,
    born himself of woman,
    God divinely human:

3 Mary hail! Though afraid,
  she believed, she obeyed.
  In her womb, God is laid:
    till the time expected,
    nurtured and protected:

4 Journey ends! Where afar
  Bethl'em shines, like a star,
  stable door stands ajar.
    Unborn Son of Mary,
    Saviour, do not tarry!

  Ring, bells, ring, ring, ring!
  Sing, choirs, sing, sing, sing!
  Jesus comes! Jesus comes!
  We will make him welcome.

        F. Pratt Green (b. 1903)
        based on Luke 2: 29, 38

GOD THE SON, REDEEMER

134

Make way

Graham Kendrick (b. 1950)

1. Make way, make way, for Christ the King in splen - dour ar - rives. Fling wide the gates and wel-come him in - to your lives.

REFRAIN

Make way, (Make way,) make way (make way) for the

King of kings; (for the King of kings;) make way, (make way,) make

way, (make way,) and let his king - dom in.

In the Refrain, high voices answer low voices.

1 Make way, make way, for Christ the King
    in splendour arrives.
Fling wide the gates and welcome him
    into your lives.

> *Make way, make way*
> *for the King of kings;*
> *make way, make way,*
> *and let his kingdom in.*

2 He comes the broken hearts to heal,
    the prisoners to free.
The deaf shall hear, the lame shall dance,
    the blind shall see.

3 And those who mourn with heavy hearts,
    who weep and sigh;
with laughter, joy and royal crown
    he'll beautify.

4 We call you now to worship him
    as Lord of all,
to have no gods before him—
    their thrones must fall!

Graham Kendrick (b. 1950)
based on Isaiah 40: 3–5; Luke 4: 18–19

135

Veni Emmanuel   88 88 (LM) with Refrain

Melody from a 15th-century
French Franciscan processional
pub. by Thomas Helmore (1811–90)
in *Hymnal Noted* (1856)

Re-joice!   Re-joice!   Em-ma - nu-el shall come to thee, O Is - ra-el.

Veni, veni, Emmanuel

1 O come, O come, Emmanuel,
    and ransom captive Israel,
        that mourns in lonely exile here
        until the Son of God appear:

            Rejoice! Rejoice!
            Emmanuel shall come to thee, O Israel.

2 O come, thou Wisdom from above
    who ord'rest all things through thy love;
        to us the path of knowledge show
        and teach us in her ways to go:

3 O come, O come, thou Lord of might,
    who to thy tribes, on Sinai's height,
        in ancient times didst give the law
        in cloud, and majesty, and awe:

4 O come, thou Rod of Jesse, free
    thine own from Satan's tyranny;
        from depths of hell thy people save,
        and give them vict'ry o'er the grave:

5 O come, thou Key of David, come,
   and open wide our heavenly home;
     make safe the way that leads on high,
     and close the path to misery:

6 O come, thou Dayspring, come and cheer ⌣
   our spirits by thine advent here;
     disperse the gloomy clouds of night,
     and death's dark shadows put to flight:

7 O come, Desire of Nations, bring ⌣
   all peoples to their Saviour King;
     thou Corner-stone, who makest one,
     complete in us thy work begun:

*8 O come, O come, Emmanuel,
   and ransom captive Israel,
     that mourns in lonely exile here
     until the Son of God appear:

18th-century Latin (or earlier)
based on The Advent Antiphons from 9th century (or earlier)
tr. *John Mason Neale* (1818–66) and others altd.

---

* Optional. The original seven 'Great O' Antiphons, on which this hymn is based, were sung, one each day, on seven days before Christmas, ending with the antiphon corresponding to verse 1 (*O come, O come, Emmanuel*) on 23rd December. This verse is now traditionally sung first; but if desired, it may be sung at the end of the hymn as well as, or instead of, at the beginning.

136

Winchester New   88 88 (LM)

Melody adapted from
Musikalisches Hand-Buch (Hamburg, 1690)
by William Henry Havergal (1793–1870)

Jordanis oras praevia

1 On Jordan's bank the Baptist's cry
   announces that the Lord is nigh;
      awake and hearken, for he brings
      glad tidings of the King of kings.

2 Then cleansed be every heart from sin;
   make straight the way for God within;
      prepare we in our hearts a home,
      where such a mighty guest may come.

3 For thou art our salvation, Lord,
   our refuge and our great reward;
      without thy grace we waste away,
      like flowers that wither and decay.

4 To heal the sick stretch forth thine hand,
   and bid the fallen sinner stand;
      shine forth, and let thy light restore
      earth's own true loveliness once more.

5 All praise, eternal Son, to thee,
   whose advent doth thy people free;
      whom with the Father we adore,
      and Holy Ghost for evermore.

Charles Coffin (1676–1749)
tr. *John Chandler* (1806–76) altd.
based on Luke 3: 1–18

137

Promised Lord   77 77 with Refrain

North American folk melody

1 Promised Lord and Christ is he:
  may we soon his kingdom see.

  Come, O Lord, quickly come,
  come in glory,
  come in glory,
  Maranatha,[1]
  quickly come.

2 Teaching, healing, once was he:
  may we soon his kingdom see.

3 Dead and buried once was he:
  may we soon his kingdom see.

4 Risen from the dead is he:
  may we soon his kingdom see.

5 Soon to come again is he:
  may we soon his kingdom see.

Roger Ruston altd.

[1] Maranatha (or Maran atha), an expression used by the
Apostle Paul in 1 Corinthians 16: 21, is an ejaculation of
prophetic utterance meaning 'Our Lord, come'.

138

Soon and very soon

Andrae Crouch

1. Soon and ve - ry soon_ we are go-ing to see the King,
2. No more cry-ing there,
3. No more dy-ing there,
4. Soon and ve - ry soon_

soon and ve - ry soon_ we are go-ing to see the King,_
no more cry-ing there,
no more dy - ing there,
soon and ve - ry soon_

soon and ve - ry soon__
no more cry - ing there,_ we are go-ing_ to see the King._
no more dy - ing there,_
soon and ve - ry soon__

— Al-le - lu - ia,_ al-le - lu - ia,_ we're going to see the King.

|1,2.| |3,4.|
— — al - le - lu - ia, al - le - lu -

1 Soon and very soon we are going to see the King,
soon and very soon we are going to see the King,
soon and very soon we are going to see the King.
Alleluia, alleluia, we're going to see the King.

2 No more crying there, we are going to see the King,
no more crying there, we are going to see the King,
no more crying there, we are going to see the King.
Alleluia, alleluia, we're going to see the King.

3 No more dying there, we are going to see the King,
no more dying there, we are going to see the King,
no more dying there, we are going to see the King.
Alleluia, alleluia, we're going to see the King.
Alleluia, alleluia, alleluia, alleluia!

4 Soon and very soon we are going to see the King,
soon and very soon we are going to see the King,
soon and very soon we are going to see the King.
Alleluia, alleluia, we're going to see the King.
Alleluia, alleluia, alleluia, alleluia!

Andrae Crouch

139

Gabriel's message   10 10 12 7 3   Basque traditional carol melody

most high-ly fa-voured la - dy.'   *Glo* - *ri* - *a!*

1 The angel Gabriel from heaven came,
   his wings as drifted snow, his eyes as flame;
   'All hail', said he, 'thou lowly maiden Mary,
      most highly favoured lady'.
         Gloria!

2 'For known a blessèd mother thou shalt be,
   all generations laud and honour thee,
   thy Son shall be Emmanuel, by seers foretold;
      most highly favoured lady.
         Gloria!

3 Then gentle Mary meekly bowed her head,
   'To me be as it pleaseth God', she said,
   'my soul shall laud and magnify his holy name':
      most highly favoured lady.
         Gloria!

*4 Of her, Emmanuel the Christ was born
   in Bethlehem, all on a Christmas morn,
   and Christian folk throughout the world will ever say
      'Most highly favoured lady'.
         Gloria!

Basque Carol
para. *Sabine Baring-Gould* (1834–1924)
based on Luke 1: 26–47

* This carol is appropriate for use on the feast of
the Annunciation of Our Lord by omitting verse 4.

140

St Stephen   86 86 (CM)

Melody by William Jones (1726–1800)
in *Ten Church Pieces for the Organ* (Nayland, 1789)

1 The Lord will come and not be slow,
    his footsteps cannot err;
before him righteousness shall go,
    his royal harbinger.

2 Mercy and truth, that long were missed,
    now joyfully are met;
sweet peace and righteousness have kissed,
    and hand in hand are set.

3 Surely to such as do him fear
    salvation is at hand;
and glory shall ere long appear
    to dwell within our land.

4 Rise, God, judge thou the earth in might,
    this wicked earth redress;
for thou art he who shall by right
    the nations all possess.

5 The nations all whom thou hast made
    shall come, and all shall frame
to bow them low before thee, Lord,
    and glorify thy name.

6 For great thou art, and wonders great
    by thy strong hand are done;
thou in thine everlasting seat
    remainest God alone.

John Milton (1608–74) altd.
based on a selection of verses from
Psalms 82, 85, 86

141

These are the days of Elijah

Robin Mark

1. These are the days of Elijah, declaring the word of the Lord; and these are the days of your servant Moses, righteousness being restored. And though these are days of great trial, of famine and darkness and sword, still we are a voice in the desert crying 'Pre-

2. These are the days of Ezekiel, the dry bones becoming as flesh; and these are the days of your servant David, rebuilding a temple of praise. These are the days of the harvest, the fields are as white in the world, and we are the labourers in your vineyard de-

1 These are the days of Elijah,
     declaring the word of the Lord;
  and these are the days of your servant Moses,
     righteousness being restored.
  And though these are days of great trial,
     of famine and darkness and sword,
  still we are a voice in the desert crying
     'Prepare ye the way of the Lord'.

  Behold he comes
  riding on the clouds,
  shining like the sun
  at the trumpet call;
  lift your voice,
  it's the year of jubilee,
  out of Zion's hill
  salvation comes.

2 These are the days of Ezekiel,
     the dry bones becoming as flesh;
  and these are the days of your servant David,
     rebuilding a temple of praise.
  These are the days of the harvest,
     the fields are as white in the world,
  and we are the labourers in your vineyard
     declaring the word of the Lord.

Robin Mark

142

Wachet auf 898 D 664 88

Melody (1598) by Philipp Nicolai (1556–1608)
adpt. J. S. Bach (1685–1750)

HIS ADVENT

Wachet auf! ruft uns die Stimme

1 Wake, O wake! With tidings thrilling
the watchmen all the air are filling,
   'Arise, Jerusalem, arise!'
Midnight strikes, no more delaying,
  'The hour has come!', we hear them saying.
   'Where are you all, you virgins wise?
     The Bridegroom comes in sight,
     raise high your torches bright!'
      Alleluia!
    The wedding song
    swells loud and strong:
    go forth and join the festal throng.

2 Zion hears the watchmen shouting,
her heart leaps up with joy undoubting,
   she stands and waits with eager eye.
See her Friend from heaven descending,
adorned with truth and grace unending!
   Her light burns clear, her star climbs high.
     Now come, our precious crown,
     Lord Jesus, God's own Son!
      Alleluia!
    Let us prepare
    to follow there,
    where in your supper we may share.

3 Every soul in you rejoices;
from earth and from angelic voices
   be glory given to you alone!
Now the gates of pearl receive us,
your presence nevermore shall leave us,
   we stand with angels round your throne.
     Earth cannot give below
     the bliss that you bestow.
      Alleluia!
    Grant us to raise,
    to length of days,
    the triumph-chorus of your praise.

Philipp Nicolai (1556–1608)
based on Matthew 25: 1–13
tr. *F. C. Burkitt* (1864–1935) altd.

143

Nativity   86 86 (CM)

Henry Lahee (1826–1912)

Alternative tunes: 551 BILLING   349 RICHMOND

1 Waken, O sleeper, wake and rise,
   salvation's day is near,
   and let the dawn of light and truth
   dispel the night of fear.

2 Let us prepare to face the day
   of judgment and of grace,
   to live as people of the light,
   and perfect truth embrace.

3 Watch, then, and pray, we cannot know
   the moment or the hour,
   when Christ, unheralded, will come
   with life-renewing power.

4 Then shall the nations gather round
   to learn his ways of peace,
   when spears to pruning-hooks are turned,
   and all our conflicts cease.

Michael Forster (b. 1946)

144

Word of justice   44 with Alleluias

Words and music by Bernadette Farrell

1. Word of jus - tice,   al - le - lu - ia,
2. Word of mer - cy,   al - le - lu - ia,
3. Word of pow - er,   al - le - lu - ia,
4. Word of free-dom,   al - le - lu - ia,

come to dwell here.   Ma-ran - a - tha!¹
live   a-mong us.   Ma-ran - a - tha!
live with-in   us.   Ma-ran - a - tha!
save your peo - ple.   Ma-ran - a - tha!

Additional or alternative verses
(a) Word of healing, ... heal our sorrow ...
(b) Word of comfort, ... bring us hope now ...
(c) Word of gladness, ... fill our hearts now ...
(d) Word of wisdom, ... come, renew us ...

¹ Maranatha (or Maran atha), an expression used by the Apostle Paul in 1 Corinthians 16: 21, is an ejaculation of prophetic utterance meaning 'Our Lord, come'.

GOD THE SON, REDEEMER

145

Day of praise   66 86 (SM)

Charles Steggall (1826–1905)

Narenza   66 86 (SM)

Adpt. by William Henry Havergal (1793–1870)
from the melody *Ave Maria klare*: cf. no. 146ii

HIS ADVENT

1 You servants of the Lord,
    each in your calling wait;
observe with care his heavenly word—
    be watchful at his gate.

2 Let all your lamps be bright
    and trim the living flame;
be ready always in his sight,
    for awesome is his name.

3 'Watch' is your Lord's command:
    the bridegroom shall appear,
for his returning is at hand,
    and while we speak he's near.

4 O happy servants they
    who wide awake are found
to greet their master on that day,
    and be with honour crowned!

5 Christ shall the banquet spread
    with his own royal hand,
and raise each faithful servant's head
    amid the_angelic band.

Philip Doddridge (1702–51) altd.
based on Matthew 25: 1–13

146

Es ist ein' Ros' entsprungen   76 76 6 76   German traditional carol melody

REFRAIN

Re - peat the hymn a - gain: 'To   God   on   high   be

glo - ry,   and   peace   on   earth.   A - men'.

Ave Maria klare   76 76 6 76

Melody from Johann Leisentritt's
Catholicum Hymnologium (1587)

REFRAIN

Re - peat   the hymn a - gain:____   'To

God   on high   be   glo - ry,   and peace on earth.   A - men.'____

Μέγα καὶ παράδοξον θαῦμα

1 A great and mighty wonder:
      redemption drawing near!
   The virgin bears the infant,
      the Prince of Peace is here!

   Repeat the hymn again:
   'To God on high be glory,
   and peace on earth. Amen'.

2 The Word becomes incarnate
      and yet remains on high;
   the shepherds hear the anthem
      as glory fills the sky.

3 The angels sing the story:
      rejoice, O distant lands;
   you valleys, forests, mountains,
      and oceans, clap your hands!

4 He comes to save all nations:
      let all now hear his word!
   Approach and bring him worship,
      the Saviour and the Lord!

   after *St. Germanus* (634–732)
   tr. *John Mason Neale* (1818–66) altd.

147

Iris (Les anges dans nos campagnes)
87 87 with Refrain

Variant of Flemish
or French carol melody

REFRAIN

Come _____ and ___ wor - ship Christ, the new - born King, ___ come _____ and ___ wor - ship, wor - ship Christ, the new - born King!

Alternative tune: 326i, 464 WESTMINSTER ABBEY

HIS INCARNATION

1 Angels, from the realms of glory,
   wing your flight o'er all the earth;
ye who sang creation's story
   now proclaim Messiah's birth:

> *Come and worship*
> *Christ, the new-born King,*
> *come and worship,*
> *worship Christ, the new-born King!*

2 Shepherds, in the field abiding,
   watching o'er your flocks by night,
God with us is now residing,
   yonder shines the infant Light:

3 Sages, leave your contemplations,
   brighter visions beam afar;
seek the great Desire of Nations;
   ye have seen his natal star:

4 Saints, before the altar bending,
   watching long in hope and fear,
suddenly the Lord, descending,
   in his temple shall appear:

5 Though an infant now we view him,
   he shall fill his Father's throne,
gather all the nations to him;
   every knee shall then bow down:

James Montgomery (1771–1854) altd.
based on Luke 2: 8–20;
Matthew 2: 1–2, 9–11

GOD THE SON, REDEEMER

148

Cherry Tree (A) 76 76 extended English traditional carol melody

Second Tune

Cherry Tree (B) 76 76 extended English traditional carol melody

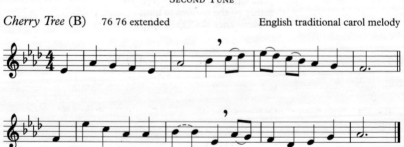

HIS INCARNATION

1 As Joseph was a-walking,
   he heard an angel sing,
   'This night shall be the birth time
   of Christ our heavenly King.

2 'He neither shall be born ‿
   in housen nor in hall,
   nor in the place of Paradise,
   but in an ox's stall.

3 'He neither shall be clothèd ‿
   in purple nor in pall,
   but in the pure white linen ‿
   as usen babies all.

4 'He neither shall be rockèd ‿
   in silver nor in gold;
   but in a wooden cradle
   that rocketh on the mould.'

5 As Joseph was a-walking,
   there did an angel sing,
   and Mary's child at midnight ‿
   was born to be our King.

6 Then be ye glad, good people,
   this night of all the year,
   and lift your hearts in joyfulness,
   his star it shineth clear.

A version of the traditional
English Cherry Tree Carol
based on Matthew 1: 18–23

When these words are sung to the first tune, the last two lines of each verse are repeated.

149

Cradle song   11 11 11 11

W. J. Kirkpatrick (1838–1921)

Normandy   11 11 11 11

Basque traditional carol melody

HIS INCARNATION

1 Away in a manger, no crib for a bed,
   the little Lord Jesus laid down his sweet head:
      the stars in the bright sky looked down where he lay,
      the little Lord Jesus asleep on the hay.

2 The cattle are lowing, the baby awakes,
   but little Lord Jesus, no crying he makes.
      I love you, Lord Jesus; look down from on high,
      and stay by my side until morning is nigh.

3 Be near me, Lord Jesus; I ask you to stay ⌣
   close by me for ever, and love me, I pray.
      Bless all the dear children in your tender care,
      and fit us for heaven, to live with you there.

attrib. *W. J. Kirkpatrick* (1838–1921) altd.
v. 3 *Charles H. Gabriel* (1892)

150

Mary's child   436 436

Words and music by Geoffrey Ainger (b. 1925)

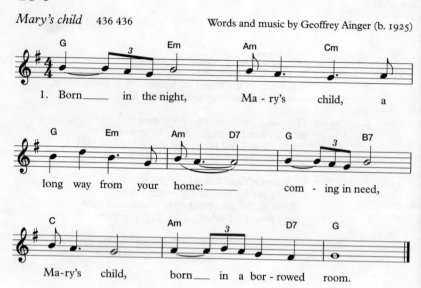

1. Born___ in the night, Ma - ry's child, a long way from your home:___ com - ing in need, Ma-ry's child, born___ in a bor - rowed room.

1 Born in the night,
  Mary's child,
  a long way from your home;
  coming in need,
  Mary's child,
  born in a borrowed room.

2 Clear shining Light,
  Mary's child,
  your face lights up our way;
  Light of the world,
  Mary's child,
  dawn on our darkened day.

3 Truth of our life,
  Mary's child,
  you tell us God is good;
  prove it is true,
  Mary's child,
  go to your cross of wood.

4 Hope of the world,
  Mary's child,
  you're coming soon to reign;
  King of the earth,
  Mary's child,
  walk in our streets again.

Geoffrey Ainger (b. 1925)

151

Bunessan (2) 55 53 D

Scots Gaelic traditional melody

For this tune with guitar chords, see no. 58.

Leanabh an áigh

1 Child in the manger,
   infant of Mary;
   outcast and stranger,
   Lord of all!
   Child who inherits
   all our transgressions,
   all our demerits
   on him fall.

2 Once the most holy
   child of salvation,
   gentle and lowly,
   lived below;
   now, as our glorious
   mighty Redeemer,
   see him victorious
   o'er each foe.

3 Prophets foretold him,
   infant of wonder;
   angels behold him
   on his throne;
   worthy our Saviour
   of all their praises;
   happy for ever
   are his own.

Mary MacDonald (1789–1872)
tr. *Lachlan MacBean (1853–1931)*

1 *Leanabh an áidh,*
   Mac Mhuire máthair,
   rugadh sa stábla,
   Rí na ndúl,
   tháinig 'n an fhásaigh,
   d'fhulaing 'nár n-áitne,
   is beannaithe go brách
   gheibh cuireadh 'na dhúin.

2 *Ní hamhlaidh don Uan so,*
   tháinig dár bhfuascailt,
   ba staidéartha, stuama
   shiúil sé ar dtúis.
   Ba naofa gan truailliú,
   b'é chruthaigh gach slua,
   is d'éirigh sé suas
   go buach ón úir.

3 *Leanabh an áidh,*
   Mar d'aithris na fáithe
   is na haingle arda,
   b'é mian a súl.
   'Sé thuilleas ár ngrá
   's ár n-urraim gach tráth,
   is beannaithe go brach
   gheibh cuireadh 'na dhúin.

From the Scots Gaelic
of *Mary MacDonald (1789–1872)*
rendered into modern Irish
by *Coslett Quin (1907–1995)*

152

Celebrations   Valerie Collison (b. 1933)

REFRAIN

Come and join the ce - le-bra-tion, it's a ve - ry spe-cial day;

come and share our ju - bi-la-tion, there's a new-born King to-day.

VERSES

Come and join the celebration,
  it's a very special day;
come and share our jubilation,
  there's a new-born King today.

1 See the shepherds hurry down to Bethlehem,
  gaze in wonder at the Son of God who lies before them:

2 Wise men journey, led to worship by a star,
  kneel in homage, bringing precious gifts from lands afar, so

3 'God is with us!'—round the world the message bring;
  he is with us—'Welcome!' all the bells on earth are pealing:

Valerie Collison (b. 1933)

153

Puer nobis nascitur (1) 88 88 (LM)

German medieval carol melody
adpt. Michael Praetorius (1571–1621)

Veni, Redemptor gentium

1 Come, thou Redeemer of the earth,
and manifest thy virgin birth:
  let every age adoring fall,
  such birth befits the God of all.

*2 Begotten of no human will,
but of the Spirit, thou art still⏑
  the Word of God, in flesh arrayed,
  the Saviour now to us displayed.

*3 A maiden's womb that burden gained
while she a virgin pure remained,
  the banners there of virtue glow,
  God in his temple dwells below.

4 Forth from his chamber goeth he,
that royal home of purity,
  a giant in twofold substance one,
  rejoicing now his course to run.

5 From God the Father he proceeds,
to God the Father back he speeds,
  runs out his course to death and hell,
  returns on God's high throne to dwell.

6 O equal to thy Father, thou!
Gird on thy fleshly mantle now,
  the weakness of our mortal state
  with deathless might invigorate.

7 Thy cradle here shall glitter bright,
and darkness glow with new-born light,
  no more shall night extinguish day,
  where love's bright beams their power display.

8 O Jesu, virgin-born, to thee⏑
eternal praise and glory be,
  whom with the Father we adore
  and Holy Spirit, evermore.

St. Ambrose (340–97)
tr. *John Mason Neale* (1818–66) and others
verses 4 & 5 based on Psalm 19: 5–6

154

Hibernia

Irish traditional melody

1. Di - a do bheath' a naoi - dhe naoimh, 'sa— mhain-séar cé taoi
2. Di - a do bheath' a Íos - a 'rís! 'Do bhea-tha, i gclí on
3. Mí - le fáil - te 'nocht i gclí le mo chroí - se dom Rí

bocht_____ meadh - rach_____ sai - bhir
Ó - igh! A Ghnú - is is
fial,_____ i ndá—— ná - dúr 'do

a tá tú 's glór-mhar id dhún féin a - nocht.____
áille ná'n ghrian, na míl - te fáil - te____ 'do Dhi - a óg!
chu - aigh, póg is fáil - te u - aim do Dhi - a!

Aodh Mac Aingil Mac Cathmhaoil (1571–1626)
adpt. *Peter Downey (b. 1956)*

1. *All hail and wel - come, ho - ly child, you poor babe in the*
2. *God bless you, Je - sus, once a - gain! Your life in its young*
3. *To-night we greet you in the flesh; my heart a - dores my*

man - ger. So hap - py and rich it
bo - dy, your face____ more love - ly
young____ King. You came____ to us in

is you are to - night__ in - side__ your cas - tle.
than the sun, a thou - sand wel - comes, Ba - by!
hu - man form, I bring you a kiss and a greet - ing.

tr. *George Otto Simms (1910–1991)*

155

Melody from Thoinot Arbeau's
Orchésographie (Langres, 1588)

Branle de l'Official   77 77 with Refrain

1 Ding dong! merrily on high
    in heav'n the bells are ringing:
  ding dong! verily the sky
    is riv'n with angels singing:

    Gloria, hosanna in excelsis!

2 E'en so here below, below,
    let steeple bells be swungen,
  and [1]*io, io, io,*
    by priest and people sungen:

3 Pray you, dutifully prime
    your matin chime, ye ringers;
  may you beautifully [2]*rime*
    your evetime song, ye singers:

George Ratcliffe Woodward (1848–1934)

[1] 'io' (pronounced 'ee-o') is an expression of joy.
[2] 'rime' is an old spelling of 'rhyme'.

156

Don oíche úd i mBeithil   77 77 D

Irish traditional melody

* The small notes refer to the Irish text only; the English text is metrically regular.

1 Don oíche úd i mBeithil beidh tagairt faoi ghrian go brách,
don oíche úd i mBeithil go dtáinig an Briathar slán;
tá gríosghrua ar spéartha 's an talamh 'na chlúdach bán;
féach Íosagán sa chliabhán, 's an Mhaighdean in aoibhneas grá.

2 Ar leaca loma sléibhe 'se 'ghlacann na haoirí scáth
ar oscailt gheal na spéire tá teachtaire Dé ar fáil,
céad glóir' anois don Athair i bhflaitheasaibh thuas go hard.
Is feasta fós ar talamh do fhearaibh dea-mhéin' síocháin.

Aodh Mac Aingil Mac Cathmhaoil (1571–1626)

1 *About that night in Bethl'hem*
all ages with joy shall tell,
that night on which our Saviour
came down with us here to dwell.
The wintry sky is glowing,
the earth is arrayed in white:
see Jesus in the cradle,
and Mary with love so bright.

2 *Upon the rocky mountain*
the shepherds in quietness lie,
the skies with brilliance open,
the angels of God are nigh.
'Let praise to God the Father
up high in the heav'ns resound,
and on the earth for ever
may peace and goodwill abound.'

tr. *Donald A. R. Caird* (b. 1925)
and *Gary Hastings* (b. 1956)
Versified *Donald Davison* (b. 1937)
based on Luke 2: 8–14

157

Highwood   11 10 11 10   Richard R. Terry (1865–1938)

1 'Glory to God!' all heav'n with joy is ringing;
    angels proclaim the gospel of Christ's birth—
'Glory to God!', and still their song is bringing
    good news of God incarnate here on earth.

2 Lowly in wonder shepherds kneel before him,
    no gift to bring save love of heart and mind.
Come like those shepherds, sing his praise, adore him,
    a babe so weak, yet Saviour of mankind.

3 Humble, yet regal, wise men kneel before him,
    gold, incense, myrrh, their gifts to Christ they bring.
Come like those wise men, sing his praise, adore him,
    a babe so poor and modest, yet a King.

4 Though now no crib or cradle is concealing
    Jesus our Lord in that far-distant shrine,
Christ at each eucharist is still revealing
    his very self in forms of bread and wine.

John E. Bowers (b. 1923)
based on Luke 2: 13–16 & Matthew 2: 1–11

158

God rest you merry 86 86 86 with Refrain English traditional carol melody

REFRAIN

O_____ ti - dings of com - fort and joy, com-fort and joy, O_____ ti - dings of com - fort and joy!

1 God rest you merry, gentlemen,
    let nothing you dismay,
  for Jesus Christ our Saviour
    was born upon this day,
  to save us all from Satan's power
    when we had gone astray:

    O tidings of comfort and joy!

2 From God our heavenly Father
    a blessèd angel came,
  and unto certain shepherds
    brought tidings of the same;
  how that in Bethlehem was born
    the Son of God by name:

3 The shepherds at those tidings
    rejoicèd much in mind,
  and left their flocks a-feeding
    in tempest, storm, and wind;
  and went to Bethlehem straightway
    this blessèd babe to find:

4 But when to Bethlehem they came,
    whereat this infant lay,
  they found him in a manger,
    where oxen feed on hay;
  his mother Mary, kneeling down,
    unto her Lord did pray:

5 Now to the Lord sing praises,
    all you within this place,
  and with true love and brotherhood
    each other now embrace.
  This holy tide of Christmas
    all others doth efface:

English traditional
based on Luke 2: 8–20

159

In dulci jubilo   66 77 78 55   German medieval carol melody

The last line of each verse is sung twice.

1 Good Christians all, rejoice
   with heart, and soul, and voice;
      give ye heed to what we say;
      Jesus Christ is born today;
   ox and ass before him bow,
   and he is in the manger now.
      Christ is born today!

2 Good Christians all, rejoice
   with heart, and soul, and voice;
      now ye hear of endless bliss:
      Jesus Christ was born for this;
   he has opened heaven's door,
   and all are blessed for evermore.
      Christ was born for this!

3 Good Christians all, rejoice
   with heart, and soul, and voice;
      now ye need not fear the grave:
      Jesus Christ was born to save:
   calls you one, and calls you all,
   to gain his everlasting hall.
      Christ was born to save!

John Mason Neale (1818–66) altd.

160

Christmas (Mendelssohn)
77 77 D with Refrain

From a chorus in
Felix Mendelssohn's *Festgesang* (1840)
adpt. 1855 W. H. Cummings (1831–1915)

Hark! the he-rald-an-gels sing glo-ry__ to the new-born King.

The rhythmic variants (shown by small notes above the stave) are from Mendelssohn's original.

1 Hark! the herald-angels sing
glory to the new-born King;
 peace on earth and mercy mild,
 God and sinners reconciled!
Joyful, all you nations, rise,
join the triumph of the skies;
 with the angelic host proclaim,
 'Christ is born in Bethlehem':

Hark! the herald angels sing
glory to the new-born King.

2 Christ, by highest heaven adored,
Christ, the everlasting Lord;
 late in time behold him come,
 offspring of a virgin's womb:
veiled in flesh the Godhead see,
hail the incarnate Deity!
 Pleased as man with us to dwell,
 Jesus our Emmanuel:

3 Hail, the heaven-born Prince of Peace!
Hail, the Sun of righteousness!
 Light and life to all he brings,
 risen with healing in his wings:
mild, he lays his glory by,
born that we no more may die;
 born to raise each child of earth,
 born to give us second birth:

Charles Wesley (1707–88) and others
based on Luke 2: 1–20

161

Es ist ein' Ros' entsprungen   76 76 6 76   German traditional carol melody

Es ist ein' Ros' entsprungen

1 I know a rose-tree springing
      forth from an ancient root,
   as prophets once were singing.
      From Jesse came the shoot
   that bore a blossom bright
      amid the cold of winter,
   when half-spent was the night.

2 This rose-tree, blossom laden,
      whereof Isaiah spake,
   is Mary, purest maiden,
      who mothered, for our sake,
   the little Child, new-born
      by God's eternal counsel
   on that first Christmas morn.

3 O Flower, whose fragrance tender
      with sweetness fills the air,
   dispel in glorious splendour
      the darkness ev'rywhere;
   true man, yet very God,
      from sin and death now save us,
   and share our every load.

vv. 1–2 Traditional Rhineland Carol (*c.* 15th cent.)
in Spierischen Gesangbuch (Cologne) 1599
v. 3 by *Friedrich Layritz* (1808–1859)
tr. *Harriet Spaeth* (1845–1925) altd.
based on Isaiah 11: 1

162

Cranham

Music by Gustav Holst (1874–1934)
Words by Christina Rossetti (1830–93)

163

Polish traditional carol melody

Infant holy   87 87 88 77

W złobie leży

1 Infant holy,
    infant lowly,
for his bed a cattle stall;
    oxen lowing,
    little knowing⌣
Christ the babe is Lord of all.
    Swift are winging⌣
    angels singing,
    nowells[1] ringing,
    tidings bringing,
Christ the babe is Lord of all,
Christ the babe is Lord of all.

2 Flocks were sleeping,
    shepherds keeping⌣
vigil till the morning new,
    saw the glory,
    heard the story,
tidings of a gospel true.
    Thus rejoicing,
    free from sorrow,
    praises voicing,
    greet the morrow,
Christ the babe was born for you!
Christ the babe was born for you!

Polish Traditional Carol
tr. *Edith M. G. Reed* (1885–1933)

[1] 'nowell' (or 'noël') = a joyous shout or song at Christmas

164

Noel   86 86 D (DCM)

English traditional melody
adpt. Arthur Sullivan (1842–1900)

1 It came upon the midnight clear,
      that glorious song of old,
   from angels bending near the earth
      to touch their harps of gold:
   'Peace on the earth, good will to all,
      from heaven's all-gracious King!';
   the world in solemn stillness lay
      to hear the angels sing.

2 Still through the cloven skies they come,
      with peaceful wings unfurled;
   and still their heavenly music floats
      o'er all the weary world:
   above its sad and lowly plains
      they bend on hovering wing;
   and ever o'er its Babel sounds
      the blessèd angels sing.

3 Yet with the woes of sin and strife
      the world has suffered long;
   beneath the angel-strain have rolled
      two thousand years of wrong;
   and warring humankind hears not
      the words of peace they bring:
   O hush the noise of human strife,
      to hear the angels sing.

4 For lo! the days are hastening on,
      by prophet bards foretold,
   when with the ever-circling years
      comes round the age of gold;
   when peace shall over all the earth
      its ancient splendours fling,
   and all the world give back the song
      which now the angels sing.

*Edmund Hamilton Sears (1810–76) altd.
based on Luke 2: 14*

165

The holly and the ivy (1)   76 87 with Refrain   English traditional carol melody

REFRAIN

So Fa-ther, we would thank you for all that you have done,

and for all that you have giv-en us through the com-ing of your Son.

At a Christingle Service

1 It's rounded like an orange,
   this earth on which we stand;
   and we praise the God who holds it
   in the hollow of his hand.

   So Father, we would thank you
   for all that you have done,
   and for all that you have given us
   through the coming of your Son.

2 A candle, burning brightly,
   can cheer the darkest night,
   and these candles tell how Jesus
   came to bring a dark world light.

3 The ribbon round the orange
   reminds us of the cost;
   how the Shepherd, strong and gentle,
   gave his life to save the lost.

4 Four seasons with their harvest
   supply the food we need,
   and the Spirit gives a harvest
   that can make us rich indeed.

5 We come with our Christingles[1]
   to tell of Jesus' birth,
   and we praise the God who blessed us
   by his coming to this earth.

Basil E. Bridge (b. 1927)

[1] A Christingle is an orange surmounted by a lighted candle and decorated with fruit and ribbon. It is received in an Advent and Christmas act of worship which originated in the Moravian Church and is now popular in other Christian traditions.

166

Antioch   86 86 (CM) extended

Melody (of unknown origin, but with echoes of Handel)
from W. Holford's *Voce di Melodia* (c.1834)

1. Joy to the world, the Lord is come! Let earth re-ceive her

King; let ev - 'ry_ heart_ pre - pare him_ room,_ and

heav'n and na - ture sing, and_ heav'n and na - ture sing, and_

heav'n, and heav'n____ and na - ture sing.

*Verse 3:

won - ders, won - ders

Alternative tune: 143 NATIVITY

1 Joy to the world, the Lord is come!
   Let earth receive her King;
   let ev'ry heart prepare him room,
   and heav'n and nature sing.

2 Joy to the world, the Saviour reigns!
   Let all their songs employ;
   while fields and floods, rocks, hills and plains
   repeat the sounding joy.

3 He rules the world with truth and grace,
   and makes the nations prove
   the glories of his righteousness
   and wonders of his love.

Isaac Watts (1674–1748) alt.
based on Psalm 98

167

Caribbean Carol

Words and music by Pamela Verrall

1. Long a-go__ and far a-way__ in Beth-le-hem, a mo-ther lay__ her new-born babe up-on the hay.__ He was the ho-ly Je-sus child, he was the ho-ly Je-sus.

2. Shep-herds on__ the moun-tain cold a-woke when an-gel voi-ces told__ 'Go and leave your lambs in fold; fol-low the star to Beth-le-hem, fol-low the star to Beth-le-hem'.

3. When they reached the o-pen door and saw that love__ had gone be-fore, they, won-d'ring, knelt on dirt-y floor, wor-ship-ping ba-by Je-sus there, wor-ship-ping ba-by Je-sus.

REFRAIN

Now-ell,[1] now-ell,__ let an-gels sing; now-ell, now-ell,__ let church bells ring; now-ell, now-ell,__ let ev-ery-thing sing al-le-lu-ia to the ba-by boy. ba-by boy.

[1] 'Nowell' (or 'Noël') = a joyous shout or song at Christmas

168

Bergers   98 98 98   French traditional carol melody

1 Lord, you were rich beyond all splendour,
    yet, for love's sake, became so poor;
leaving your throne in glad surrender,
    sapphire-paved courts for stable floor:
Lord, you were rich beyond all splendour,
    yet, for love's sake, became so poor.

2 You are our God beyond all praising,
    yet, for love's sake, became a man;
stooping so low, but sinners raising
    heav'nwards, by your eternal plan:
you are our God, beyond all praising,
    yet, for love's sake, became a man.

3 Lord, you are love beyond all telling,
    Saviour and King, we worship you;
Emmanuel, within us dwelling,
    make us and keep us pure and true:
Lord, you are love beyond all telling,
    Saviour and King, we worship you.

Frank Houghton (1894–1972)
based on 2 Corinthians 8: 9

169

Christmas bells   46 77 5

Armas Maasalo (1885–1960)

Lis - ten!   Lis - ten!   Christ-mas bells are   ring - ing!

vv. 2–4

Fine   OPTIONAL BRIDGE BETWEEN VERSES

Je - sus Christ is   come!

1 Listen! Listen!
   Christmas bells are ringing!
   From the heaven's glory bright,
   angel voices echoing:
    Jesus Christ is come!

2 Listen! Listen!
   Christmas bells are ringing!
   All across the frosty sky,
   even stars are singing:
    Jesus Christ is come!

3 Listen! Listen!
   Christmas bells are ringing!
   See, in every window clear,
   Christmas candles shining:
    Jesus Christ is come!

4 Listen! Listen!
   Christmas bells are ringing!
   Over all the hills and fields,
   children joyful singing:
    Jesus Christ is come!

5 Listen! Listen!
   Christmas bells are ringing!
   Can you hear from heaven high,
   angel voices answering?:
    Jesus Christ is come!

Helmi Auvinen
tr. *Christopher Bruce Warren* (b. 1936)

170

Gartan (1)   67 67   Irish traditional melody

1 Love came down at Christmas,
　　Love all lovely, Love divine;
　Love was born at Christmas,
　　star and angels gave the sign.

2 Worship we the Godhead,
　　Love incarnate, Love divine;
　worship we our Jesus:
　　but wherewith for sacred sign?

3 Love shall be our token,
　　Love be yours and love be mine,
　Love to God and all men,
　　Love for plea and gift and sign.

Christina Rossetti (1830–94)
based on Matthew 2: 1–11;
Luke 2: 8–18

171

Dean Street   86 86 D (DCM)   J. T. (Jock) Horne (1894–1978)

Alternative tune: 685ii CLAUDIUS

1 O Bethl'hem is a small place,
      and very far away,
   but ah! my heart's in Bethlehem,
      for this is Christmas Day.
   And well I know, in Bethl'hem town
      the Christmas bells they ring,
   where long ago, the heavenly host
      proclaimed the infant King.

2 Far would I fare to hear those bells,
      to pass the little door,
   and look upon the silver star
      that shines upon the floor.
   Fain would I see him as he was
      once on that holy spot,
   Mary's sweet Child, Emmanuel,
      my Saviour, in his cot.

3 I may not go to Bethl'hem town,
      but he will come to me;
   and in his Father's holy place,
      his glory I shall see:
   for I shall kneel at his fair board,
      who lives now, and was dead,
   to cry with joy, to Christ adored,
      'This is the ¹House of Bread'.

Richard S. Breene (1886–1974) altd.

¹ House of Bread—the meaning of the Hebrew name for Bethlehem

172

Adeste fideles

Melody possibly by John F. Wade (*c.*1711–86)

Adeste, fideles

1 O come, all ye faithful,
     joyful and triumphant,
   O come ye, O come ye to Bethlehem;
     come and behold him ⌣
     born, the King of angels:

       O come, let us adore him,
       Christ the Lord.

2 God of God,
     Light of Light,
   Lo! he abhors not the Virgin's womb;
     very God,
     begotten, not created:

    Adeste, fideles,
       laeti, triumphantes,
   venite, venite in Bethlehem;
       natum videte
       regem angelorum:

           venite, adoremus Dominum.

    Deum de Deo,
       Lumen de Lumine,
   gestant puellae viscera;
       Deum verum,
       genitum, non factum:
         venite ...

*3   See how the shepherds,
       summoned to his cradle,
  leaving their flocks, draw nigh with lowly fear;
      we too will thither
      bend our joyful footsteps:

*4   Lo! star-led chieftains,
      Magi,[1] Christ adoring,
  offer him incense, gold and myrrh;
      we to the Christ-child
      bring our heart's oblations:

*5   Child, for us sinners
      poor and in the manger,
  fain we embrace thee, with awe and love;
      who would not love thee,
      loving us so dearly?

6   Sing, choirs of angels,
      sing in exultation,
  sing, all ye citizens of heaven above;
      glory to God
      in the highest:

(On Christmas Day only)
7a   Yea, Lord, we greet thee,
      born this happy morning,
  Jesu, to thee be glory given;
      Word of the Father,
      now in flesh appearing:

(From Christmas to Epiphany)
7b   Yea, Lord, we bless thee,
      born for our salvation,
  Jesu, to thee be glory given;
      Word of the Father,
      now in flesh appearing:

vv. 1, 2, 6, 7 18th-century Latin
tr. *Frederick Oakeley* (1802–80) adpt.
vv. 3, 5 *Abbé E. J. F. Borderies* (1764–1852)
vv. 4 19th-century Latin
tr. *W. T. Brooke* (1848–1917) adpt.
based on Luke 2: 11–15;
Matthew 2: 11; John 1: 14

Magi (pronounced May-jai) were normally members of a priestly caste of
Ancient Persia. For generations the name has applied to the wise men or
kings from the East who brought gifts to the infant Christ.

173

O Jesulein süss 10 8 88 10

German carol melody from
Samuel Scheidt's *Tabulaturbuch* (1650)

O Jesulein süss

1 O Jesu so meek, O Jesu so kind,
  thou hast fulfilled thy Father's mind,
    hast come from heaven down to earth
    in human flesh through human birth.
  O Jesu so meek, O Jesu so kind.

2 O Jesu so good, O Jesu so meek,
  to do thy will is all we seek:
    for all we are or have is thine:
    do thou our hearts to thee incline.
  O Jesu so good, O Jesu so meek.

Valentin Thilo (1607–62)
tr. *Geoffrey W. Daisley* (1877–1939)

174

Forest Green 86 86 D (DCM)

English traditional melody
coll. & arr. R. Vaughan Williams (1872–1958)

1 O little town of Bethlehem,
    how still we see thee lie!
Above thy deep and dreamless sleep
    the silent stars go by;
yet in thy dark streets shineth
    the everlasting Light;
the hopes and fears of all the years
    are met in thee tonight.

2 O morning stars, together
    proclaim the holy birth,
and praises sing to God the King,
    and peace to all on earth.
For Christ is born of Mary;
    and, gathered all above,
while mortals sleep, the angels keep
    their watch of wondering love.

3 How silently, how silently,
    the wondrous gift is given!
So God imparts to human hearts
    the blessings of his heaven.
No ear may hear his coming;
    but in this world of sin,
where meek souls will receive
    him, still
    the dear Christ enters in.

4 O holy Child of Bethlehem,
    descend to us, we pray;
cast out our sin, and enter in;
    be born in us today.
We hear the Christmas angels
    the great glad tidings tell;
O come to us, abide with us,
    our Lord, Emmanuel.

Phillips Brooks (1835–93)
based on Micah 5: 2; Luke 2: 4–7

174

Christmas carol   86 86 D (DCM)   H. Walford Davies (1869–1941)

1 O little town of Bethlehem,
     how still we see thee lie!
   Above thy deep and dreamless sleep
     the silent stars go by;
   yet in thy dark streets shineth
     the everlasting Light;
   the hopes and fears of all the years
     are met in thee tonight.

2 O morning stars, together
     proclaim the holy birth,
   and praises sing to God the King,
     and peace to all on earth.
   For Christ is born of Mary;
     and, gathered all above,
   while mortals sleep, the angels keep
     their watch of wondering love.

3 How silently, how silently,
     the wondrous gift is given!
   So God imparts to human hearts
     the blessings of his heaven.
   No ear may hear his coming;
     but in this world of sin,
   where meek souls will receive
     him, still
     the dear Christ enters in.

4 O holy Child of Bethlehem,
     descend to us, we pray;
   cast out our sin, and enter in;
     be born in us today.
   We hear the Christmas angels
     the great glad tidings tell;
   O come to us, abide with us,
     our Lord, Emmanuel.

Phillips Brooks (1835–93)
based on Micah 5: 2; Luke 2: 4–7

175

Corde natus (Divinum mysterium)
87 87 877

Later form of a plainsong melody
as given in *Piae Cantiones* (1582)

ev - er-more and ev - er - more.

Corde natus ex Parentis

1 Of the Father's heart begotten
    ere the worlds began to be,
he is Alpha and Omega,
    he the source, the ending he,
of the things that are, that have been,
    and that future years shall see,
        evermore and evermore.

2 At his word they were created;
    he commanded; it was done:
heaven and earth and depths of ocean
    in their threefold order one;
all that grows beneath the shining
    of the light of moon and sun,
        evermore and evermore.

3 O that birth for ever blessèd,
    when the Virgin, full of grace,
by the Spirit's power conceiving,
    bore the Saviour of our race;
and the babe, the world's Redeemer,
    first revealed his sacred face,
        evermore and evermore.

4 This is he whom seers and sages
    sang of old with one accord,
whom the writings of the prophets
    promised in their faithful word:
now he shines, the long-expected;
    let creation praise its Lord,
        evermore and evermore.

5 Let the heights of heaven adore him;
    angel hosts, his praises sing;
powers, dominions, bow before him,
    and extol our God and King;
let no tongue on earth be silent,
    every voice in concert ring,
        evermore and evermore.

Marcus Aurelius Clemens Prudentius (c.348–413)
tr. *John Mason Neale* (1818–66),
Henry Williams Baker (1821–77) and others

176

Sussex carol 88 88 88

English traditional melody

The first two lines of each stanza are sung twice.

1 On Christmas night all Christians sing,
  to hear the news the angels bring,
    news of great joy, news of great mirth,
    news of our merciful King's birth.

2 Then why should we on earth be so sad,
  since our Redeemer made us glad,
    when from our sin he set us free,
    all for to gain our liberty?

3 When sin departs before his grace,
  then life and health come in its place;
    heaven and earth with joy may sing,
    all for to see the new-born King.

4 All out of darkness we have light,
  which made the angels sing this night;
    'Glory to God, on earth be peace,
    goodwill to all shall never cease'.

English traditional
after *Luke Wadding* (d. 1686)

Music: © 1919 Stainer & Bell Ltd

177

Irby 87 87 77

Henry J. Gauntlett (1805–76)

1 Once in royal David's city
    stood a lowly cattle shed,
where a mother laid her baby
    in a manger for his bed;
Mary was that mother mild,
    Jesus Christ her little child.

2 He came down to earth from heaven
    who is God and Lord of all,
and his shelter was a stable,
    and his cradle was a stall;
with the poor, and mean and lowly
    lived on earth our Saviour holy.

3 And through all his wondrous childhood
    he would honour and obey,
love and watch the lowly maiden
    in whose gentle arms he lay;
Christian children all should be
    kind, obedient, good as he.

*4 For he is our childhood's pattern,
    day by day, like us, he grew;
he was little, weak and helpless,
    tears and smiles like us he knew;
and he feeleth for our sadness,
    and he shareth in our gladness.

5 And our eyes at last shall see him,
    through his own redeeming love,
for that child so dear and gentle
    is our Lord in heaven above;
and he leads his children on
    to the place where he is gone.

6 Not in that poor lowly stable,
    with the oxen standing by,
we shall see him; but in heaven,
    set at God's right hand on high;
when like stars his children crowned
    all in white shall wait around.

Cecil Frances (Fanny) Alexander (1818–95) altd.

GOD THE SON, REDEEMER

178

Lourdes 11 11 with Refrain

French traditional melody

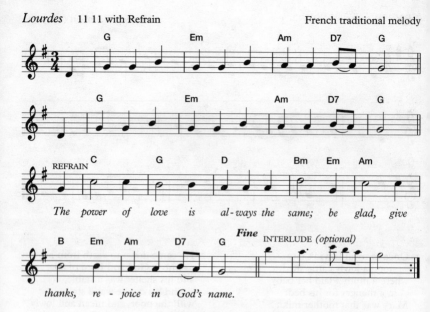

The power of love is al-ways the same; be glad, give thanks, re-joice in God's name.

At a Christingle Service

1 Round orange, round orange, you serve as a sign
   that God made the round world with purpose divine.

   The power of love is always the same;
   be glad, give thanks, rejoice in God's name.

2 Red ribbon, you tell us of bloodshed and pain
   which led to forgiveness when Jesus was slain.

3 Ripe fruits, freely given, this truth you recall,
   when God hands out presents, they're meant for us all.

4 Bright candle, the message you carry is clear,
   the true light from God found a home with us here.

5 Christingle,[1] christingle, shine out in the night
   to kindle among us that marvellous light,

Elizabeth Cosnett (b. 1936)

[1] A Christingle is an orange surmounted by a lighted candle and decorated with fruit
and ribbon. It is received in an Advent and Christmas act of worship which originated
in the Moravian Church and is now popular in other Christian traditions.

179

Humility   77 77 with Refrain

John Goss (1800–80)

REFRAIN

Hail, thou ev - er - bless - ed morn! hail, re-demp-tion's hap - py dawn!

sing through all Je - ru - sa - lem: 'Christ is born in Beth - le - hem!'

1 See amid the winter's snow,
   born for us on earth below,
      see the tender Lamb appears,
      promised from eternal years.

   Hail, thou ever-blessèd morn!
   hail, redemption's happy dawn!
   sing through all Jerusalem:
   'Christ is born in Bethlehem!'

2 Lo, within a manger lies
   he who built the starry skies;
      he who, throned in height sublime,
      sits amid the cherubim!

*3 Say, ye holy shepherds, say
   what your joyful news today;
      wherefore have ye left your sheep
      on the lonely mountain steep?

*4 'As we watched at dead of night,
   lo, we saw a wondrous light;
      angels singing "Peace on earth"
      told us of the Saviour's birth':

5 Sacred Infant, all divine,
   what a tender love was thine,
      thus to come from highest bliss
      down to such a world as this!

6 Teach, O teach us, holy Child,
   by thy face so meek and mild,
      teach us to resemble thee,
      in thy sweet humility.

Edward Caswall (1814–78)
based on Luke 2: 1–20

180

Quem pastores   88 87   14th-century German carol melody

Quem pastores laudavere

1 Shepherds came, their praises bringing,
   who had heard the angels singing:
   'Far from you be fear unruly,
      Christ is King of glory born'.

2 Wise men, whom a star had guided,
   incense, gold and myrrh provided,
   made their sacrifices duly
      to the King of glory born.

3 Jesus born the King of heaven,
   Christ to us through Mary given,
   to your praise and honour truly
      be resounding glory done.

14th-century Latin
tr. *George B. Caird* (1917–84)

181

St Cedma 55 65

George A. Beattie (1902–88)

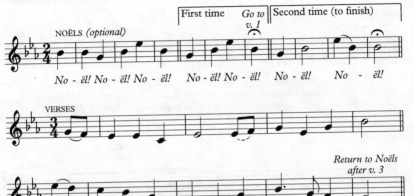

No - ël! No - ël! No - ël! No - ël! No - ël! No - ël! No - ël!

Noël![1] *Noël! Noël! Noël! Noël!*

1 The snow on the ground,
    the star in the sky,
  and here is the inn
    with the manger hard by.

2 The door's on the latch,
    so we softly creep in
  and gaze down in wonder
    on Jesus within.

3 The snow on the ground,
    the star in the sky,
  and Mary is singing
    a sweet lullaby.

Noël! Noël! Noël! Noël! Noël!

George A. Beattie (1902–88)

[1] 'Noël' (or 'Nowell') = a joyous shout or song at Christmas

182

Stille Nacht

Later form of a carol by
Franz X. Gruber (1787–1863)

1. Si - lent night, ho - ly night, all is calm,
2. Si - lent night, ho - ly night, shep - herds quake
3. Si - lent night, ho - ly night, Son of God,

all is bright round yon vir - gin mo - ther and child.
at the sight, glo - ries stream from hea - ven a - far,
love's pure light rad - iant beams from thy ho - ly face,

Ho - ly in - fant so ten - der and mild, sleep in hea - ven-ly
hea - ven-ly hosts sing al - le - lu - ia; Christ the Sav - iour is
with the dawn of re - deem - ing grace, Je - sus, Lord, at thy

peace, sleep in hea - ven-ly peace.
born! Christ the Sav - iour is born!
birth, Je - sus, Lord, at thy birth.

Stille Nacht, heilige Nacht!

1 Silent night, holy night,
  all is calm, all is bright
round yon virgin mother and child.
Holy Infant so tender and mild,
  sleep in heavenly peace,
  sleep in heavenly peace.

2 Silent night, holy night,
  shepherds quake at the sight,
glories stream from heaven afar,
heavenly hosts sing alleluia;
  Christ the Saviour is born!
  Christ the Saviour is born!

3 Silent night, holy night,
  Son of God, love's pure light
radiant beams from thy holy face,
with the dawn of redeeming grace,
  Jesus, Lord, at thy birth,
  Jesus, Lord, at thy birth.

Joseph Mohr (1792–1848)
tr. *J. F. Young* (1820–85)

183

The holly and the ivy (2)   76 96 with Refrain   English traditional carol melody

O the ris-ing of the sun,— and the run-ning of the deer,

the— play-ing of the mer-ry or - gan, sweet sing-ing in the quire.

1 The holly and the ivy
   now both are full well grown;
of all the trees that are in the wood,
   the holly bears the crown:

   *O the rising of the sun,
      and the running of the deer,
   the playing of the merry organ,
   sweet singing in the* ¹*quire.*

2 The holly bears a blossom
   as white as lily-flower;
and Mary bore sweet Jesus Christ
   to be our sweet Saviour:

3 The holly bears a berry
   as red as any blood;
and Mary bore sweet Jesus Christ
   to do poor sinners good:

4 The holly bears a prickle
   as sharp as any thorn;
and Mary bore sweet Jesus Christ
   on Christmas Day in the morn:

5 The holly bears a bark
   as bitter as any gall;
and Mary bore sweet Jesus Christ
   for to redeem us all:

6 The holly and the ivy
   now both are full well grown;
of all the trees that are in the wood,
   the holly bears the crown:

English traditional folk carol

¹ 'quire' is old English spelling for 'choir'.

184

Puer nobis nascitur (2)   76 777

German medieval carol melody
from *Piae Cantiones* (1582)

Puer nobis nascitur

1 Unto us is born a Son,
    King of quires[1] supernal:
  see on earth his life begun,
    of lords the Lord eternal,
    of lords the Lord eternal.

2 Christ, from heav'n descending low,
    comes on earth a stranger;
  ox and ass their owner know,
    becradled in a manger,
    becradled in a manger.

3 This did Herod sore affray,
    and grievously bewilder;
  so he gave the word to slay,
    and slew the little childer,
    and slew the little childer.

4 Of his love and mercy mild,
    this the Christmas story;
  O that Mary's gentle child
    might lead us up to glory,
    might lead us up to glory.

5 We adore him [2]A and O
    [3]*cum cantibus in choro;*
  let our merry organ go,
    [4]*benedicamus Domino,*
    benedicamus Domino.

15th-century Latin
based on Isaiah 9: 6; Matthew 2: 16
tr. *George R. Woodward* (1848–1934) and others

[1] 'quire' is old English spelling for 'choir'.

[2] A (alpha) and O (omega) are the first and last letters of
the Greek alphabet, and refer to Christ as the beginning
and the end (see Revelation 1: 8; 21: 6; 22: 13).

[3] (Latin) with songs in the choir

[4] (Latin) let us bless the Lord

185

Quem pastores   88 87   14th-century German carol melody

vv. 1 & 4

1 Virgin-born, we bow before thee:
  blessèd was the womb that bore thee;
    Mary, maid and mother mild,
    blessèd was she in her child.

2 Blessèd was the breast that fed thee;
  blessèd was the hand that led thee;
    blessèd was the parent's eye
    that watched thy slumbering infancy.

3 Blessèd she by all creation,
  who brought forth the world's Salvation;
    blessèd they, for ever blessed,
    who love thee most and serve thee best.

4 Virgin-born, we bow before thee:
  blessèd was the womb that bore thee;
    Mary, maid and mother mild,
    blessèd was she in her child.

Reginald Heber (1783–1826)

HIS INCARNATION

Melody contributed by Louis Bourgeois (c.1510–61)
to the *French Psalter* (1542)

Mon Dieu, prête moi l'oreille
88 77 D

1. Vir - gin - born, we bow be - fore thee: bless - ed
3. Bless - ed she by all cre - a - tion, who brought

was the womb that bore thee; Ma - ry, maid and mo-ther mild,___
forth the world's Sal - va - tion; bless-ed they, for ev - er blessed, who

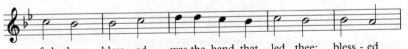

bless-ed was she in her child. 2. Bless-ed was the breast that
love thee most and serve thee best. 4. Vir - gin - born, we bow be -

fed thee; bless - ed was the hand that led thee; bless - ed
-fore thee: bless - ed was the womb that bore thee; Ma - ry,

was the par-ent's eye that watched thy slum-bering in-fan - cy.
maid and mo-ther mild,___ bless - ed was she in her child.

186

Hermon   86 86 6

Jeremiah Clarke (1673–1707)

1 What Adam's disobedience cost,
    let holy scripture say:
  mankind estranged, an Eden lost,
    and then a judgment day:
    each day a judgment day.

2 An Ark of Mercy rode the Flood;
    but man, where waters swirled,
  rebuilt, impatient of the good,
    another fallen world:
    an unrepentant world.

3 And now a Child is Adam's heir,
    is Adam's hope, and Lord.
  Sing joyful carols everywhere
    that Eden is restored:
    in Jesus is restored.

4 Regained is Adam's blessedness;
    the angels sheathe their swords.
  In joyful carols all confess
    the Kingdom is the Lord's:
    the glory is the Lord's!

F. Pratt Green (b. 1903)

187

When the crimson sun had set 87 87 with Refrain
(Les anges dans nos campagnes)

Variant of Flemish or French
traditional carol melody

REFRAIN

Glo - - - - - ri - a in ex-cel-sis De - o, Glo - - - - ri - a in ex-cel-sis De - o!

1 When the crimson sun had set,
    sinking 'neath the frosty plain,
on a bright and cold midnight
    broke the glad angelic strain:

    Gloria in excelsis Deo![1]

2 Shepherds, watching by their flocks,
    upward look with wond'ring gaze,
in the sky bright hosts espy,
    filling all the heav'nly ways:

3 Hie they then with quick accord,
    hasting to the manger-throne,
bending low with hearts aglow,
    God of God the Babe they own:

4 Joy with us, good Christians all,
    Christ is come to set us free;
he was born on Christmas morn,
    sing the glad nativity:

Anon.
edited by *J. A. Jennings*
based on Luke 2: 8–14

[1] Glory to God in the highest

188

Winchester Old   86 86 (CM)   Melody from T. Este's *Psalmes* (1592)

1 While shepherds watched their flocks by night,
   all seated on the ground,
the angel of the Lord came down,
   and glory shone around.

2 'Fear not,' said he (for mighty dread
   had seized their troubled mind),
'glad tidings of great joy I bring
   to you and all mankind.

3 'To you, in David's town, this day,
   is born of David's line
a Saviour, who is Christ the Lord;
   and this shall be the sign:

4 'The heavenly babe you there shall find
   to human view displayed,
all meanly wrapped in swaddling clothes,
   and in a manger laid.'

5 Thus spake the seraph; and forthwith
   appeared a shining throng
of angels, praising God, who thus
   addressed their joyful song:

6 'All glory be to God on high,
   and to the earth be peace!
Goodwill henceforth from heaven to earth
   begin, and never cease.'

Nahum Tate (1652–1715) altd.
based on Luke 2: 8–14

189

From a chorale by Conrad Kocher (1786–1872)
abridged by William Henry Monk (1823–89)

Dix   77 77 77

1 As with gladness men of old
  did the guiding star behold;
    as with joy they hailed its light,
    leading onward, beaming bright;
  so, most gracious Lord, may we
  evermore be led to thee.

2 As with joyful steps they sped,
  Saviour, to thy lowly bed;
    there to bend the knee before
    thee whom heaven and earth adore;
  so may we with willing feet
  ever seek thy mercy-seat.

3 As they offered gifts most rare
  at thy cradle rude and bare;
    so may we with holy joy,
    pure and free from sin's alloy,
  all our costliest treasures bring,
  Christ, to thee, our heavenly King.

4 Holy Jesus, every day
  keep us in the narrow way;
    and, when earthly things are past,
    bring our ransomed soul at last
  where they need no star to guide,
  where no clouds thy glory hide.

5 In the heavenly country bright
  need they no created light;
    thou its light, its joy, its crown,
    thou its sun, which goes not down:
  there for ever may we sing
  alleluias to our King.

William Chatterton Dix (1837–98)
based on Matthew 2: 1–11

190

FIRST TUNE

Epiphany   11 10 11 10

J. F. Thrupp (1827–67)

SECOND TUNE

Liebster Immanuel   11 10 11 10   Melody adpt. from *Himmels-Lust* (Jena, 1679)

1 Brightest and best of the suns of the morning,
    dawn on our darkness and come to our aid;
star of the east, the horizon adorning,
    guide where our infant Redeemer is laid.

2 Cold on his cradle the dew-drops are shining,
    low lies his head with the beasts of the stall;
angels adore him in slumber reclining,
    Maker and Monarch and Saviour of all.

3 What shall we give him, in costly devotion?
    Shall we bring incense and offerings divine,
gems of the mountain and pearls of the ocean,
    myrrh from the forest or gold from the mine?

4 Vainly we offer each lavish oblation,
    vainly with gifts would his favour secure;
richer by far is the heart's adoration,
    dearer to God are the prayers of the poor.

5 Brightest and best of the suns of the morning,
    dawn on our darkness and come to our aid;
star of the east, the horizon adorning,
    guide where our infant Redeemer is laid.

Reginald Heber (1783–1826) altd.
based on Matthew 2: 1–11

GOD THE SON, REDEEMER

191

FIRST TUNE

Old 120th   66 66 66

Melody as given in Este's *Psalmes* (1592)

SECOND TUNE

Hail to the Lord   66 66 66

Malcolm Williamson (b. 1931)

1. Hail to the Lord who comes, comes to his
tem - ple gate! Not with his an - gel host,
not in his king - ly state; no shouts pro - claim him
nigh, no crowds his com - ing wait;___

HIS EPIPHANY

1 Hail to the Lord who comes,
   comes to his temple gate!
Not with his angel host,
   not in his kingly state;
no shouts proclaim him nigh,
   no crowds his coming wait;

2 but borne upon the throne
   of Mary's gentle breast,
watched by her duteous love,
   in her fond arms at rest;
thus to his Father's house
   he comes, the heavenly guest.

3 There Joseph at her side
   in reverent wonder stands;
and, filled with holy joy,
   old Simeon in his hands
takes up the promised Child,
   the glory of all lands.

4 Hail to the great First-born
   whose ransom price they pay!
The Son before all worlds,
   the Child of man today,
that he might ransom us
   who still in bondage lay.

5 O Light of all the earth,
   thy children wait for thee!
Come to thy temples here,
   that we, from sin set free,
before thy Father's face
   may all presented be!

John Ellerton (1826–93)

192

Wie schön leuchtet   887 D 484 8

Later form of a melody by
Philipp Nicolai (1556–1608)

Wie herrlich strahlt der Morgenstern

1 How brightly beams the morning star!
What sudden radiance from afar
   now cheers us with its shining!
Brightness of God, that breaks our night
and fills the darkened souls with light
   who once for truth were pining!
      Your word, Jesus,
      inly feeds us,
      rightly leads us,
      life bestowing.
Praise, O praise such love o'erflowing.

2 Through you alone can we be blessed;
then deep be on our hearts impressed
   the love that you have borne us;
so make us ready to fulfil
with burning zeal your holy will,
   though some may vex or scorn us.
      Saviour, never
      let us lose you;
      for we choose you,
      thirst to know you;
all we are and have we owe you!

3 All praise to him who came to save,
who conquered death and burst the grave;
   each day new praise is sounding
to him the Lamb who once was slain,
the friend whom none shall trust in vain,
   whose grace is still abounding;
      sing, you people,
      tell the story
      of his glory,
      till his praises
flood with light earth's darkest places!

Philipp Nicolai (1556–1608)
and *Johann Schlegel* (1721–93)
tr. *Catherine Winkworth* (1827–78) altd.

193

Alleluia, dulce carmen   87 87 87   Melody from
An Essay on the Church Plain Chant (1782)
probably by Samuel Webbe the elder (1740–1816)

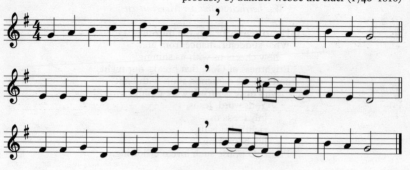

THE PRESENTATION OF CHRIST IN THE TEMPLE
FEBRUARY 2

1 In his temple now behold him,
  see the long-expected Lord!
ancient prophets had foretold him;
  God hath now fulfilled his word.
Now to praise him his redeemèd
  shall break forth with one accord.

2 In the arms of her who bore him,
  Virgin pure, behold him lie,
while his agèd saints adore him,
  ere in perfect faith they die:
Alleluia, alleluia!
  Lo! the incarnate God most high!

3 Jesus, by thy Presentation,
  thou who didst for us endure,
make us see thy great salvation,
  seal us with thy promise sure;
and present us in thy glory,
  to thy Father, cleansed and pure.

4 Prince and author of salvation,
  be thy boundless love our theme!
Jesus, praise to thee be given
  by the world thou didst redeem,
with the Father and the Spirit,
  Lord of majesty supreme!

Henry J. Pye (1825–93)
based on Luke 2: 22–40

194

Stuttgart   87 87

Adapted from a melody in C. F. Witt's
Harmonia Sacra (Gotha, 1715)

1 Earth has many a noble city:
      Bethl'em, thou dost all excel;
   out of thee the Lord from heaven
      came to rule his Israel.

2 Fairer than the sun at morning
      was the star that told his birth,
   to the world its God announcing
      seen in fleshly form on earth.

3 Eastern sages at his cradle
      make oblations rich and rare;
   see them give, in deep devotion,
      gold and frankincense and myrrh.

4 Sacred gifts of mystic meaning:
      incense doth their God disclose,
   gold the King of kings proclaimeth,
      myrrh his sepulchre foreshows.

5 Jesus, whom the Gentiles worshipped
      at thy glad Epiphany,
   unto thee, with God the Father
      and the Spirit, glory be.

Marcus Aurelius Clemens Prudentius (c.348–413)
      tr. *Edward Caswall (1814–78) altd.*
            based on Matthew 2: 1–11

195

Shine, Jesus, shine

Words and music by Graham Kendrick (b. 1950)

1. Lord, the light of your love is shin - ing
2. Lord, I come to your awe - some pres - ence,
3. As we gaze on your king - ly bright - ness,

in the midst of the dark - ness, shin - ing;
from the sha - dows in - to your rad - iance;
so our fa - ces dis - play your like - ness,

Je - sus, Light of the world, shine up - on___ us,
by the blood I may en - ter your bright - ness,
ev - er chan - ging from glo - ry to glo - ry,

set us free by the truth you now bring___ us,
search me, try me, con - sume all my dark - ness.
mir - rored here may our lives tell your sto - ry.

HIS EPIPHANY

based on John 1: 1–5; 3: 19–21;
2 Corinthians 3: 18; 1 John 1: 7

196

Was lebet, was schwebet (1)   12 10 12 10

Melody from the *Rheinhardt MS*
(Üttingen, 1754)

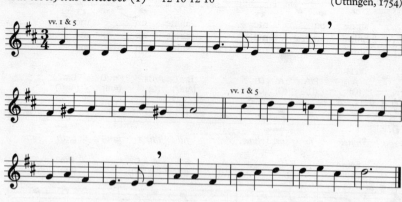

1 O worship the Lord in the beauty of holiness!
    Bow down before him, his glory proclaim;
with gold of obedience, and incense of lowliness,
    kneel and adore him, the Lord is his name!

2 Low at his feet lay thy burden of carefulness,
    high on his heart he will bear it for thee,
comfort thy sorrows, and answer thy prayerfulness,
    guiding thy steps as may best for thee be.

3 Fear not to enter his courts in the slenderness
    of the poor wealth thou wouldst reckon as thine:
truth in its beauty, and love in its tenderness,
    these are the offerings to lay on his shrine.

4 These, though we bring them in trembling and fearfulness,
    he will accept for the name that is dear;
mornings of joy give for evenings of tearfulness,
    trust for our trembling and hope for our fear.

5 O worship the Lord in the beauty of holiness!
    Bow down before him, his glory proclaim;
with gold of obedience, and incense of lowliness,
    kneel and adore him, the Lord is his name!

John S. B. Monsell (1811–75)
based on Psalms 29: 2; 96: 9; Matthew 2: 11

197

St Edmund   77 77 D

Charles Steggall (1826–1905)

Alternative tune: 37 ST GEORGE'S, WINDSOR

1 Songs of thankfulness and praise,
  Jesu, Lord, to thee we raise,
    manifested by the star
    to the sages from afar;
  branch of royal David's stem
  in thy birth at Bethlehem;
    anthems be to thee addressed,
    God in Man made manifest.

2 Manifest at Jordan's stream,
  Prophet, Priest and King supreme;
    and at Cana wedding-guest
    in thy Godhead manifest;
  manifest in power divine,
  changing water into wine;
    anthems be to thee addressed,
    God in Man made manifest.

3 Manifest in making whole
  palsied limbs and fainting soul;
    manifest in valiant fight,
    quelling all the devil's might;
  manifest in gracious will,
  ever bringing good from ill;
    anthems be to thee addressed,
    God in Man made manifest.

*4 Sun and moon shall darkened be,
  stars shall fall, the heavens shall flee;
    Christ will then like lightning shine,
    all will see his glorious sign;
  all will then the trumpet hear,
  all will see the Judge appear;
    thou by all will be confessed,
    God in Man made manifest.

5 Grant us grace to see thee, Lord,
  mirrored in thy holy word;
    may we imitate thee now,
    and be pure, as pure art thou;
  that we like to thee may be
  at thy great Epiphany,
    and may praise thee, ever blessed,
    God in Man made manifest.

Christopher Wordsworth (1807–85) altd.
based on Matthew 2: 1–11;
Luke 5: 17–26; John 2: 1–11

263

198

The first Nowell

English traditional carol melody from William Sandys'
Christmas Carols Ancient and Modern (1833)

No - well,___ No - well, No - well, No - well,

born is the King___ of Is - ra - el.

HIS EPIPHANY

1 The first Nowell[1] the angel did say
  was to certain poor shepherds in fields as they lay;
    in fields where they lay keeping their sheep
    on a cold winter's night that was so deep:

    Nowell, Nowell, Nowell, Nowell,
    born is the King of Israel.

2 They lookèd up and saw a star
  shining in the east beyond them far,
    and to the earth it gave great light,
    and so it continued both day and night:

3 And by the light of that same star
  three wise men came from country far;
    to seek for a king was their intent,
    and to follow the star wherever it went:

4 This star drew nigh to the north-west,
  o'er Bethlehem it took its rest,
    and there it did both stop and stay
    right over the place where Jesus lay:

5 Then entered in those wise men three
  most reverently upon their knee,
    and offered there in his presence,
    their gold and myrrh and frankincense:

6 Then let us all with one accord
  sing praises to our heavenly Lord,
    that hath made heaven and earth of nought,
    and with his blood mankind hath bought:

from William Sandys'
Christmas Carols, Ancient and Modern (1833)
based on Luke 2: 10–11 & Matthew 2: 1–11

[1] 'Nowell' (or 'Noël') = a joyous shout or song at Christmas

199

Dundee (French)   86 86 (CM)

Melody from *The CL Psalmes of David*
(Edinburgh, 1615)

For the significance of the small notes, see the Musical Preface. See also no. 629.

1 The people that in darkness walked
   a glorious light have seen;
   the light has shined on them who long
   in shades of death have been.

2 To hail thee, Sun of righteousness,
   the gathering nations come;
   they joy as when the reapers bear
   their harvest treasures home.

3 For unto us a Child is born,
   to us a Son is given,
   and on his shoulder ever rests
   all power in earth and heaven.

4 His name shall be the Prince of Peace,
   for evermore adored;
   the Wonderful, the Counsellor,
   the Everlasting Lord.

5 His power, increasing, still shall spread,
   his reign no end shall know:
   justice shall guard his throne above,
   and peace abound below.

John Morison (1750–98) altd.
based on Isaiah 9: 2–7

200

Solemnis haec festivitas   88 88 (LM)   Melody from the *Paris Gradual* (1685)

Alternative tunes: 153 PUER NOBIS NASCITUR   136, 238 WINCHESTER NEW

1 The sinless one to Jordan came
 to share our fallen nature's blame;
   God's righteousness he thus fulfilled
   and chose the path his Father willed.

2 Uprising from the waters there,
 the voice from heaven did witness bear
   that he, the Son of God, had come
   to lead his scattered people home.

3 Above him see the heavenly Dove,
 the sign of God the Father's love,
   now by the Holy Spirit shed
   upon the Son's anointed head.

4 How blessed that mission then begun
 to heal and save a race undone;
   straight to the wilderness he goes
   to wrestle with his people's foes.

5 Dear Lord, let those baptized from sin
 go forth with you, a world to win;
   and send the Holy Spirit's power
   to shield them in temptation's hour.

6 On you shall all your people feed
 and know you are the Bread indeed,
   who gives eternal life to those
   that with you died, and with you rose.

George B. Timms (1910–97)
based on Mark 1: 9–11

201

Kings of Orient   88 86 with Refrain

John H. Hopkins (1820–92)
published 1865

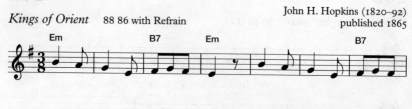

REFRAIN

O— star of won-der, star of night, star with roy-al beau-ty bright;

west-ward lead-ing, still pro-ceed-ing, guide us to thy per-fect light!

INTERLUDE *(optional)*

1 *The kings*   We three kings of Orient are;
bearing gifts we traverse afar
field and fountain, moor and mountain,
following yonder star:

O star of wonder, star of night,
star with royal beauty bright;
westward leading, still proceeding,
guide us to thy perfect light!

2 *First king*   Born a king on Bethlehem plain,
gold I bring to crown him again—
king for ever, ceasing never ⌣
over us all to reign:

3 *Second king*   Frankincense to offer have I;
incense owns a Deity nigh;
prayer and praising gladly raising,
worship him, God Most High:

4 *Third king*   Myrrh is mine; its bitter perfume
breathes a life of gathering gloom;
sorrowing, sighing, bleeding, dying,
sealed in the stone-cold tomb:

5 *The kings*   Glorious now, behold him arise,
King, and God, and Sacrifice!
Heav'n sings alleluia: alle- ⌣
-luia the earth replies:

John H. Hopkins (1820–91)
based on Matthew 2: 1–11

Verses 1 and 5 are sung by all; if possible, verses 2, 3 and 4 should be
sung as a solo or by a small group of voices.

202

Greensleeves   87 87 68 67

English traditional carol melody
from Will Ballet's *MS. Lute-Book* (*c*.1600)
in the Library of Trinity College, Dublin

HIS EPIPHANY

1 What child is this, who, laid to rest,
   on Mary's lap is sleeping,
whom angels greet with anthems sweet,
   while shepherds watch are keeping?
This, this is Christ the King,
   whom shepherds guard and angels sing:
haste, haste to bring him laud,
   the babe, the son of Mary!

2 Why lies he in such mean estate,
   where ox and ass are feeding?
Good Christian, fear; for sinners here
   the silent Word is pleading:
nails, spear, shall pierce him through,
   the cross be borne, for me, for you:
hail, hail, the Word made flesh,
   the babe, the son of Mary!

3 So bring him incense, gold, and myrrh,
   come, peasant, king, to own him.
The King of kings salvation brings:
   let loving hearts enthrone him.
Raise, raise the song on high!
   The virgin sings her lullaby:
joy, joy, for Christ is born,
   the babe, the son of Mary!

William Chatterton Dix (1837–98)

203

Lourdes 11 11 with Refrain

French traditional melody

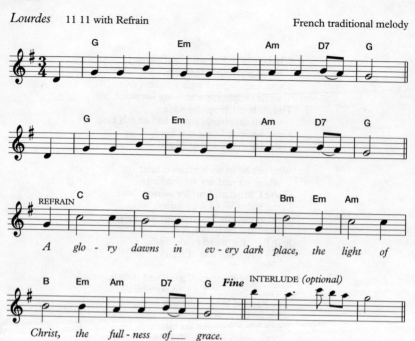

REFRAIN

A glo - ry dawns in ev - ery dark place, the light of Christ, the full - ness of___ grace.

Fine INTERLUDE *(optional)*

THE PRESENTATION OF CHRIST IN THE TEMPLE
FEBRUARY 2

*When verses 10 and 11 are omitted, the word 'we'
should be substituted for 'they' in verse 12.*

1 When candles are lighted on Candlemas[1] Day,
the dark is behind us and spring's on the way.

  *A glory dawns in every dark place,
  the light of Christ, the fullness of grace.*

2 The kings have departed, the shepherds have gone,
the child and his parents are left on their own.

3 They go to the temple, obeying the law,
and offer two pigeons, the gift of the poor.

4 But Anna and Simeon recognise there
  the Christ-child who came at the turn of the year.

*5 The old, who have suffered and waited so long,
  see hope for the world as they welcome the young.

*6 They gaze at God's wonderful answer to prayer,
  the joy of the Jews and the Gentiles' desire.

*7 The light is increasing and spring's in the air.
  Look back with thanksgiving! Look forward with awe!

8 They see before Mary a heart-piercing grief,
  but trust is complete at the end of their life.

9 For Mary will follow, with tears in her eyes,
  her saviour and son to the foot of the cross.

*10 O Spirit of God, with like courage inspire‿
  your everyday saints who face up to despair.

*11 They pass through temptation, through failure, through death.
  When darkness descends, they plod onward in faith.

12 Like Anna, like Simeon, may they *(we)* have trust,
  the eyes to see Jesus and peace at the last.

13 The candles invite us to praise and to pray
  when Christmas greets Easter on Candlemas Day.

Elizabeth Cosnett (b. 1936)
based on Luke 2: 22–40

---

[1] As Christmas is a popular name for the Nativity of Christ, so Candlemas is often used to describe the feast of the Presentation of Christ in the Temple, and is a reference to the ancient custom of lighting candles on that day to symbolise the 'Light that lightens the Gentiles'.

204

Crüger   76 76 D

adpt. by William Henry Monk (1823–89)
from a chorale by Johann Crüger (1598–1662)
in his *Gesangbuch* (Berlin, 1640)

HIS EPIPHANY

1 When Jesus came to Jordan
  to be baptized by John,
he did not come for pardon,
  but as his Father's Son.
He came to share repentance
  with all who mourn their sins,
to speak the vital sentence
  with which good news begins.

2 He came to share temptation,
  our utmost woe and loss;
for us and our salvation
  to die upon the cross.
So when the Dove descended ⌣
  on him, the Son of Man,
the hidden years had ended,
  the age of grace began.

3 Come, Holy Spirit, aid us
  to keep the vows we make;
this very day invade us,
  and every bondage break;
come, give our lives direction,
  the gift we covet most—
to share the resurrection
  that leads to Pentecost

F. Pratt Green (b. 1903)
based on Mark 1: 9–11

GOD THE SON, REDEEMER

205

FIRST TUNE

Feniton   78 78 with Alleluias   Sydney H. Nicholson (1875–1947)

Al - le - lu - ia,   Al - le - lu - ia,   Al - le - lu - ia!

SECOND TUNE

St Albinus   78 78 with Alleluia   Henry J. Gauntlett (1805–76)

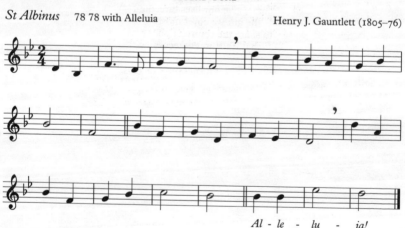

Al - le - lu - ia!

276

THE TRANSFIGURATION OF OUR LORD
AUGUST 6

1 Christ, upon the mountain peak,
   stands alone in glory blazing.
 Let us, if we dare to speak,
   join the saints and angels praising:
     Alleluia!

2 Trembling at his feet we saw
   Moses and Elijah speaking.
 All the Prophets and the Law
   shout through them their joyful greeting:
     Alleluia!

3 Swift the cloud of glory came,
   God, proclaiming in its thunder,
 Jesus as the Son by name!
   Nations, cry aloud in wonder:
     Alleluia!

4 This is God's beloved Son!
   living hope of every nation.
 Hear and heed him everyone;
   sing, with earth and all creation:
     Alleluia!

Brian Wren (b. 1936)
based on Matthew 17: 1–8;
Mark 9: 2–8; Luke 9: 28–36

206

Kilmarnock   86 86 (CM)

Melody by Neil Dougall (1776–1862)

1 Come, let us to the Lord our God
   with contrite hearts return;
   our God is gracious, nor will leave
   the desolate to mourn.

2 His voice commands the tempest forth,
   and stills the stormy wave;
   and though his arm be strong to smite,
   'tis also strong to save.

3 Long has the night of sorrow reigned,
   the dawn shall bring us light:
   God shall appear, and we shall rise
   with gladness in his sight.

4 Our hearts, if God we seek to know,
   shall know him and rejoice;
   his coming like the morn shall be,
   like morning songs his voice.

5 As dew upon the tender herb,
   diffusing fragrance round;
   as showers that usher in the spring
   and cheer the thirsty ground,

6 so shall his presence bless our souls,
   and shed a joyful light;
   that hallowed morn shall chase away
   the sorrows of the night.

John Morison (1750–98) altd.
based on Hosea 6: 1–4

207

Heinlein (Aus der Tiefe)   77 77

Melody in *Nürnbergisches Gesangbuch* (1676)
attrib. Martin Herbst (1654–81)

1 Forty days and forty nights
   thou wast fasting in the wild;
forty days and forty nights
   tempted, and yet undefiled:

2 sunbeams scorching all the day,
   chilly dew-drops nightly shed;
prowling beasts about thy way;
   stones thy pillow, earth thy bed.

3 Let us thy endurance share,
   and from earthly joys abstain,
with thee watching unto prayer,
   with thee strong to suffer pain.

4 And if Satan, vexing sore,
   flesh or spirit should assail,
thou, his vanquisher before,
   grant we may not faint nor fail.

5 So shall we have peace divine;
   holier gladness ours shall be;
round us too shall angels shine,
   such as ministered to thee.

6 Keep, O keep us, Saviour dear,
   ever constant by thy side;
that with thee we may appear
   at the eternal Eastertide.

George H. Smyttan (1822–70)
and *Francis Pott* (1832–1909)
based on Mark 1: 12–13

208

Attende, Domine

Plainsong melody, mode v

Hear-ken, O Lord, have mer-cy up-on us, for we have sin-ned a - gainst thee.

The refrain is sung at the beginning and after each verse. Traditionally, each verse is sung by a cantor and the following refrain is sung by all: at the beginning, the first phrase of the refrain is sung by the cantor and the second phrase by all. However, other arrangements are possible; for example, the verses may be sung by part or all of the choir, all present joining in the refrain.

The Lent Prose—'Attende, Domine'

Hearken, O Lord, have mercy upon us,
for we have sinnèd against thee.

1 To thee, Redeemer, King of highest heaven,
   lift we our eyes in grief and deep abasement:
   listen, O Saviour, to our supplications.

2 Head of the Corner, right hand of the Father,
   way of salvation, gate of life eternal,
   wash thou away the stain of our offences.

3 Lord, we beseech thee, from thy throne of glory
   bow down thine ear to hear our cry of sorrow,
   look down in mercy on our sore transgressions.

4 All our misdoings now we lay before thee,
   unveil with contrite heart each guilty secret:
   Saviour, in pity grant us thy forgiveness.

5 Guiltless, a captive taken unresisting,
   by false accusers brought to condemnation,
   save, Lord, and help the souls thou hast redeemèd.

Latin, tr. Compilers Hymns A.M. 1950

209

Providence 84 84

Richard R. Terry (1865–1938)

THE TRANSFIGURATION OF OUR LORD
AUGUST 6

1 Here in this holy time and place,
      transfigured Lord,
   grant us to know your perfect grace
      by sign and word.

2 Then let us on our journey move,
      leaving behind
   passions and cares which hindrance prove
      for heart and mind.

3 Let us not seek for cheap relief
      from loss and shame,
   but tread the holy path of grief,
      Christ, in your name.

4 Here may we celebrate the grace
      so long concealed,
   now in the glory of your face
      fully revealed.

Michael Forster (b. 1946)

210

Rex gloriae 87 87 D

Henry Smart (1813–79)

1 Holy God, of righteous glory,
   see your people gathered here,
in a solemn congregation,
   your forgiving word to hear.
God of love and slow to anger,
   gracious, longing to restore,
hear your priests and people calling,
   give us grace to sin no more.

2 We confess the pride we suffer,
   needs which none can satisfy;
how we love the praise of mortals,
   swift to flow'r and quick to die.
Let us find rewards eternal
   as we quietly seek your face,
and our open, public living
   witness only to your grace.

3 Free us from our self-bound living,
   better witnesses to be,
to the world by grace appealing,
   telling forth the mystery:
how creation's pure Redeemer
   walked among us undefiled,
by his deathless love proclaiming,
   God with us is reconciled.

Michael Forster (b. 1946)

211

Bishopthorpe   86 86 (CM)

Melody from Gardner's
Select Portions of the Psalms (London, *c.*1786)
ascribed to Jeremiah Clarke (*c.*1673–1707)

Version of bar 1 in 1960 edition:

etc.

Alternative tunes: 11ii HARESFIELD   547 STRACATHRO

1 Immortal love for ever full,
  for ever flowing free,
for ever shared, for ever whole,
  a never-ebbing sea!

2 Our outward lips confess the name,
  all other names above;
love only knoweth whence it came
  and comprehendeth love.

3 We may not climb the heavenly
    steeps
  to bring the Lord Christ down;
in vain we search the lowest deeps,
  for him no depths can drown;

4 but warm, sweet, tender, even yet
  a present help is he;
and faith has still its Olivet,
  and love its Galilee.

*5 The healing of his seamless dress
  is by our beds of pain;
we touch him in life's throng and press,
  and we are whole again.

*6 Through him the first fond prayers
    are said
  our lips of childhood frame;
the last low whispers of our dead
  are burdened with his name.

7 Alone, O Love ineffable,
  thy saving name is given;
to turn aside from thee is hell,
  to walk with thee is heaven.

John G. Whittier (1807–92)
based on Philippians 2: 9–11;
Romans 10: 6–7; Mark 5: 25–29

212

Song 13 (2)   77 77

Later form of melody
by Orlando Gibbons (1583–1625)

For the original form of this tune, see no. 626ii.

1 Jesus, grant me this, I pray,
  ever in thy heart to stay;
    let me evermore abide
    hidden in thy wounded side.

2 If the world or Satan lay
  tempting snares about my way,
    I am safe when I abide
    in thy heart and wounded side.

3 If the flesh, more dangerous still,
  tempt my soul to deeds of ill,
    naught I fear when I abide
    in thy heart and wounded side.

4 Death will come one day to me;
  Jesus, cast me not from thee;
    dying, let me still abide
    in thy heart and wounded side.

Henry Williams Baker (1821–77)

213

Au clair de la lune (1)   11 11 11 11   French traditional melody

1 Jesus' hands were kind hands, doing good to all,
  healing pain and sickness, blessing children small;
  washing weary feet, and saving those who fall;
  Jesus' hands were kind hands, doing good to all.

2 Take my hands, Lord Jesus, let them work for you,
  make them strong and gentle, kind in all I do;
  let me watch you, Jesus, till I'm gentle too,
  till my hands are kind hands, quick to work for you.

Margaret Cropper (1886–1980)

214

Eisenach   88 88 (LM)

Melody by J. H. Schein (1586–1630)
in his revised *Cantional* (1645)

O amor quam ecstaticus

1 O Love, how deep, how broad, how high!
It fills the heart with ecstasy
   that God, the Son of God, should take
   our mortal form for mortals' sake.

*2 He sent no angel to our race
of higher or of lower place,
   but wore the robe of human frame
   himself, and to this lost world came.

3 For us he was baptized, and bore
his holy fast, and hungered sore;
   for us temptations sharp he knew;
   for us the tempter overthrew.

4 For us he prayed, for us he taught,
for us his daily works he wrought;
   by words, and signs, and actions thus
   still seeking not himself but us.

5 For us to wicked hands betrayed,
scourged, mocked, in purple robe arrayed,
   he bore the shameful cross and death;
   for us at length gave up his breath.

6 For us he rose from death again,
for us he went on high to reign,
   for us he sent his Spirit here
   to guide, to strengthen, and to cheer.

7 To him whose boundless love has won
salvation for us through his Son,
   to God the Father, glory be
   both now and through eternity.

Anon. 15th-century Latin
tr. *Benjamin Webb* (1820–85) altd.

215

Herzliebster Jesu   11 11 11 5

Later form of a melody
by Johann Crüger (1598–1662)

Herzliebster Jesu

1 Ah, holy Jesu, how hast thou offended,
   that we to judge thee have in hate pretended:
      by foes derided, by thine own rejected,
         O most afflicted.

2 Who was the guilty? Who brought this upon thee?
   Alas, my treason, Jesu, hath undone thee.
      'Twas I, Lord Jesu, I it was denied thee:
         I crucified thee.

*3 Lo, the good Shepherd for the sheep is offered;
   the slave hath sinnèd, and the Son hath suffered;
      for man's atonement, while he nothing heedeth,
         God intercedeth.

*4 For me, kind Jesu, was thy incarnation,
   thy mortal sorrow, and thy life's oblation;
      thy death of anguish and thy bitter passion,
         for my salvation.

5 Therefore, kind Jesu, since I cannot pay thee,
   I do adore thee, and will ever pray thee,
      think on thy pity and thy love unswerving,
         not my deserving.

Robert Bridges (1844–1930)
based on an 11th cent. Latin meditation by
Johann Heerman (1585–1647)

216

Alleluia, my Father

Tim Cullen

Alleluia, my Father, for giving us your Son;
sending him into the world to die for ev'ryone,
knowing we would bruise him and smite him from the earth.
Alleluia, my Father, in his death is my birth.
Alleluia, my Father, in his life is my life.

Tim Cullen

217

St Theodulph
(Valet will ich dir geben)   76 76 D

Melchior Teschner (1584–1635)

REFRAIN

All glo-ry, laud, and hon-our to thee, Re-deem-er, King,

Fine

to whom the lips of child-ren made sweet ho-san-nas ring.

D.C.

* Alternative:

Gloria, laus et honor tibi sit

All glory, laud, and honour
to thee, Redeemer, King,
to whom the lips of children
made sweet hosannas ring.

1 Thou art the King of Israel,
    thou David's royal Son,
who in the Lord's name comest,
    the King and blessèd one:

2 The company of angels
    are praising thee on high;
and mortal flesh, and all things
    created, make reply:

3 The people of the Hebrews
    with palms to meet thee went;
our praise and prayer and anthems
    before thee we present:

4 To thee, before thy Passion,
    they sang their hymns of praise;
to thee, now high exalted,
    our melody we raise:

5 Thou didst accept their praises;
    accept the prayers we bring,
who in all good delightest,
    thou good and gracious King:

St. Theodulf of Orleans (d. 821)
tr. John Mason Neale (1818–66) altd.
based on Matthew 21: 8–9

218

Sagina   88 88 88 extended

From Thomas Campbell's
The Bouquet (1825)

(Repeat lines 5 & 6)

Alternative tune: 395 SURREY (CAREY'S)

The last two lines of each stanza are sung twice.

1 And can it be that I should gain
    an interest in the Saviour's blood?
Died he for me, who caused his pain;
    for me, who him to death pursued?
Amazing love! how can it be
that thou, my God, shouldst die for me?

2 He left his Father's throne above—
    so free, so infinite his grace—
emptied himself of all but love,
    and bled for Adam's helpless race.
'Tis mercy all, immense and free;
for, O my God, it found out me!

3 Long my imprisoned spirit lay
    fast bound in sin and nature's night:
thine eye diffused a quickening ray—
    I woke, the dungeon flamed with light;
my chains fell off, my heart was free.
I rose, went forth, and followed thee.

4 No condemnation now I dread;
    Jesus, and all in him, is mine!
Alive in him, my living head,
    and clothed in righteousness divine,
bold I approach the eternal throne,
and claim the crown, through Christ, my own.

Charles Wesley (1707–88)

219

The Servant King

Words and music by Graham Kendrick (b. 1950)

1. From heav'n you came, help-less babe, en-tered our world, your glo - ry veiled; not to be served but to serve, and give your life that we might live. *This is our God,___ the Ser-vant King,___ he calls us now to fol - low him,___ to bring our lives as a dai-ly of-fer - ing of wor-ship to___ the Ser-vant King. King.*

1 From heav'n you came, helpless babe,
entered our world, your glory veiled;
not to be served but to serve,
and give your life that we might live.

This is our God, the Servant King,
he calls us now to follow him,
to bring our lives as a daily offering
of worship to the Servant King.

2 There in the garden of tears,
my heavy load he chose to bear;
his heart with sorrow was torn,
'Yet not my will but yours', he said.

3 Come see his hands and his feet,
the scars that speak of sacrifice,
hands that flung stars into space
to cruel nails surrendered.

4 So let us learn how to serve,
and in our lives enthrone him;
each other's needs to prefer,
for it is Christ we're serving.

Graham Kendrick (b. 1950)

220

Caswall   65 65

Melody by Friedrich Filitz (1804–76)
in his *Choralbuch* (1847)

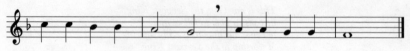

Viva, viva, Gesù

1 Glory be to Jesus,
　　who, in bitter pains,
　poured for me the life-blood
　　from his sacred veins.

2 Grace and life eternal
　　in that blood I find:
　blessed be his compassion
　　infinitely kind.

3 Abel's blood for vengeance
　　pleaded to the skies,
　but the blood of Jesus
　　for our pardon cries.

4 When that blood is sprinkled
　　on our guilty hearts,
　Satan in confusion
　　terror-struck departs.

5 When this earth exulting
　　lifts its praise on high,
　angel hosts rejoicing
　　make their glad reply.

6 Raise your thankful voices,
　　swell the mighty flood;
　louder still and louder
　　praise the precious blood.

Italian (*c.*1815)
tr. *Edward Caswall* (1814–78) altd.

221

Bryn Calfaria   87 87 47 extended   William Owen (1813–1893)

vv. 1 & 2. 'It is fin - ished,   it is fin - ished,   it is fin - ished!'
v. 3. Al - le - lu - ia,   al - le - lu - ia,   al - le - lu - ia,____

1 Hark! the voice of love and mercy
     sounds aloud from Calvary;
   see, it tears the temple curtain,
     shakes the earth and veils the sky:
   'It is finished, it is finished!'—
     hear the dying Saviour cry.

2 Finished—all the types and shadows
     of the ceremonial law;
   God fulfils what he had promised—
     death and hell shall reign no more:
   'It is finished, it is finished!'—
     Christ has opened heaven's door.

3 Saints and angels shout his praises,
     his great finished work proclaim;
   all on earth and all in heaven
     join to bless Emmanuel's name:
   'Alleluia, alleluia,
     endless glory to the Lamb!'

                        J. Evans (1748–1809) altd.
                        based on John 19: 30

222

Here is love   87 87 D

Robert Lowry (1826–99)

1 Here is love, vast as the ocean,
    loving kindness as the flood,
  when the Prince of life, our ransom,
    shed for us his precious blood.
  Who his love will not remember?
    Who can cease to sing his praise?
  He can never be forgotten
    throughout heaven's eternal days.

2 On the mount of crucifixion
    fountains opened deep and wide;
  through the floodgates of God's mercy
    flowed a vast and gracious tide.
  Grace and love, like mighty rivers,
    poured incessant from above,
  and heaven's peace and perfect justice
    kissed a guilty world in love.

Robert Lowry (1826–99)

223

Hosanna in the highest

Music and words by Carl Tuttle

1. Ho - san - na, ho - san - na, ho-san-na in the high - est. Ho -
2. Glo - ry, glo - ry, glo-ry to the King of kings.

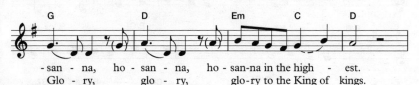

-san - na, ho - san - na, ho-san-na in the high - est.
Glo - ry, glo - ry, glo-ry to the King of kings.

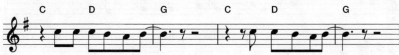

Lord, we lift up your name, with hearts full of praise.

Be ex-alt-ed, O_ Lord my God, (1) ho-san-na in the high - est.
(2) glo-ry to the King of kings.

1 Hosanna, hosanna, hosanna in the highest.
Hosanna, hosanna, hosanna in the highest.
Lord, we lift up your name,
with hearts full of praise.
Be exalted, O Lord my God,
hosanna in the highest.

2 Glory, glory, glory to the King of kings.
Glory, glory, glory to the King of kings.
Lord, we lift up your name,
with hearts full of praise.
Be exalted, O Lord my God,
glory to the King of kings.

Carl Tuttle

224

How deep the Father's love   87 87 D

Stuart Townend

BRIDGE AND CODA *(optional)*

1 How deep the Father's love for us,
  how vast beyond all measure,
  that he should give his only Son
  to make a wretch his treasure!
  How great the pain of searing loss:
  the Father turns his face away
  as wounds which mar the chosen one
   bring many sons to glory!

2 Behold the man upon a cross,
  my sin upon his shoulders;
  ashamed, I hear my mocking voice
  call out among the scoffers.
  It was my sin that held him there
  until it was accomplished;
  his dying breath has brought me life—
  I know that it is finished.

3 I will not boast in anything,
  no gifts, no power, no wisdom;
  but I will boast in Jesus Christ,
  his death and resurrection.
  Why should I gain from his reward?
  I cannot give an answer;
  but this I know with all my heart,
  his wounds have paid my ransom.

Stuart Townend

225

FIRST TUNE

Gott will's machen 87 87

J. L. Steiner (1688–1761)
pub. Zurich (1735)

SECOND TUNE

Wychbold 87 87

Walter G. Whinfield (1865–1919)

1 In the cross of Christ I glory,
    towering o'er the wrecks of time;
all the light of sacred story
    gathers round its head sublime.

2 When the woes of life o'ertake me,
    hopes deceive and fears annoy,
never shall the cross forsake me,
    lo! it glows with peace and joy.

3 When the sun of bliss is beaming
    light and love upon my way,
from the cross the radiance streaming,
    adds more lustre to the day.

4 Bane and blessing, pain and pleasure,
    by the cross are sanctified;
peace is there that knows no measure,
    joys that through all time abide.

John Bowring (1792–1872)
based on Galatians 6: 14

226

Herongate   88 88 (LM)

English traditional melody (Essex)
coll. and arr. R. Vaughan Williams (1872–1958)

1 It is a thing most wonderful,
    almost too wonderful to be,
  that God's own Son should come from heaven,
    and die to save a child like me.

2 And yet I know that it is true;
    he chose a poor and humble lot,
  and wept and toiled and mourned and died,
    for love of those who loved him not.

3 I cannot tell how he could love
    a child so weak and full of sin;
  his love must be most wonderful
    if he could die my love to win.

4 I sometimes think about the cross,
    and shut my eyes and try to see
  the cruel nails and crown of thorns,
    and Jesus crucified for me.

5 But even could I see him die,
    I could but see a little part
  of that great love which, like a fire,
    is always burning in his heart.

*6 It is most wonderful to know
    his love for me so free and sure;
  but 'tis more wonderful to see
    my love for him so faint and poor.

7 And yet I want to love thee, Lord,
    O light the flame within my heart,
  and I will love thee more and more,
    until I see thee as thou art.

W. Walsham How (1823–97)
based on Romans 5: 8

227

Gethsemane 77 78

Philipp Bliss (1838–76)

Al - le - lu - ia! What a Sav - iour!

1 Man of sorrows! What a name
for the Son of God, who came
ruined sinners to reclaim:
 Alleluia! What a Saviour!

2 Mocked by insults harsh and crude,
in my place condemned he stood;
sealed my pardon with his blood:
 Alleluia! What a Saviour!

3 Guilty, helpless, lost were we:
blameless Lamb of God was he,
sacrificed to set us free:
 Alleluia! What a Saviour!

4 He was lifted up to die:
'It is finished' was his cry;
now in heaven exalted high:
 Alleluia! What a Saviour!

5 When he comes, our glorious king,
all his ransomed home to bring;
then again this song we'll sing:
 Alleluia! What a Saviour!

Philipp Bliss (1838–76)
based on Isaiah 53: 3

228

Meekness and majesty

Words and music by Graham Kendrick (b. 1950)

1. Meek-ness and ma - jes - ty, man-hood and de - i - ty,
   in per - fect har-mo-ny— the man who is God:
   Lord of e - ter-ni-ty dwells in hu - man-i-ty,
   kneels in hu - mi-li-ty__ and__ wash-es our feet.

2. Fa - ther's pure ra - di-ance, per - fect in in-no-cence,
   yet learns o - be - di-ence to death on a cross:
   suf-fering to give us life, con-quering through sac-ri-fice—
   and, as they cru-ci-fy,__ prays, 'Fa - ther, for - give'.

3. Wis - dom un - search-a-ble, God the in - vis-i-ble,
   love in - de - struct-i - ble in frail - ty ap - pears:
   Lord of in - fi-ni-ty, stoop - ing so ten-der-ly,
   lifts our hu - man-i-ty__ to the heights of his throne.

REFRAIN

O what a mys-te - ry— meek-ness and ma-jes-ty:____
bow down and wor - ship,_____ for this is your God,__

1 Meekness and majesty,
   manhood and deity,
   in perfect harmony—
   the man who is God:
   Lord of eternity
   dwells in humanity,
   kneels in humility
   and washes our feet.

   O what a mystery—
   meekness and majesty:
   bow down and worship,
   for this is your God,
   this is your God!

2 Father's pure radiance,
   perfect in innocence,
   yet learns obedience
   to death on a cross:
   suffering to give us life,
   conquering through sacrifice—
   and, as they crucify,
   prays, 'Father, forgive'.

3 Wisdom unsearchable,
   God the invisible,
   love indestructible
   in frailty appears:
   Lord of infinity,
   stooping so tenderly,
   lifts our humanity
   to the heights of his throne.

Graham Kendrick
based on John 3: 13–16; Philippians 2: 6–11

GOD THE SON, REDEEMER

229

FIRST TUNE

Belgrave   86 86 (CM)   William Horsley (1774–1858)

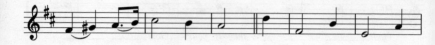

SECOND TUNE

St Francis Xavier   86 86 (CM)   John Stainer (1840–1901)

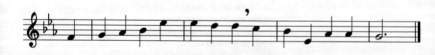

Alternative tune: 111 EPWORTH

1 My God I love thee; not because ⌣
 I hope for heaven thereby,
nor yet because who love thee not
 are lost eternally.

2 Thou, O my Jesus, thou didst me ⌣
 upon the cross embrace;
for me didst bear the nails and spear,
 and manifold disgrace,

3 and griefs and torments numberless,
 and sweat of agony;
yea, death itself, and all for me
 who was thine enemy.

4 Then why, most loving Jesus Christ,
 should I not love thee well?
Not for the sake of winning heaven,
 nor of escaping hell;

5 not with the hope of gaining aught,
 nor seeking a reward;
but as thyself hast lovèd me,
 O ever-loving Lord.

6 So would I love thee, dearest Lord,
 and in thy praise will sing,
solely because thou art my God,
 and my most loving King.

17th cent.
tr. *Edward Caswall* (1814–78)

230

What love?

Words and music by Graham Kendrick (b. 1950)

1 My Lord, what love is this that pays so dearly, that I, the guilty one, may go free.

Amazing love, O what sacrifice, the Son of God given for me. My debt he pays and my death he dies,

(2) so, they watched him die, despised, rejected; but O, the blood he shed flowed for me.

(3) now this love of Christ shall flow like rivers; come, wash your guilt away, live again!

1 My Lord, what love is this
   that pays so dearly,
   that I, the guilty one,
   may go free.

   Amazing love,
   O what sacrifice,
   the Son of God
   given for me.
   My debt he pays
   and my death he dies,
   that I might live.

2 And so, they watched him die,
   despised, rejected;
   but O, the blood he shed
   flowed for me.

3 And now this love of Christ
   shall flow like rivers;
   come, wash your guilt away,
   live again!

   Graham Kendrick (b. 1950)

231

Love unknown   66 66 44 44   John Ireland (1879–1962)

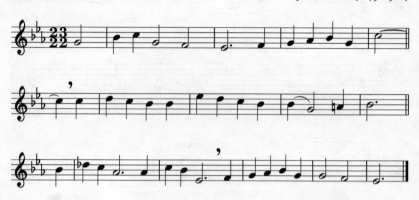

1 My song is love unknown,
    my Saviour's love to me,
  love to the loveless shown,
      that they might lovely be.
        O who am I,
          that for my sake
          my Lord should take
        frail flesh, and die?

2 He came from his blessed throne,
    salvation to bestow;
  but we made strange, and none
      the longed-for Christ would know.
        But O, my Friend,
          my Friend indeed,
          who at my need
        his life did spend.

3 Sometimes they strew his way,
    and his sweet praises sing,
  resounding all the day
      hosannas to their King.
        Then 'Crucify!'
          is all their breath,
          and for his death
        they thirst and cry.

*4 Why, what hath my Lord done?
    What makes this rage and spite?
He made the lame to run,
    he gave the blind their sight.
      Sweet injuries!
        Yet they at these
        themselves displease,
    and 'gainst him rise.

*5 They rise, and needs will have
    my dear Lord made away;
a murderer they save,
    the Prince of life they slay.
      Yet cheerful he
        to suffering goes,
        that he his foes
    from thence might free.

6 In life, no house, no home
    my Lord on earth might have;
in death, no friendly tomb
    but what a stranger gave.
      What may I say?
        Heav'n was his home;
        but mine the tomb
    wherein he lay.

7 Here might I stay and sing,
    no story so divine;
never was love, dear King,
    never was grief like thine!
      This is my Friend,
        in whose sweet praise
        I all my days
    could gladly spend.

Samuel Crossman (1624–83) altd.

GOD THE SON, REDEEMER

232

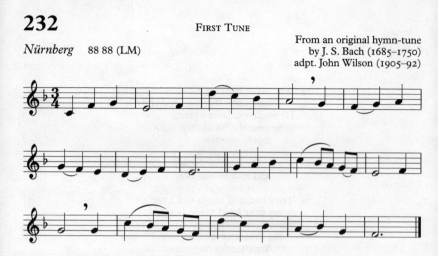

Nürnberg 88 88 (LM)

FIRST TUNE

From an original hymn-tune
by J. S. Bach (1685–1750)
adpt. John Wilson (1905–92)

SECOND TUNE

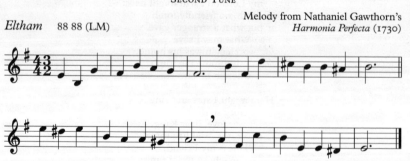

Eltham 88 88 (LM)

Melody from Nathaniel Gawthorn's
Harmonia Perfecta (1730)

Alternative tune: 589i GALILEE

1 Nature with open volume stands,
    to spread her maker's praise abroad;
and every labour of his hands
    shows something worthy of a God.

2 But in the grace that rescued man,
    his brightest form of glory shines;
here, on the cross, 'tis fairest dawn
    in precious blood, and crimson lines.

*3 Here his whole name appears complete:
    nor wit can guess, nor reason prove,
which of the letters best is writ,
    the power, the wisdom, or the love.

4 O the sweet wonders of that cross
    where Christ my Saviour loved and died!
Her noblest life my spirit draws
    from his dear wounds and bleeding side.

5 I would for ever speak his name
    in sounds to mortal ears unknown,
with angels join to praise the Lamb,
    and worship at his Father's throne.

Isaac Watts (1674–1748)

233

FIRST TUNE

Bristol   86 86 (CM)

From Thomas Ravenscroft's *Psalmes* (1621)

For the significance of the small notes above the stave, see the Musical Preface.

SECOND TUNE

Ayrshire   86 86 (CM)

Kenneth Finlay (1882–1974)

1 O dearest Lord, thy sacred head ‿
      with thorns was pierced for me;
   O pour thy blessing on my head
      that I may think for thee.

2 O dearest Lord, thy sacred hands ‿
      with nails were pierced for me;
   O shed thy blessing on my hands
      that they may work for thee.

3 O dearest Lord, thy sacred feet ‿
      with nails were pierced for me;
   O pour thy blessing on my feet
      that they may follow thee.

4 O dearest Lord, thy sacred heart ‿
      with spear was pierced for me;
   O pour thy Spirit in my heart
      that I may live for thee.

Henry E. Hardy [*Father Andrew*] (1869–1946)

234

Vater unser   88 88 88

Melody from Schumann's *Geistliche Lieder*
(Leipzig, 1539)

1 O Love divine, what hast thou done?
    The immortal God hath died for me!
  The Father's co-eternal Son
    bore all my sins upon the tree;
  The immortal God for me hath died!
  My Lord, my Love is crucified.

2 Behold him, all ye that pass by,
    the bleeding Prince of life and peace!
  Come, sinners, see your maker die,
    and say, was ever grief like his?
  Come, feel with me his blood applied:
  My Lord, my Love is crucified:

3 is crucified for me and you,
    to bring us rebels back to God:
  believe, believe the record true,
    ye all are bought with Jesu's blood.
  Pardon for all flows from his side:
  My Lord, my Love is crucified.

4 Then let us sit beneath his cross,
    and gladly catch the healing stream,
  all things for him account but loss,
    and give up all our hearts to him;
  of nothing think or speak beside:
  My Lord, my Love is crucified.

Charles Wesley (1707–88)
based on Lamentations 1: 12

235

Passion Chorale
(*Herzlich thut mich verlangen*)   76 76 D

Secular melody in H. L. Hassler's
Lustgarten (1601)

O Haupt voll Blut und Wunden

1 O sacred head, sore wounded,
   with grief and scorn weighed down;
O kingly head, surrounded
   with thorns, thine only crown.
Death's pallor now comes o'er thee,
   the glow of life decays;
yet hosts of heaven adore thee
   and tremble as they gaze.

2 What language shall I borrow
   to praise thee, dearest friend,
for this thy dying sorrow,
   thy pity without end?
O agony and dying!
   O love to sinners free!
Jesus, all grace supplying,
   turn thou thy face on me.

3 In this thy bitter passion,
   good Shepherd, think of me
with thy most sweet compassion,
   unworthy though I be:
beneath thy cross abiding
   for ever would I rest,
in thy dear love confiding,
   and with thy presence blessed.

4 Be thou my consolation,
   my shield, when I must die;
remind me of thy passion
   when my last hour draws nigh.
Mine eyes shall then behold thee,
   upon thy cross shall dwell,
my heart by faith enfold thee;
   who dieth thus, dies well.

Paul Gerhardt (1607–76)
from Salve caput cruentatum
attrib. *Bernard of Clairvaux* (1091–1153)
tr. *Henry Williams Baker* (1821–77)
and *James Waddell Alexander* (1804–59)

236

The old rugged cross

George Bennard (1873–1958)

REFRAIN

So I'll che - rish the old rug - ged cross,____ till my

tro - phies at last I lay down;____ I will cling to the old rug - ged

cross____ and ex - change it some day for a crown.____

1 On a hill far away stood an old rugged cross,
    the emblem of suff'ring and shame;
and I love that old cross where the dearest and best
    for a world of lost sinners was slain.

    So I'll cherish the old rugged cross,
        till my trophies at last I lay down;
    I will cling to the old rugged cross
        and exchange it some day for a crown.

2 O, the old rugged cross, so despised by the world,
    has a wondrous attraction for me;
for the dear Lamb of God left his glory above
    to bear it to dark Calvary.

3 In the old rugged cross, stained with blood so divine,
    a wondrous beauty I see;
for 'twas on that old cross Jesus suffered and died
    to pardon and sanctify me.

4 To the old rugged cross I will ever be true,
    its shame and reproach gladly bear;
then he'll call me some day to my home far away,
    where his glory for ever I'll share.

George Bennard (1873–1955)
based on Hebrews 12: 2; James 1: 12

237

North Coates   65 65

Timothy R. Matthews (1826–1910)

Alternative tune: 220 CASWALL

1 O my Saviour, lifted
    from the earth for me,
  draw me, in thy mercy,
    nearer unto thee.

2 Speed these lagging footsteps,
    melt this heart of ice,
  as I scan the marvels
    of thy sacrifice.

3 Lift my earth-bound longings,
    fix them, Lord, above;
  draw me with the magnet
    of thy mighty love.

4 Lord, thine arms are stretching
    ever far and wide,
  to enfold thy children
    to thy loving side.

5 And I come, O Jesus;
    dare I turn away?
  No, thy love hath conquered,
    and I come today:

6 bringing all my burdens,
    sorrow, sin and care,
  at thy feet I lay them,
    and I leave them there.

W. Walsham How (1823–97)

238

Winchester New   88 88 (LM)

Melody adapted from *Musikalisches Hand-Buch*
(Hamburg, 1690)
by William Henry Havergal (1793–1870)

1 Ride on, ride on in majesty,
 hark, all the tribes 'Hosanna' cry!
   O Saviour meek, pursue thy road
   with palms and scattered garments strowed.

2 Ride on, ride on in majesty:
 in lowly pomp ride on to die;
   O Christ, thy triumphs now begin
   o'er captive death and conquered sin.

3 Ride on, ride on in majesty:
 the angel armies of the sky
   look down with sad and wondering eyes
   to see the approaching sacrifice.

4 Ride on, ride on in majesty:
 thy last and fiercest strife is nigh;
   the Father on his sapphire throne
   awaits his own anointed Son.

5 Ride on, ride on in majesty:
 in lowly pomp ride on to die;
   bow thy meek head to mortal pain;
   then take, O God, thy power, and reign.

Henry H. Milman (1791–1868) altd.
based on Matthew 21: 8–9;
Zechariah 9: 9

GOD THE SON, REDEEMER

239

Yellow Bittern   88 88 (LM)

Adrian Beecham (1904–1982)

Alternative tune: 599 BRESLAU

1 See, Christ was wounded for our sake,
    and bruised and beaten for our sin,
  so by his sufferings we are healed,
    for God has laid our guilt on him.

2 Look on his face, come close to him—
    see, you will find no beauty there:
  despised, rejected, who can tell
    the grief and sorrow he must bear?

3 Like sheep that stray we leave God's path,
    to choose our own and not his will;
  like sheep to slaughter he has gone,
    obedient to his Father's will.

4 Cast out to die by those he loved,
    reviled by those he died to save,
  see how sin's pride has sought his death,
    see how sin's hate has made his grave.

5 For on his shoulders God has laid
    the weight of sin that we should bear;
  so by his passion we have peace,
    through his obedience and his prayer.

Brian Foley (b. 1919)
based on Isaiah 53

240

Cross of Jesus   87 87

John Stainer (1840–1901)
from *The Crucifixion*

1 Sweet the moments, rich in blessing,
   which before the cross I spend,
life and health and peace possessing,
   from the sinners' dying Friend.

2 Here I find my hope of heaven,
   while upon the Lamb I gaze;
loving much, and much forgiven,
   let my heart o'erflow in praise.

3 For thy sorrows we adore thee,
   for the pains that wrought our peace,
gracious Saviour, we implore thee,
   in our souls thy love increase.

4 Lord, in ceaseless contemplation,
   fix our hearts and eyes on thee,
till we taste thy full salvation,
   and thine unveiled glory see.

Walter Shirley (1725–86)

GOD THE SON, REDEEMER

241

Pange lingua   87 87 87

Plainsong melody (Sarum form), mode iii

A - men.___

SECOND TUNE

Grafton   87 87 87

French *Tantum ergo* melody in
Chants Ordinaires de l'Office Divin (Paris, 1881)

When this tune is sung in unison, all ♪♪ ♪♪ groups may be alternatively be sung ♪♪♪, as in the second half of the penultimate bar.

Alternative tune: 427 PICARDY

Pange, lingua, gloriosi proelium certaminis

1 Sing, my tongue, the glorious battle,
    sing the last, the dread affray;
o'er the cross, the victor's trophy,
    sound the high triumphal lay,
how, the pains of death enduring,
    earth's Redeemer won the day.

2 When at length the appointed fulness
    of the sacred time was come,
he was sent, the world's Creator,
    from the Father's heavenly home,
and was found in human fashion,
    offspring of the Virgin's womb.

3 When the thirty years were ended
    which on earth he willed to see,
willingly he meets his passion,
    born to set his people free;
on the cross the Lamb is lifted,
    there the sacrifice to be.

4 There the nails and spear he suffers,
    vinegar and gall and reed;
from his sacred body piercèd
    blood and water both proceed:
precious flood, which all creation
    from the stain of sin has freed.

5 Faithful cross, above all other,
    one and only noble tree,
none in foliage, none in blossom,
    none in fruit thy peer may be;
sweet the wood and sweet the iron,
    and thy load, most sweet is he.

6 Praise and honour to the Father,
    praise and honour to the Son,
praise and honour to the Spirit,
    ever Three and ever One:
One in might and One in glory,
    while eternal ages run. Amen.

Venantius Honorius Fortunatus (530–609)
tr. *John Mason Neale* (1818–66) altd.

GOD THE SON, REDEEMER

242

FIRST TUNE

Verbum supernum   88 88 (LM)   Plainsong melody, mode viii

A - men.

SECOND TUNE

Eisenach   88 88 (LM)   Melody by J. H. Schein (1586–1630)
in his revised *Cantional* (1645)

Part 1
Verbum supernum prodiens

1 The heavenly Word proceeding forth,
    yet leaving not the Father's side,
went forth unto his work on earth
    until he reached life's eventide.

2 By false disciple to be given ‿
    to foemen for his death athirst,
himself the Bread of life from heaven,
    he gave to his disciples first.

3 By birth their fellow-man was he;
    their meat, when sitting at the board;
he died, their ransomer to be;
    he ever reigns, their great reward.

Part 2
O salutaris hostia

4 O saving Victim, opening wide ‿
    the gate of heaven to us below,
our foes press on from every side;
    thine aid supply, thy strength bestow.

5 All praise and thanks to thee ascend
    for evermore, blessed One in Three;
O grant us life that shall not end
    in our true native land with thee.

Thomas Aquinas (1227–74)
tr. *John Mason Neale* (1818–66)

243

Vexilla Regis 88 88 (LM)

Sarum plainsong melody: mode i

A - men.

Gonfalon Royal 88 88 (LM)

Percy C. Buck (1871–1947)

After v. 6

A - - men.

Vexilla Regis prodeunt

1 The royal banners forward go,
 the cross shines forth in mystic glow;
   where he in flesh, our flesh who made,
   our sentence bore, our ransom paid.

2 His feet and hands outstretching there,
 he willed the piercing nails to bear;
   for us, and our redemption's sake
   a victim of himself to make.

3 There whilst he hung, his sacred side ⌣
 by soldier's spear was opened wide,
   to cleanse us in the precious flood ⌣
   of water mingled with his blood.

4 Fulfilled is now what David told
 in true prophetic song of old,
   to all the nations, 'Lo!' saith he,
   'Our God is reigning from the tree'.

5 O tree of glory, tree most fair,
 ordained those holy limbs to bear,
   how bright in purple robe it stood,
   the purple of a Saviour's blood!

6 To thee, eternal Three in One,
 let homage meet by all be done:
   as by the cross thou dost restore,
   so rule and guide us evermore.
     Amen.

Venantius Honorius Fortunatus (530–609)
tr. *John Mason Neale* (1818–66) altd.

244

Horsley　　86 86 (CM)　　　　　　　　　　　William Horsley (1774–1858)

1　There is a green hill far away,
　　　without[1] a city wall,
　　where the dear Lord was crucified,
　　　who died to save us all.

2　We may not know, we cannot tell
　　　what pains he had to bear,
　　but we believe it was for us
　　　he hung and suffered there.

3　He died that we might be forgiven,
　　　he died to make us good,
　　that we might go at last to heaven,
　　　saved by his precious blood.

4　There was no other good enough
　　　to pay the price of sin;
　　he only could unlock the gate
　　　of heaven, and let us in.

5　O dearly, dearly has he loved,
　　　and we must love him too,
　　and trust in his redeeming blood,
　　　and try his works to do.

Cecil Frances (Fanny) Alexander (1818–95)
based on Mark 15: 22–24

[1] without = outside

245

Contributed by Thomas Tallis (1515–85)
to Parker's *The Whole Psalter* (1567)
with the melody in the tenor
edited John Wilson (1905–92)

Third mode melody   86 86 D (DCM)

1. To mock your reign, O dear-est Lord, they made a crown of thorns;
2. In mock ac-claim, O gra-cious Lord, they snatched a pur-ple cloak,
3. A scep-tred reed, O pa-tient Lord, they thrust in-to your hand,

set you with taunts a-long that road from which no one re-turns.
your pas-sion turned, for all they cared, in-to a sol-dier's joke.
and act-ed out their grim cha-rade to its ap-point-ed end.

They could not know, as we do now, how glo-rious is that crown:
They could not know, as we do now, that though we me-rit blame,
They could not know, as we do now, though em-pires rise and fall,

that thorns would flower up-on your brow, your sor-rows heal our own.
you will your robe of mer-cy— throw, a-round our na-ked shame.
your King-dom shall not cease to— grow till love em-bra-ces all.

F. Pratt Green (b. 1903)
based on John 19

246

Were you there?

North American traditional spiritual

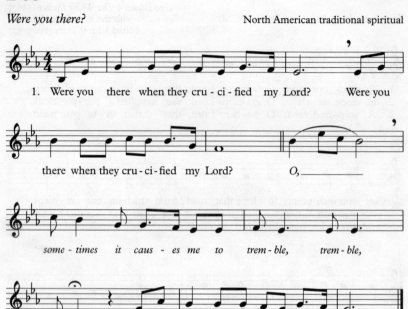

1. Were you there when they cru-ci-fied my Lord? Were you there when they cru-ci-fied my Lord? O, _____ some-times it caus-es me to trem-ble, trem-ble, trem-ble; were you there when they cru-ci-fied my Lord?

If v. 6 is omitted, the v. 6 ending (sung to 'tomb') may be used for v. 5.

1 Were you there when they crucified my Lord?
Were you there when they crucified my Lord?
O, sometimes it causes me to tremble, tremble, tremble;
were you there when they crucified my Lord?

2 Were you there when they nailed him to the tree? *etc.*

3 Were you there when they pierced him in the side? *etc.*

4 Were you there when the sun refused to shine? *etc.*

5 Were you there when they laid him in the tomb? *etc.*

*6 Were you there when God raised him from the dead? *etc.*

North American traditional spiritual

247

Rockingham   88 88 (LM)

Adapted by Edward Miller (1731–1807)
from a melody in *A Second Supplement
to Psalmody in Miniature* (c.1780)

1 When I survey the wondrous cross
    on which the Prince of Glory died,
 my richest gain I count but loss,
    and pour contempt on all my pride.

2 Forbid it, Lord, that I should boast,
    save in the cross of Christ, my God;
 all the vain things that charm me most,
    I sacrifice them to his Blood.

3 See from his head, his hands, his feet,
    sorrow and love flow mingled down;
 did e'er such love and sorrow meet,
    or thorns compose so rich a crown?

4 Were the whole realm of nature mine,
    that were an offering far too small;
 love so amazing, so divine,
    demands my soul, my life, my all.

Isaac Watts (1674–1748)
based on Galatians 6: 14;
Philippians 3: 7–8

248

Bow Brickhill   88 88 (LM)   Sydney H. Nicholson (1875–1947)

Alternative tune: 599 BRESLAU

1 We sing the praise of him who died,
   of him who died upon the cross;
  the sinner's hope though all deride,
   for this we count the world but loss.

2 Inscribed upon the cross we see
   in shining letters, 'God is love';
  he bears our sins upon the tree;
   he brings us mercy from above.

3 The cross, it takes our guilt away;
   it holds the fainting spirit up;
  it cheers with hope the gloomy day,
   and sweetens every bitter cup.

4 It makes the coward spirit brave,
   and nerves the feeble arm for fight;
  it takes the terror from the grave,
   and gilds the bed of death with light;

5 the balm of life, the cure of woe,
   the measure and the pledge of love,
  the sinner's refuge here below,
   the angels' theme in heaven above.

Thomas Kelly (1769–1855) altd.

249

Later form of melody
by Orlando Gibbons (1583–1625)

Song 13 (2)   77 77

For the original form of this tune, see no. 626ii.

1 When my love for Christ grows weak,
  when for deeper faith I seek,
    then in thought I go to thee,
    Garden of Gethsemane.

2 There I walk amid the shades,
  while the lingering twilight fades,
    see that suffering, friendless one,
    weeping, praying there alone.

3 When my love for man grows weak,
  when for stronger faith I seek,
    Hill of Calvary, I go
    to thy scenes of fear and woe:—

4 there behold his agony,
  suffered on the bitter tree:
    see his anguish, see his faith,
    Love triumphant still in death.

5 Then to life I turn again,
  learning all the worth of pain,
    learning all the might that lies
    in a full self-sacrifice;

6 and I praise with firmer faith
  Christ, who vanquished pain and death;
    and to Christ enthroned above
    raise my song of selfless love.

John R. Wreford (1800–81)
and *Samuel Longfellow* (1819–92) altd.

250

Miles Lane   86 86 (CM) extended   William Shrubsole (1760–1806)

... crown him,

crown him, crown him, crown him Lord of all.

SECOND TUNE

Diadem   86 86 (CM) extended   James Ellor (1819–99)

crown _____ him, crown him,

crown him, crown him, and crown __ him Lord of all.

1 All hail the power of Jesu's name,
    let angels prostrate fall;
bring forth the royal diadem
    to crown him Lord of all.

2 Crown him, ye martyrs of your God,
    who from his altar call;
extol him in whose path ye trod,
    and crown him Lord of all.

3 Ye seed of Israel's chosen race,
    ye ransomed of the fall,
hail him who saves you by his grace,
    and crown him Lord of all.

4 Sinners, whose love can ne'er forget
    the wormwood and the gall,
go, spread your trophies at his feet,
    and crown him Lord of all.

5 Let every kindred, every tribe,
    on this terrestrial ball,
to him all majesty ascribe,
    and crown him Lord of all.

6 O that with yonder sacred throng,
    we at his feet may fall;
we'll join the everlasting song,
    and crown him Lord of all.

Edward Perronet (1726–92)
and *John Rippon* (1751–1836)
based on Revelation 4: 9–11

251

Lux eoi   87 87 D

Arthur Sullivan (1842–1900)

Alternative tune: 3, 38 or 318 ABBOT'S LEIGH

1 Alleluia! Alleluia!
    Hearts to heaven and voices raise;
sing to God a hymn of gladness,
    sing to God a hymn of praise;
he who on the cross a victim
    for the world's salvation bled,
Jesus Christ, the King of glory,
    now is risen from the dead.

2 Christ is risen, Christ the first-fruits
    of the holy harvest-field,
which will all its full abundance
    at his second coming yield;
then the golden ears of harvest
    will their heads before him wave,
ripened by his glorious sunshine
    from the furrows of the grave.

3 Christ is risen, we are risen;
    shed upon us heavenly grace,
rain and dew and gleams of glory
    from the brightness of thy face;
so that we, with hearts in heaven,
    here on earth may fruitful be;
and by angel-hands be gathered,
    and be ever, Lord, with thee.

4 Alleluia! Alleluia!
    Glory be to God on high!
Alleluia to the Saviour,
    who has gained the victory!
Alleluia to the Spirit,
    fount of love and sanctity!
Alleluia, alleluia
    to the blessèd Trinity!

Christopher Wordsworth (1807–85)

252

Alleluia no. 1

Donald E. Fishel (b. 1950)

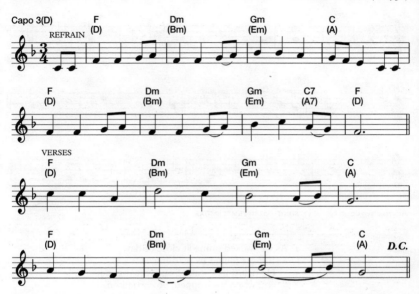

Alleluia, alleluia, give thanks to the risen Lord!
Alleluia, alleluia, give praise to his name.

1 Jesus is Lord of all the earth.
   He is the King of creation.

2 Spread the good news through all the earth,
   Jesus has died and is risen:

3 We have been crucified with Christ—
   now we shall live for ever:

4 God has proclaimed the just reward—
   life for the world, alleluia!

5 Come, let us praise the living God,
   joyfully sing to our Saviour!

Donald E. Fishel (b. 1950)

253

The Silkie   88 88 (LM)

Scottish traditional melody

Alternative tunes: 399 FOLK SONG   613ii TEMPLEMORE

1 As we walked home at close of day,
   a stranger joined us on our way.
       He heard us speak of one who'd gone,
       and when we stopped, he carried on.

2 'Why wander further without light?
   Please stay with us this troubled night.
       We've shared the truth of how we feel,
       and now would like to share a meal.'

3 We sat to eat our simple spread,
   then watched the stranger take the bread;
       and, as he said the blessing prayer,
       we knew that someone else was there.

4 No stranger he; it was our eyes
   which failed to see in stranger's guise,
       the Lord who, risen from the dead,
       met us when ready to be fed.

5 Alleluia! Alleluia!
   Alleluia! Alleluia!
       As Mary and our sisters said,
       'The Lord is risen from the dead!'

John L. Bell (b. 1949)
and *Graham Maule* (b. 1958)
based on Luke 24: 13–15, 28–31

254

Salzburg (Alle Menschen müssen sterben) Melody from J. Hintze (1622–1702)
77 77 D

Ad regias Agni dapes

1 At the Lamb's high feast we sing
   praise to our victorious King,
      who hath washed us in the tide
      flowing from his piercèd side.
   Praise we him, whose love divine
   gives his guests his blood for wine,
      gives his body for the feast;
      Christ the victim, Christ the priest.

2 Where the paschal blood is poured,
   death's dark angel sheathes his sword;
      Israel's hosts triumphant go
      through the wave that drowns the foe.
   Praise we Christ, whose blood was shed,
   paschal victim, paschal bread;
      with sincerity and love
      eat we manna from above.

3 Mighty victim from on high,
   hell's fierce powers beneath thee lie;
      thou hast conquered in the fight;
      thou hast brought us life and light.
   Now no more can death appal,
   now no more the grave enthral;
      thou hast opened paradise,
      and in thee thy saints shall rise.

4 Easter triumph, Easter joy,
   sin alone can this destroy;
      from sin's power do thou set free
      souls new-born, O Lord, in thee.
   Hymns of glory and of praise,
   risen Lord, to thee we raise;
      holy Father, praise to thee,
      with the Spirit, ever be.

7th-century Latin
tr. *Robert Campbell* (1814–68) altd.

255

Morgenlied   87 87 D with Refrain   Frederick C. Maker (1844–1927)

REFRAIN

Christ is ris - en, al - le - lu - ia! ris - en our vic - tor-ious head;

sing his prais-es, al - le - lu - ia! Christ is ris - en from the dead.

1 Christ is risen, alleluia!
    risen our victorious head;
sing his praises, alleluia!
    Christ is risen from the dead.
Gratefully our hearts adore him,
    as his light once more appears,
bowing down in joy before him,
    rising up from grief and tears.

Christ is risen, alleluia!
    risen our victorious head;
sing his praises, alleluia!
    Christ is risen from the dead.

2 Christ is risen! all the sadness ‿
    of this earthly life is o'er;
through the open gates of gladness
    he returns to life once more;
death and hell before him bending,
    he doth rise the victor now,
angels on his steps attending,
    glory round his wounded brow:

3 Christ is risen! henceforth never ‿
    death or hell shall us enthral,
we are Christ's, in him for ever ‿
    we have triumphed over all;
all the doubting and dejection
    of our trembling hearts have ceased.
'tis the day of resurrection;
    let us rise and keep the feast.

John S. B. Monsell (1811–75)

256

Christis risen as he said   77 77

John Carter

1. Christ is ris - en
3. Lord of life, he
5. Christ who died our
7. Son of God, his

as__ he said, Christ the first - born from the dead:
lives__ a - gain; Lord of lords, to rule and reign:
life__ to win, Christ has con - quered death and sin:
life__ he gave, Son of Man, to seek and save:

2. See, the stone is rolled a - way, See the place where Je - sus lay.
4. Ev - ery tongue con - fess him now, Ev - ery knee be - fore him bow.
6. Now is all his war - fare done, Now is ev - ery tri - umph won.
8. Ris - en now, the Son who died, Risen, as - cend - ed,

glo - ri - fied, risen, as - cend - ed, glo - ri - fied.

An Easter Antiphon

1 *Versicle:* Christ is risen as he said,
   Response: Christ the firstborn from the dead:

2 *V.* See, the stone is rolled away,
   R. See the place where Jesus lay.

3 *V.* Lord of life, he lives again;
   R. Lord of lords, to rule and reign:

4 *V.* Every tongue confess him now,
   R. Every knee before him bow.

5 *V.* Christ who died our life to win,
   R. Christ has conquered death and sin:

6 *V.* Now is all his warfare done,
   R. Now is every triumph won.

7 *V.* Son of God, his life he gave,
   R. Son of Man, to seek and save:

8 *V.* Risen now, the Son who died,
   R. Risen, ascended, glorified.

Timothy Dudley-Smith (b. 1926)

257

Moville 76 76 D

Irish traditional melody

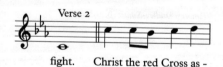

fight.   Christ the red Cross as -

All glo - ry

Christus Redemptor omnium

1 Christ is the world's Redeemer,
    the lover of the pure,
the fount of heavenly wisdom,
    our trust and hope secure;
the armour of his soldiers,
    the Lord of earth and sky;
our health while we are living,
    our life when we shall die.

2 Christ has our host surrounded
    with clouds of martyrs bright,
who wave their palms in triumph,
    and fire us for the fight.
Christ the red Cross ascended
    to save a world undone,
and suffering, for the sinful,
    our full redemption won.

3 Down in the realm of darkness
    he lay a captive bound,
but at the hour appointed
    he rose a victor crowned.
And now, to heaven ascended,
    he sits upon the throne,
in glorious dominion,
    his Father's and his own.

4 All glory to the Father,
    the unbegotten One;
all honour be to Jesus,
    his sole-begotten Son;
and to the Holy Spirit—
    the perfect Trinity.
Let all the worlds give answer,
    'Amen—so let it be!'

attrib. *Columba* (*c.*520–597)
tr. *Duncan MacGregor* (1854–1923) altd.

258

FIRST TUNE

Nassau (Würtemburg) (1)
77 77 with Alleluia

Later form of a melody in *Hundert
Geistlicher Arien* (Dresden, 1694)
adapted by William Henry Monk (1823–89)

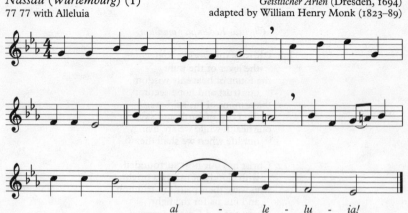

al - le - lu - ia!

SECOND TUNE

Orientis partibus (2)   77 77 with Alleluia

French medieval melody from the Office of
Pierre de Corbeil (d. 1222)

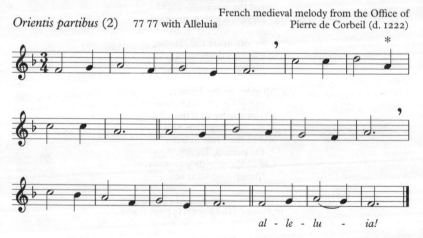

al - le - lu - ia!

* This note is sometimes sung as B flat.

Christ ist erstanden

1 Christ the Lord is risen again!
Christ has broken every chain!
    Hark! angelic voices cry,
    singing evermore on high,
      alleluia!

2 He who gave for us his life,
who for us endured the strife,
    is our Paschal Lamb to-day;
    we too sing for joy, and say
      alleluia!

3 He who bore all pain and loss
comfortless upon the cross,
    lives in glory now on high,
    pleads for us, and hears our cry:
      alleluia!

*4 He whose path no records tell,
who descended into hell,
    who the strong man armed hath bound,
    now in highest heaven is crowned.
      Alleluia!

5 He who slumbered in the grave
is exalted now to save;
    now through Christendom[1] it rings
    that the Lamb is King of kings.
      Alleluia!

6 Now he bids us tell abroad
how the lost may be restored,
    how the penitent forgiven,
    how we too may enter heaven.
      Alleluia!

*7 Thou, our paschal Lamb indeed,
Christ thy ransomed people feed;
    take our sins and guilt away:
    let us sing by night and day
      alleluia!

Michael Weiss (c.1480–1534)
tr. *Catherine Winkworth (1829–78)*

[1] Christendom = the entire Christian world

259

Guiting Power   85 85 78

John Barnard (b. 1948)

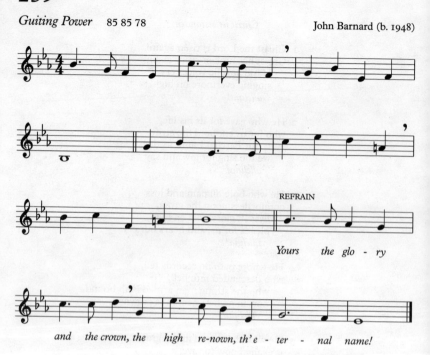

REFRAIN

Yours   the glo - ry   and   the crown, the   high   re-nown, th'e - ter - nal   name!

Alternative tunes: 346 ANGEL VOICES   453 ARTHOG

1 Christ triumphant, ever reigning,
      Saviour, Master, King!
   Lord of heaven, our lives sustaining,
      hear us as we sing:

      Yours the glory and the crown,
      the high renown, th'eternal name!

2 Word incarnate, truth revealing,
      Son of Man on earth!
   Power and majesty concealing
      by your humble birth:

3 Suffering servant, scorned, ill-treated,
      victim crucified!
   Death is through the cross defeated,
      sinners justified:

4 Priestly King, enthroned for ever
      high in heaven above!
   Sin and death and hell shall never ‿
      stifle hymns of love:

5 So, our hearts and voices raising
      through the ages long,
   ceaselessly upon you gazing,
      this shall be our song:

      Michael Saward (b. 1932)

260

Truro   88 88 (LM)

Melody from Thomas Williams'
Psalmodia Evangelica (1789)

1 Christ is alive! Let Christians sing.
    The cross stands empty to the sky.
Let streets and homes with praises ring.
    Love drowned in death, shall never die.

2 Christ is alive! No longer bound
    to distant years in Palestine,
but saving, healing, here and now,
    and touching every place and time.

3 In every insult, rift and war,
    where colour, scorn, or wealth divide,
Christ suffers still, yet loves the more,
    and lives, where even hope has died.

4 Women and men, in age and youth,
    can feel the Spirit, hear the call,
and find the way, the life, the truth,
    revealed in Jesus, freed for all.

5 Christ is alive, and comes to bring
    good news to this and every age,
till earth and sky and ocean ring
    with joy, with justice, love and praise.

Brian Wren (b. 1936)

261

Norman   87 87

Melody from J. F. Doles'
Choralbuch (Leipzig, 1785)

Aeterne Rex altissime

1 Christ, above all glory seated!
   King triumphant, strong to save!
Dying, thou hast death defeated,
   buried, thou hast spoiled the grave.

2 Thou art gone, where now is given
   what no mortal might could gain,
on the eternal throne of heaven
   in thy Father's power to reign.

3 We, O Lord, with hearts adoring,
   follow thee beyond the sky;
hear our prayers thy grace imploring,
   lift our souls to thee on high.

4 So when thou again in glory
   on the clouds of heaven shalt shine,
we thy flock may stand before thee,
   owned for evermore as thine.

5 Hail! All hail! In thee confiding,
   Jesus, thee shall all adore,
in thy Father's might abiding
   with one Spirit evermore.

Latin *c.* 5th cent.
tr. *James R. Woodford* (1820–85)

262

St John Damascene   76 76 D   Arthur Henry Brown (1830–1926)

SECOND TUNE

Ave virgo virginum (Gaudeamus pariter)
76 76 D

German medieval melody as given in
Leisentritt's *Catholicum
Hymnologium Germanicum*
(Cologne, 1584)

Ἄίσωμεν πάντες λαοί

1 Come, ye faithful, raise the strain ‿
　　of triumphant gladness;
　God has brought his Israel
　　into joy from sadness;
　loosed from Pharaoh's bitter yoke
　　Jacob's sons and daughters,
　led them with unmoistened foot
　　through the Red Sea waters.

2 'Tis the spring of souls today;
　　Christ has burst his prison,
　and from three days' sleep in death
　　as a sun has risen;
　all the winter of our sins,
　　long and dark, is flying
　from his light, to whom we give ‿
　　laud and praise undying.

3 Now the queen of seasons, bright ‿
　　with the day of splendour,
　with the royal feast of feasts,
　　comes its joy to render;
　comes to glad Jerusalem,
　　who with true affection
　welcomes in unwearied strains
　　Jesu's resurrection.

4 Alleluia, now we cry
　　to our King immortal,
　who triumphant burst the bars ‿
　　of the tomb's dark portal;
　alleluia, with the Son
　　God the Father praising;
　Alleluia, yet again,
　　to the Spirit raising!

　　　　John of Damascus (c.675–c.750)
　　　　tr. *John Mason Neale (1818–66) altd.*
　　　　based on Exodus 15; Luke 24

263

Diademata   66 86 D (DSM)   George J. Elvey (1816–93)

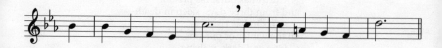

1 Crown him with many crowns,
    the Lamb upon his throne,
hark! how the heavenly anthem drowns
    all music but its own:
awake, my soul, and sing
    of him who died for thee,
and hail him as thy matchless King
    through all eternity.

*2 Crown him the Virgin's Son,
    the God incarnate born,
  whose conquering arm those trophies won
    which now his brow adorn:
  the Saviour long foretold,
    the branch of Jesse's stem,
the eternal shepherd of his fold,
    the babe of Bethlehem.

3 Crown him the Lord of love;
   behold his hands and side,
those wounds, yet visible above,
   in beauty glorified:
no angel in the sky
   can fully bear that sight,
but downward bends his wondering eye
   at mysteries so bright.

4 Crown him the Lord of life
   who triumphed o'er the grave,
and rose victorious in the strife,
   for those he came to save:
his glories now we sing,
   who died and rose on high,
who died eternal life to bring,
   and lives that death may die.

*5 Crown him the Lord of peace,
   whose power a sceptre sways
from pole to pole, that wars may cease,
   and all be love and praise:
his reign shall know no end;
   and round his piercèd feet
the thousand tones of earth shall blend
   in concord ever sweet.

6 Crown him the Lord of years,
   the Potentate of time,
creator of the rolling spheres,
   ineffably sublime:
all hail, Redeemer, hail!
   for thou hast died for me;
thy praise shall never, never fail
   throughout eternity.

Matthew Bridges (1800–94)
and *Godfrey Thring* (1823–1903) altd.
based on Revelation 19: 12

264

Surrexit　88 88 (LM)

A. Gregory Murray (1905–92)

Al - le - lu - ia,　al - le - lu - ia!

Finita iam sunt proelia

1 Finished the strife of battle now,
   gloriously crowned the victor's brow:
   sing with gladness, hence with sadness:
      Alleluia!

2 After the death that him befell,
   Jesus Christ has harrowed hell:[1]
   songs of praising we are raising:
      Alleluia!

3 On the third morning he arose,
   shining with victory o'er his foes;
   earth is singing, heaven is ringing:
      Alleluia!

4 Lord, by your wounds on you we call,
   now that from death you've freed us all:
   may our living be thanksgiving:
      Alleluia!

Latin (17th cent.?)
tr. *John Mason Neale* (1818–66)
based on 1 Corinthians 15: 53–57

---

[1] The 'Harrowing of Hell' is the medieval term for the defeat of the powers of evil, and the release of its victims, by the descent of Christ into hell after his death.

For another translation of the same Latin text, see no. 286.

265

Cherry Tree (B)   76 76   English traditional carol melody

1 Good Joseph had a garden,
    close by that sad green hill,
  where Jesus died a bitter death
    to save us all from ill.

2 One evening in that garden,
    their faces dark with gloom,
  they laid the Saviour's body
    within good Joseph's tomb.

3 There came the holy women
    with spices and with tears;
  the angels tried to comfort them,
    but could not calm their fears.

4 Came Mary to that garden,
    and sobbed with heart forlorn;
  she thought she heard the gardener ask
    'Whom do you seek this morn?'

5 She heard her own name spoken,
    and then she lost her care:
  all in his strength and beauty,
    the risen Lord stood fair!

6 Good Joseph had a garden;
    amid its trees so tall
  the Lord Christ rose on Easter Day:
    he lives to save us all.

7 And as he rose at Easter
    he is alive alway,
  the very same Lord Jesus Christ
    who hears us sing today.

8 Go tell the Lord Christ's message,
    the Easter triumph sing,
  till all his waiting children know
    that Jesus is their king.

Alda M. Milner-Barry (1877–1941)
based on John 20: 10–18

266

Llanfair   77 77 with Alleluias

Robert Williams (1781–1821)

1 Hail the day that sees him rise, *alleluia!*
   to his throne above the skies; *alleluia!*
     Christ the Lamb for sinners given, *alleluia!*
     enters now the highest heaven. *Alleluia!*

2 There for him high triumph waits;
  lift your heads, eternal gates!
    he has conquered death and sin;
    take the King of glory in!

*3 See! the heaven its Lord receives,
   yet he loves the earth he leaves;
     though returning to his throne,
     still he calls the world his own.

*4 See! he lifts his hands above;
   see, he shows the prints of love;
     Hark, his gracious lips bestow
     blessings on his Church below!

*5 Still for us he intercedes,
   his prevailing death he pleads;
     near himself prepares our place,
     first-fruits of the human race.

6 Lord, though parted from our sight,
  far above the starry height,
    grant our hearts may thither rise,
    following thee beyond the skies.

7 There we shall with thee remain,
  partners of thine endless reign;
    there thy face unclouded see,
    find our heaven of heavens in thee.

Charles Wesley (1707–88) altd.
v. 2 based on Psalm 24: 7–10

267

Regent Square   87 87 87   Henry Smart (1813–79)

Al - le - lu - ia,   al - le - lu - ia,

Alternative tunes: 130 ST THOMAS   84, 275i NEANDER

1 Hail the risen Lord, ascending
 to his holy Father's side,
angels, lost in awe and wonder,
 now acclaim the Lord who died.
  Alleluia, alleluia,
 Christ triumphant, glorified.

2 He who once, from royal splendour,
 came to share our state of blame,
now ascends, in clouds of glory,
 to the heights from which he came.
  Alleluia, alleluia,
 Christ for evermore the same!

3 He will grant his praying servants,
 from the riches of his pow'r,
grace to live as risen people
 in this present watching hour.
  Alleluia, alleluia,
 God on us his blessing shower.

4 Now he bids us tell the story,
 where the lost and fearful roam:
he will come again triumphant,
 and will lead his people home.
  Alleluia, alleluia,
 Maranatha![1] Come, Lord, come.

Michael Forster (b. 1946)

[1] Maranatha, an expression used by the Apostle
Paul in 1 Corinthians 16: 22, is an ejaculation of
prophetic utterance meaning "Our Lord, come".

268

Hyfrydol   87 87 D   Melody by Rowland Hugh Pritchard (1811–87)

1 Hail, thou once-despisèd Jesus!
   Hail, thou Galilean king!
Thou didst suffer to release us,
   thou didst free salvation bring.
Hail, thou universal Saviour,
   bearer of our sin and shame;
by thy merits we find favour;
   life is given through thy name!

2 Paschal Lamb, by God appointed,
   all our sins on thee were laid;
by almighty love anointed,
   thou hast full atonement made.
All thy people are forgiven
   through the virtue of thy blood;
opened is the gate of heaven,
   we are reconciled with God.

3 Jesus, hail, enthroned in glory,
   there for ever to abide!
All the heavenly hosts adore thee,
   seated at thy Father's side.
There for sinners thou art pleading,
   there thou dost our place prepare,
ever for us interceding,
   till in glory we appear.

4 Worship, honour, power and blessing
   thou art worthy to receive;
loudest praises, without ceasing,
   meet it is for us to give.
Help, ye bright angelic spirits,
   bring your sweetest, noblest lays;
help to sing our Saviour's merits,
   help us chant Emmanuel's praise.

John Bakewell (1721–1819) altd.

269

St Ambrose (St Oswald)　87 87　　　　　　John Bacchus Dykes (1823–76)

1 Hark ten thousand voices sounding
　　far and wide throughout the sky,
'tis the voice of joy abounding,
　　Jesus lives, no more to die.

2 Jesus lives, his conflict over,
　　lives to claim his great reward;
angels round the Victor hover,
　　crowding to behold their Lord.

3 Yonder throne for him erected
　　now becomes the Victor's seat;
lo, the Man on earth rejected,
　　angels worship at his feet.

4 All the powers of heaven adore him,
　　all obey his sovereign word;
day and night they cry before him,
　　'Holy, Holy, Holy, Lord!'

Thomas Kelly (1769–1855)

270

Church triumphant   88 88 (LM)   James William Elliot (1833–1915)

1 I know that my Redeemer lives—
   what joy the blessed assurance gives!
      He lives, he lives, who once was dead;
      he lives, my everlasting head.

2 He lives, to bless me with his love;
   he lives, to plead for me above;
      he lives, my hungry soul to feed,
      he lives, to help in time of need.

3 He lives, and grants me daily breath;
   he lives, and I shall conquer death;
      he lives, my mansion to prepare;
      he lives, to lead me safely there.

4 He lives, all glory to his name;
   he lives, my Saviour, still the same;
      what joy the blessed assurance gives,
      I know that my Redeemer lives!

Samuel Medley (1738–99)
based on Job 19: 25

271

Easter Hymn   77 77 with Alleluias

Adpt. in *The Compleat Psalmodist* (1749)
from a melody in *Lyra Davidica* (1708)

Surrexit Christus hodie

1 Jesus Christ is risen today, *alleluia!*
   our triumphant holy day, *alleluia!*
      who did once, upon the cross, *alleluia!*
      suffer to redeem our loss, *alleluia!*

2 Hymns of praise then let us sing,
   unto Christ, our heavenly King,
      who endured the cross and grave,
      sinners to redeem and save.

3 But the pains that he endured,
   our salvation have procured;
      now above the sky he's King,
      where the angels ever sing.

Anon., Lyra Davidica (1708)
based on a 14th-century MS altd.

272

St Albinus   78 78 with Alleluia   Henry J. Gauntlett (1805–76)

Jesus lebt

1 Jesus lives: thy terrors now
    can no more, O death, appal us;
Jesus lives: by this we know
    now the grave cannot enthral us.
        Alleluia!

2 Jesus lives: for us he died;
    then may we, for Jesus living,
pure in heart, in him abide,
    glory to our Saviour giving.
        Alleluia!

3 Jesus lives: our hearts know well
    naught from us his love shall sever;
life, nor death, nor powers of hell
    tear us from his keeping ever.
        Alleluia!

4 Jesus lives: henceforth is death
    but the gate of life immortal;
this shall calm our trembling breath,
    when we pass its gloomy portal.
        Alleluia!

5 Jesus lives: to him the throne
    over all the world is given;
may we go where he is gone,
    live and reign with him in heaven.
        Alleluia!

Christian F. Gellert (1715–69)
tr. Frances E. Cox (1812–97) altd.

273

Like a lamb

Words and music by
Graham Kendrick (b. 1950)

INTRODUCTION

VERSES

1. Led like a lamb to the slaugh-ter, in si-lence and shame,
2. At break of dawn, poor Ma - ry, still weep-ing she came,
3. At the right hand of the Fa - ther, now seat-ed on high,

there on your back you car-ried a world of vio-lence and pain,
when through her grief she heard your voice now speak-ing her name.
you have be - gun your e-ter - nal reign of jus - tice and joy.

bleed - ing,___ dy - ing,___
¹Ma - ry!___ Mas - ter!___
Glo - ry,___ glo - ry,___

bleed - ing,___ dy - ing.___
Ma - ry!___ Mas - ter!___
glo - ry,___ glo - ry.___

REFRAIN

You're a-

¹ It is effective if the men sing 'Mary!' and the women reply 'Master!'

- live, you're a-live, you have ris-en, al-le-lu-ia! ___ And the
(al-le-lu-ia! al-le-lu-ia!)

power and the glo-ry is giv-en, al-le-lu-ia, ___ Je-sus to
(al-le-lu-ia, al-le-lu-ia,)

you.

* The word 'alleluia' can be sung antiphonally, as indicated,
the people having been divided into three equal groups.

1 Led like a lamb to the slaughter,
  in silence and shame,
  there on your back you carried
  a world of violence and pain,
  bleeding, dying, bleeding, dying.

  You're alive, you're alive, you have risen,
  alleluia!
  And the power and the glory is given,
  alleluia,
  Jesus to you.

2 At break of dawn, poor Mary,
  still weeping she came,
  when through her grief she heard your voice
  now speaking her name.
  ¹Mary! Master! Mary! Master!

3 At the right hand of the Father,
  now seated on high,
  you have begun your eternal reign
  of justice and joy.
  Glory, glory, glory, glory.

Graham Kendrick (b. 1950)
based on Isaiah 53: 4–7;
John 20: 11–16

367

274

Lasst uns erfreuen (Easter Song)
88 88 (LM) with Alleluias

Melody from *Geistliche Kirchengesäng*
(Cologne, 1623)

Al - le - lu - ia! Al - le - lu - ia!

Al - le - lu - ia! Al - le - lu - ia! Al - le -

-lu - ia! Al - le - lu - ia! Al - le - lu - ia!

Aurora lucis rutilat

1 Light's glittering morn bedecks the sky;
 heaven thunders forth its victor-cry:
   Alleluia!
   The glad earth shouts her triumph high,
   and groaning hell makes wild reply:
   Alleluia!

2 While he, the King, the mighty King,
 despoiling death of all its sting,
   and trampling down the powers of night,
   brings forth his ransomed saints to light.

3 His tomb of late the threefold guard ⌣
 of watch and stone and seal had barred;
   but now, in pomp and triumph high,
   he comes from death to victory.

4 The pains of hell are loosed at last,
 the days of mourning now are past;
   an angel robed in light has said,
   'The Lord is risen from the dead'.

5 O Lord of all, with us abide
 in this our joyful Eastertide;
   from every weapon death can wield
   your own redeemed for ever shield.

6 All praise be yours, O risen Lord,
 from death to endless life restored!
   All praise to God the Father be
   and Spirit blessed eternally!

Latin *c.*4th cent.
tr. *John Mason Neale* (1818–66) altd.

GOD THE SON, REDEEMER

275

FIRST TUNE

Neander (Unser Herrscher)   87 87 87

Melody from Joachim Neander's
Alpha and Omega (Bremen, 1680)

SECOND TUNE

Triumph   87 87 87

Henry J. Gauntlett (1805–76)

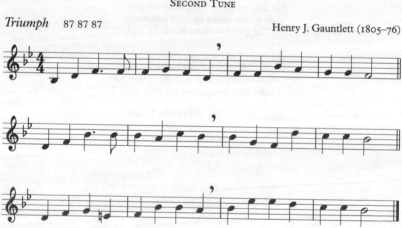

1 Look, ye saints, the sight is glorious,
     see the Man of sorrows now;
 from the fight returned victorious,
     every knee to him shall bow;
         crown him! crown him!
     crowns become the Victor's brow.

2 Crown the Saviour, angels crown him,
     rich the trophies Jesus brings;
 in the seat of power enthrone him,
     while the vault of heaven rings;
         crown him! crown him!
     crown the Saviour 'King of kings'.

3 Sinners in derision crowned him,
     mocking thus the Saviour's claim:
 saints and angels crowd around him,
     own his title, praise his name:
         crown him! crown him!
     spread abroad the Victor's fame.

4 Hark those bursts of acclamation!
     Hark those loud triumphant chords!
 Jesus takes the highest station;
     O what joy the sight affords!
         Crown him! crown him!
     'King of kings and Lord of lords'.

Thomas Kelly (1769–1854)

276

Majesty

Words and music by
Jack W. Hayford (b. 1934)

Ma - jes-ty,＿＿＿ wor-ship his ma - jes-ty,＿＿＿ un - to

Je - sus be glo - ry, hon-our and praise.＿＿＿

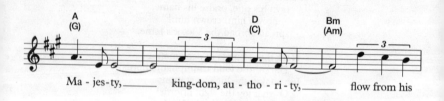

Ma - jes-ty,＿＿＿ king-dom, au - tho - ri - ty,＿＿＿ flow from his

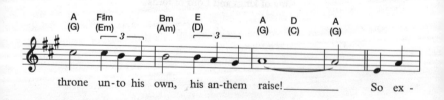

throne un-to his own, his an-them raise!＿＿＿ So ex -

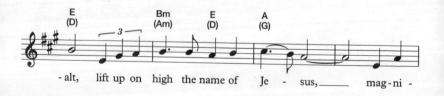

- alt, lift up on high the name of Je - sus,＿＿＿ mag-ni -

-fy, come glo - ri - fy Christ Je - sus the King.

Ma - jes - ty, wor-ship his ma - jes - ty, Je-sus who

died, now glo - ri - fied, King of all kings.

Majesty, worship his majesty,
unto Jesus be glory, honour and praise.
Majesty, kingdom, authority,
flow from his throne unto his own,
his anthem raise!
So exalt, lift up on high the name of Jesus,
magnify, come glorify Christ Jesus the King.
Majesty, worship his majesty,
Jesus who died, now glorified,
King of all kings.

Jack W. Hayford (b. 1934)

277

Savannah (Herrnhut)   77 77

Melody from MS. *Choralbuch*
(Herrnhut, *c.*1740)
as given in John Wesley's
Foundery Collection (1742)

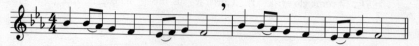

Alternative tune: 258i NASSAU (singing 'Alleluia' at the end of each verse)

1 Love's redeeming work is done;
   fought the fight, the battle won:
      Lo! our Sun's eclipse is o'er;
      Lo! he sets in blood no more.

2 Vain the stone, the watch, the seal;
   Christ hath burst the gates of hell;
      death in vain forbids him rise;
      Christ hath opened Paradise.

3 Lives again our glorious King;
   where, O death, is now thy sting?
      Dying once he all doth save:
      where thy victory, O grave?

4 Soar we now where Christ hath led,
   following our exalted Head;
      made like him, like him we rise;
      ours the cross, the grave, the skies.

5 Hail! the Lord of earth and heaven,
   praise to thee by both be given;
      thee we greet triumphant now,
      hail the resurrection thou.

Charles Wesley (1707–88)

278

Noël nouvelet   11 11 10 11

French traditional carol melody

Love   is   come a - gain,   like   wheat that springs up   green.

1 Now the green blade rises from the buried grain,
  wheat that in the dark earth many days has lain;
      Love lives again, that with the dead had been:
      Love is come again, like wheat that springs up green.

2 In the grave they laid him, Love by hatred slain,
  thinking that he never would awake again,
      laid in the earth like grain that sleeps unseen:

3 Forth he came at Easter, like the risen grain,
  he that for the three days in the grave had lain,
      quick[1] from the dead, my risen Lord is seen:

4 When our hearts are wintry, grieving, or in pain,
  then your touch can call us back to life again,
      fields of our hearts, that dead and bare have been:

John M. C. Crum (1872–1958) altd.

[1] Quick is an archaic way of expressing 'alive'.

279

O filii et filiae 888 with Alleluias

French Easter carol melody
from *Airs sur les hymnes sacrez* (Paris, 1623)

Al - le - lu - ia!___ Al - le - lu - ia! Al - le - lu - ia!

VERSES

REFRAIN *(all verses)*

Al - le - lu - ia!

* Opening Alleluias to precede verse 1 only

O filii et filiae

*As an alternative to singing all of the following verses, congregations may sing
either verses 1, 2, 3 and 9 (relating the women's visit to
the empty tomb) or verses 1 and 4–9 (relating the story of Thomas).*

Alleluia! Alleluia! Alleluia!

1 O sons and daughters, let us sing!
   The King of heaven, the glorious King
   o'er death today rose triumphing:
   alleluia!

2 That Easter morn, at break of day,
   the faithful women went their way,
   their spices o'er the dead to lay:
   alleluia!

3 An angel robed in white they see,
who sat and spoke unto the three,
'Your Lord is gone to Galilee':
  alleluia!

4 That night the apostles met in fear;
amidst them came their Lord most dear
and said, 'My peace be on all here':
  alleluia!

5 When Thomas first the tidings heard,
he doubted if it were the Lord
until he came and spoke the word:
  alleluia!

6 'My piercèd side, O Thomas, see;
behold my hands and feet', said he,
'not faithless but believing be':
  alleluia!

7 No longer Thomas then denied;
he saw the feet, the hands, the side;
'You are my Lord and God', he cried:
  alleluia!

8 How blessed are they who have not seen,
and yet whose faith has constant been,
for they eternal life shall win:
  alleluia!

9 On this most holy day of days
our hearts and voices, Lord, we raise
in laud and jubilee and praise:
  alleluia!

Jean Tisserand (d. 1494)
tr. *John Mason Neale* (1818–66) altd.
based on John 20: 1–29

GOD THE SON, REDEEMER

280

FIRST TUNE

Zörbig (O Ursprung)   11 11 12 11 11

Melody by Thomas Selle (1599–1663)
from *Neue Musikalische Fest-Andachten*
(Lüneberg, 1655)

O sing al-le-lu-ia, O sing al-le-lu-ia, O sing al-le-lu-ia, be joy-ful and sing, Christ Je-sus is King!

SECOND TUNE

Our Lord Christ hath risen

John Kelly

1. Our Lord Christ hath ris-en, the tempt-er is foiled, his le-gions are scat-tered, his strong-holds are spoiled. O sing al-le-

378

1   Our Lord Christ hath risen,
         the tempter is foiled,
     his legions are scattered,
         his strongholds are spoiled.
   O sing alleluia, O sing alleluia,
       O sing alleluia, be joyful and sing,
       Our great foe is baffled—*Christ Jesus is King!*

2   O death, we defy thee!
         A stronger than thou ⌣
     hath entered thy palace,
         we fear thee not now.
   O sing alleluia, O sing alleluia,
       O sing alleluia, be joyful and sing,
       the grave cannot scare us—*Christ Jesus is King!*

3   O sin thou art vanquished,
         thy long reign is o'er;
     though still thou dost vex us,
         we dread thee no more.
   O sing alleluia, O sing alleluia,
       O sing alleluia, be joyful and sing,
       who now can condemn us? *Christ Jesus is King!*

4   Our Lord Christ hath risen,
         day breaketh at last;
     the long night of weeping
         is now well-nigh past.
   O sing alleluia, O sing alleluia,
       O sing alleluia, be joyful and sing,
       our foes are all conquered—*Christ Jesus is King!*

William C. Plunkett (1828–97)

281

Gopsal   66 66 88

G. F. Handel (1685–1759)

REFRAIN

1–4. Lift   up   your   heart,   lift   up   your voice;
5. We   soon   shall   hear the arch - an - gel's voice;

re - joice!   A - gain   I____ say: Re - joice!
the trump   of   God   shall_ sound: Re - joice!

1 Rejoice, the Lord is King!
   Your Lord and King adore;
   mortals, give thanks and sing,
   and triumph evermore.

   Lift up your heart, lift up your voice;
   rejoice! Again I say: Rejoice!

2 Jesus the Saviour reigns,
   the God of truth and love;
   when he had purged our stains,
   he took his seat above:

3 His kingdom cannot fail,
   he rules o'er earth and heaven;
   the keys of death and hell
   are to our Jesus given:

4 He sits at God's right hand
   till all his foes submit,
   and bow to his command,
   and fall beneath his feet:

5 Rejoice in glorious hope;
   Jesus the Judge shall come,
   and take his servants up
   to their eternal home.

   We soon shall hear the archangel's voice;
   the trump of God shall sound: Rejoice!

Charles Wesley (1707–88)
based on Philippians 4: 4

282

Surrexit Christus

Jacques Berthier (1923–94)
for the Taizé Community

(hum) Sur - re - xit Christ-us, al - le - lu - ia!

(hum) Can - ta - te Do-mi-no, al - le - lu - ia!¹

VERSES (Cantor)

1. Give thanks to the Lord, for he is good,
for his love has no end. * 2. The
Lord is my strength, the Lord is my song;
he has been my Sav - iour.
3. I shall not die, I shall live,
I shall live and re - count his deeds.

¹ Translation: Christ is risen, alleluia! Sing to the Lord, alleluia!

* Choose either part.

The refrain is sung repeatedly by all while a cantor sings the verses over the hummed phrases.

For verses from the Benedicite for use with this chant, see no. 711.

283

Ellacombe 76 76 D

Melody from *Würtemberg Gesangbuch* (1784)

Ἀναστάσεως ἡμέρα

1 The Day of Resurrection,
    earth, tell it out abroad—
the passover of gladness,
    the passover of God!
From death to life eternal,
    from earth unto the sky,
our Christ has brought us over,
    with hymns of victory.

2 Our hearts be pure from evil,
    that we may see aright
the Lord in rays eternal
    of resurrection light:
and, listening to his accents,
    may hear, so calm and plain,
his own 'All hail!' and, hearing,
    may raise the victor-strain.

3 Now let the heavens be joyful,
    let earth her song begin,
the round world keep high triumph,
    and all that is therein;
let all things seen and unseen
    their notes of gladness blend,
for Christ the Lord is risen,
    our joy that has no end.

John of Damascus (c.675–c.750)
tr. John Mason Neale (1818–66) altd.

284

Weybridge 86 86 (CM) Charles Edward Miller (1856–1933)

Alternative tunes: 467ii CREDITON 378 ST STEPHEN

1 The golden gates are lifted up,
   the doors are opened wide,
 the King of glory is gone in
   unto his Father's side.

2 Thou art gone up before us, Lord,
   to make for us a place,
 that we may be where now thou art,
   and see thee face to face.

3 And ever on our earthly path
   a gleam of glory lies;
 a light still breaks behind the cloud
   that veils thee from our eyes.

4 Lift up our hearts, lift up our minds,
   let thy pure grace be given,
 that, while we journey here below,
   our treasure be in heaven:

5 that, where thou art at God's right hand,
   our hope, our love may be:
 dwell in us now, that we may dwell
   for evermore in thee.

Cecil Frances (Fanny) Alexander (1818–95) altd.

285

St Magnus   86 86 (CM)

Melody probably by
Jeremiah Clarke (*c.*1673–1707)

1 The head that once was crowned with thorns
    is crowned with glory now;
  a royal diadem adorns
    the mighty victor's brow.

2 The highest place that heaven affords
    is his, is his by right,
  the King of kings, and Lord of lords,
    and heaven's eternal light.

3 The joy of all who dwell above:
    the joy of all below,
  to whom he manifests his love,
    and grants his name to know.

4 To them the cross, with all its shame,
    with all its grace, is given:
  their name an everlasting name,
    their joy the joy of heaven.

5 They suffer with their Lord below,
    they reign with him above,
  their profit and their joy to know
    the mystery of his love.

6 The Cross he bore is life and health,
    though shame and death to him;
  his people's hope, his people's wealth,
    their everlasting theme.

Thomas Kelly (1769–1854)
based on Revelation 17: 14; 19: 12, 16

286

Vulpius (Gelobt sei Gott) 888 with Alleluias

Melody from M. Vulpius's
Gesangbuch (1609)

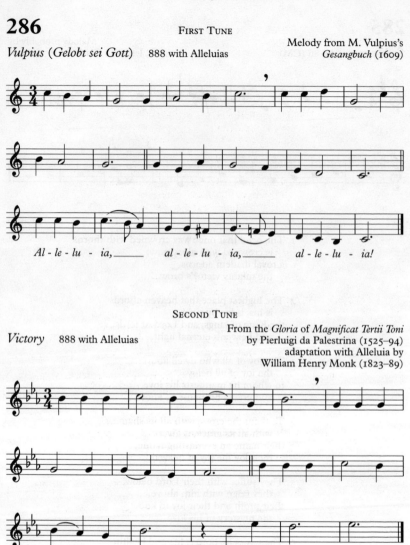

Al - le - lu - ia,_____ al - le - lu - ia,_____ al - le - lu - ia!

SECOND TUNE

Victory 888 with Alleluias

From the *Gloria* of *Magnificat Tertii Toni*
by Pierluigi da Palestrina (1525–94)
adaptation with Alleluia by
William Henry Monk (1823–89)

Al - le - lu - ia!

Finita iam sunt proelia

1 The strife is o'er, the battle done;
now is the victor's triumph won;
O let the song of praise be sung:

   Alleluia![1]

2 Death's mightiest powers have done their worst,
and Jesus has his foes dispersed;
let shouts of praise and joy outburst:

3 On the third morn he rose again,
glorious in majesty to reign;
O let us swell the joyful strain:

*4 He broke the bonds of death and hell,
the bars from heav'n's high portals fell;
let hymns of praise his triumph tell:

*5 Lord, by the stripes which wounded thee
from death's dread sting thy servants free,
that we may live, and sing to thee:

From the Latin Symphonia Sirenum Selectarum (Cologne 1695)
tr. *Francis Pott* (1832–1909) altd.
based on 1 Corinthians 15: 53–57

[1] When the tune VULPIUS is used, the word 'Alleluia' is sung three times.

For another translation of the same Latin text, see no. 264.

287

Lasst uns erfreuen (Easter Song)
88 44 88 with Alleluias

Melody from *Geistliche Kirchengesäng*
(Cologne, 1623)

Christ is ris - en! Al - le - lu - ia!

Al - le - lu - ia! Christ is ris - en! Al - le -

-lu - ia! Christ is ris - en! Al - le - lu - ia!

Die ganze Welt

1 The whole bright world rejoices now,
   the birds sing out on every bough;
      Christ is risen! Alleluia!
   Then shout beneath the racing skies
   to him who rose that we may rise:
      Alleluia! Christ is risen!
      Alleluia! Christ is risen! Alleluia!

2 Let us rejoice! All shall be well,
   friends severed now, in heaven shall dwell:
      Christ is risen! Alleluia!
   The end of all our ways is love;
   then rise with him to things above:
      Alleluia! Christ is risen!
      Alleluia! Christ is risen! Alleluia!

3 Now let all living things rejoice,
   let young and old lift heart and voice:
      Christ is risen! Alleluia!
   He rose to cheer us on our ways,
   he lives to bless us all our days:
      Alleluia! Christ is risen!
      Alleluia! Christ is risen! Alleluia!

German (1623)
tr. *Percy Dearmer* (1867–1936) altd.

288

Maccabaeus   10 11 11 11 with Refrain

G. F. Handel (1685–1759)
adpt. from a chorus in
Judas Maccabaeus (1746)

Thine   be   the   glo - ry,   ris - en,__ con-quering Son,

end - less__ is   the   vic - tory   thou o'er death hast won.

1 Thine be the glory, risen, conquering Son,
  endless is the victory thou o'er death hast won;
     angels in bright raiment rolled the stone away,
     kept the folded grave-clothes where thy body lay:

> *Thine be the glory, risen, conquering Son,*
> *endless is the victory thou o'er death hast won.*

2 Lo, Jesus meets us, risen from the tomb;
  lovingly he greets us, scatters fear and gloom;
     let the Church with gladness hymns of triumph sing,
     for her Lord now liveth, death hath lost its sting:

3 No more we doubt thee, glorious Prince of Life;
  life is nought without thee: aid us in our strife;
     make us more than conquerors through thy deathless love;
     bring us safe through Jordan to thy home above:

Edmond Budry (1854–1932)
tr. *R. B. Hoyle* (1875–1939)

289

Vruechten (Easter Carol)   67 67 with Refrain

Melody in *David's Psalmen*
(Amsterdam, 1685)

REFRAIN

Had Christ, that once was slain, ne'er burst his three-day pri - son, our faith had been in vain: but now hath Christ a - ris - en, a - ris - en, a - ris - en, a - ris - - - en.

1 This joyful Eastertide
       away with sin and sorrow!
   My Love, the crucified,
       hath sprung to life this morrow:

       *Had Christ, that once was slain,
           ne'er burst his three-day prison,
       our faith had been in vain:
           but now hath Christ arisen.*

*2 My flesh in hope shall rest,
       and for a season slumber;
    till trump from east to west
       shall wake the dead in number:

3 Death's flood hath lost its chill,
       since Jesus crossed the river;
   Lover of souls, from ill ‿
       my passing soul deliver:

       George R. Woodward (1848–1934) altd.
       Refrain based on 1 Corinthians 15: 13–14
       v. 2 based on Psalm 16: 9

290

Au clair de la lune (2)   65 65 65 75   French traditional melody

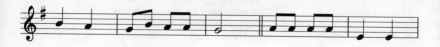

1 Walking in a garden at the close of day,
   Adam tried to hide him when he heard God say:
      'Why are you so frightened, why are you afraid?
      You have brought the winter in, made the flowers fade'.

2 Walking in a garden where the Lord had gone,
   three of the disciples—Peter, James and John;
      they were very weary, could not keep awake,
      while the Lord was kneeling there, praying for their sake.

3 Walking in a garden at the break of day,
   Mary asked the gardener where the body lay;
      but he turned towards her, smiled at her and said:
      'Mary, spring is here to stay, only death is dead'.

Hilary Greenwood (b. 1929)
based on Genesis 3: 8–10; Mark 14: 32–42;
John 20: 15–17

291

Melcombe   88 88 (LM)

Melody by Samuel Webbe the Elder (1740–1816) in his
An Essay on the Church Plain Chant (London, 1782)

1 Where high the heavenly temple stands,
the house of God not made with hands,
   a great high priest our nature wears,
   the guardian of our race appears.

2 He who for us as surety stood
and poured on earth his precious blood,
   pursues in heaven his mighty will,
   our saviour and our helper still.

3 Though now ascended up on high,
he sees us with a brother's eye;
   he shared with us the human name
   and knows the frailty of our frame.

4 In every pang that rends the heart
the Man of Sorrows had a part,
   he sympathises with our grief,
   and to the sufferer sends relief.

5 With boldness, therefore, at the throne
let us make all our sorrows known,
   and ask the aid of heavenly power
   to help us in the evil hour.

Michael Bruce (1746–67) altd.
based on Hebrews 4: 14–16

292

St Fulbert   86 86 (CM)

Henry J. Gauntlett (1805–76)

After last verse

Al - le - lu - ia!   A - men.

Chorus novae Jerusalem

1 Ye choirs of new Jerusalem,
  your sweetest notes employ,
the paschal victory to hymn
  in strains of holy joy.

2 For Judah's lion bursts his chains
  to crush the serpent's head,
and cries aloud through death's domains
  to wake the imprisoned dead.

3 Devouring depths of hell their prey
    at his command restore;
  his ransomed hosts pursue their way
    where Jesus goes before.

4 Triumphant in his glory now,
    to him all power is given;
  to him in one communion bow
    all saints in earth and heaven.

5 While we, his servants, praise our king,
    his mercy we implore,
  within his palace bright to bring
    and keep us evermore.

6 All glory to the Father be,
    all glory to the Son,
  all glory Holy Ghost, to thee
    while endless ages run.
      Alleluia! Amen!

Fulbert of Chartres (d. 1028)
tr. *Robert Campbell* (1814–68) altd.

293

FIRST TUNE

Spiritus Dei 66 86 (SM) Frederick Ellis (1896)

SECOND TUNE

Eastville 66 86 (SM) Kenneth Naylor (1931–1991)

Alternative tune: 382 DOMINICA

1 Breathe on me, Breath of God,
   fill me with life anew,
  that I may love what thou dost love,
   and do what thou wouldst do.

2 Breathe on me, Breath of God,
   until my heart is pure;
  until with thee I will one will
   to do and to endure.

3 Breathe on me, Breath of God,
   till I am wholly thine;
  until this earthly part of me
   glows with thy fire divine.

4 Breathe on me, Breath of God,
   so shall I never die,
  but live with thee the perfect life
   of thine eternity.

Edwin Hatch (1835–89)
based on Job 33: 4

294

Down Ampney   6 6 11 D

R. Vaughan Williams (1872–1958)

Discendi, Amor santo

1   Come down, O Love divine,
      seek thou this soul of mine,
  and visit it with thine own ardour glowing;
     O Comforter, draw near,
      within my heart appear,
  and kindle it, thy holy flame bestowing.

2   O let it freely burn,
      till earthly passions turn
  to dust and ashes in its heat consuming;
     and let thy glorious light
      shine ever on my sight,
  and clothe me round, the while my path illuming.

3   Let holy charity
      mine outward vesture be,
  and lowliness become mine inner clothing:
     true lowliness of heart,
      which takes the humbler part,
  and o'er its own shortcomings weeps with loathing.

4   And so the yearning strong,
      with which the soul will long,
  shall far outpass the power of human telling;
     for none can guess its grace,
      till we become the place
  wherein the Holy Spirit makes his dwelling.

Bianco da Siena (d. 1434)
tr. *Richard F. Littledale* (1833–90)
based on John 14: 16, 26

295

Birling   88 88 (LM)

Melody from an early 19th-century
Nottingham collection

Alternative tunes: 242ii VERBUM SUPERNUM   457 WARRINGTON

1 Come, gracious Spirit, heavenly Dove,
   with light and comfort from above;
       be thou our guardian, thou our guide;
       o'er every thought and step preside.

2 The light of truth to us display,
   and make us know and choose thy way;
       plant holy fear in every heart,
       that we from God may ne'er depart.

3 Lead us to Christ, the living Way,
   nor let us from his pastures stray;
       lead us to holiness, the road
       that we must take to dwell with God.

4 Lead us to heaven, that we may share
   fullness of joy for ever there;
       lead us to God, our final rest,
       to be with him for ever blest.

Simon Browne (1680–1732)

296

Veni, Creator Spiritus   88 88 (LM) with Doxology

Mechlin form of mode viii
Plainsong melody

Praise to thy e - ter-nal me-rit,   Fa-ther, Son, and Ho-ly Spi-rit.   A - men.

Veni, Creator Spiritus

1 Come, Holy Ghost, our souls inspire,
  and lighten with celestial fire;
      thou the anointing Spirit art,
      who dost thy seven-fold gifts impart.

2 Thy blessèd unction from above
  is comfort, life, and fire of love;
      enable with perpetual light
      the dullness of our blinded sight.

3 Anoint and cheer our soilèd face
  with the abundance of thy grace;
      keep far our foes, give peace at home:
      where thou art guide no ill can come.

4 Teach us to know the Father, Son,
  and thee, of both, to be but One,
      that through the ages all along,
      this may be our endless song:

  Praise to thy eternal merit,
  Father, Son, and Holy Spirit. Amen.

John Cosin (1594–1672)
based on Veni, Creator Spiritus
attrib. *Rhabanus Magnentius Maurus* (776–856)

297

Veni, Sancte Spiritus   777 D

Samuel Webbe the elder (*c.*1740–1816)
in his *An Essay on the Church Plain Chant*
(London, 1782)

Veni, Sancte Spiritus

1 Come, thou Holy Spirit, come,
  and from thy celestial home
    shed a ray of light divine;
  come, thou Father of the poor,
  all good gifts are from thy store,
    in us let thy radiance shine:

2 thou of comforters the best,
  thou the soul's most welcome guest,
    glad refreshment here below;
  in our labour rest most sweet,
  grateful coolness in the heat,
    solace in the midst of woe.

3 O most blessèd Light divine,
  shine within these hearts of thine,
    and our inmost being fill;
  where thou art not, we have naught,
  nothing good in deed or thought,
    nothing free from taint of ill.

4 Heal our wounds; our strength renew;
  on our dryness pour thy dew;
    wash the stains of guilt away;
  bend the stubborn heart and will;
  melt the frozen, warm the chill;
    guide the steps that go astray.

5 On thy servants, who adore ⌣
    and confess thee, evermore ⌣
      in thy sevenfold gifts descend;
    grant us virtue's sure reward,
    grant us thy salvation, Lord,
      grant us joys that never end.

From a 13th-century Latin hymn
Attrib. *Stephen Langton* (*c.*1160–1228)
and *Edward Caswall* (1814–78) altd.

298

FIRST TUNE

Farley Castle   10 10 10 10   Henry Lawes (1596–1662)

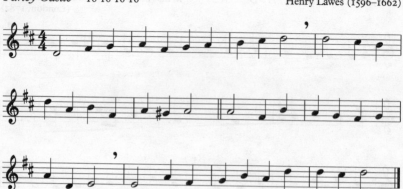

SECOND TUNE

Morestead   10 10 10 10   Sydney Watson (b. 1903)

1 Filled with the Spirit's power, with one accord
the infant Church confessed its risen Lord;
    O Holy Spirit, in the Church today
    no less your power of fellowship display.

2 Now with the mind of Christ set us on fire,
that unity may be our great desire;
    give joy and peace; give faith to hear your call,
    and readiness in each to work for all.

3 Widen our love, good Spirit, to embrace
with your compassion all the human race;
    like wind and fire with life among us move,
    till we are known as Christ's, and Christians prove.

J. R. Peacey (1896–1971) altd.

299

All for Jesus 87 87

John Stainer (1840–1901)
from *The Crucifixion*

1 Holy Spirit, come, confirm us
    in the truth that Christ makes known;
  we have faith and understanding
    through your helping gifts alone.

2 Holy Spirit, come, console us,
    come as advocate to plead,
  loving Spirit from the Father,
    grant in Christ the help we need.

3 Holy Spirit, come, renew us,
    come yourself to make us live,
  holy through your loving presence,
    holy through the gifts you give.

4 Holy Spirit, come, possess us,
    you the love of Three in One,
  Holy Spirit of the Father,
    Holy Spirit of the Son.

Brian Foley (b. 1919)
based on John 14: 25–27; 16: 12–15

300

Song 13 (1)   77 77

Original form of melody
by Orlando Gibbons (1583–1625)

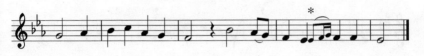

* This decorative figure is in the original, but may be omitted if desired.
For a later (simpler) form of this tune, see no. 212 or no. 249.

1 Holy Spirit, truth divine,
    dawn upon this soul of mine:
        voice of God, and inward light,
        wake my spirit, clear my sight.

2 Holy Spirit, love divine,
    glow within this heart of mine:
        kindle every high desire,
        purify me with your fire.

3 Holy Spirit, power divine,
    fill and nerve this will of mine:
        boldly may I always live,
        bravely serve and gladly give.

4 Holy Spirit, law divine,
    reign within this soul of mine:
        be my law, and I shall be
        firmly bound, for ever free.

5 Holy Spirit, peace divine,
    still this restless heart of mine:
        speak to calm this tossing sea.
        Grant me your tranquillity.

6 Holy Spirit, joy divine,
    gladden now this heart of mine:
        in the desert ways I sing—
        spring, O living water, spring!

Samuel Longfellow (1819–92) altd.
based on Galatians 5: 22

301

Ludgate   666 D

John Dykes Bower (1905–81)

Alternative tune: 344i LAUDES DOMINI

1 Let every Christian pray,
  this day, and every day,
    come, Holy Spirit, come!
  Was not the Church we love
  commissioned from above?
    Come, Holy Spirit, come!

2 The Spirit brought to birth
  the Church of Christ on earth
    to seek and save the lost:
  never has he withdrawn,
  since that tremendous dawn,
    his gifts at Pentecost.

3 Age after age, he strove
  to teach her how to love:
    come, Holy Spirit, come!
  Age after age, anew
  she proved the gospel true:
    come, Holy Spirit, come!

4 Only the Spirit's power
  can fit us for this hour:
    come, Holy Spirit, come!
  Instruct, inspire, unite;
  and make us see the light:
    come, Holy Spirit, come!

F. Pratt Green (b. 1903)

302

FIRST TUNE
adpt. by William Henry Havergal (1793–1870)
from a melody in Speiss's
Davids Harpffen Spiel (Heidelberg, 1745)

Swabia   66 86 (SM)

SECOND TUNE

Doncaster   66 86 (SM)

Samuel Wesley (1766–1837)

1 Lord God the Holy Ghost,
  in this accepted hour,
as on the day of Pentecost,
  descend in all thy power.

2 We meet with one accord
  in our appointed place,
and wait the promise of our Lord,
  the Spirit of all grace.

3 Like mighty rushing wind
  upon the waves beneath,
move with one impulse every mind,
  one soul, one feeling breathe:

4 the young, the old inspire ‿
  with wisdom from above;
and give us hearts and tongues of fire
  to pray, and praise, and love.

5 Spirit of truth, be thou ‿
  in life and death our guide;
O Spirit of adoption, now ‿
  may we be sanctified.

James Montgomery (1771–1854)

303

Londonderry Air (1)   11 10 11 10 D

Irish traditional melody
from Limavady, Co. Londonderry

1 Lord of the Church, we pray for our renewing:
    Christ over all, our undivided aim.
Fire of the Spirit, burn for our enduing,
    wind of the Spirit, fan the living flame!
We turn to Christ amid our fear and failing,
    the will that lacks the courage to be free,
the weary labours, all but unavailing,
    to bring us nearer what a church should be.

2 Lord of the Church, we seek a Father's blessing,
    a true repentance and a faith restored,
a swift obedience and a new possessing,
    filled with the Holy Spirit of the Lord!
We turn to Christ from all our restless striving,
    unnumbered voices with a single prayer:
the living water for our souls' reviving,
    in Christ to live, and love and serve and care.

3 Lord of the Church, we long for our uniting,
    true to one calling, by one vision stirred;
one cross proclaiming and one creed reciting,
    one in the truth of Jesus and his word!
So lead us on; till toil and trouble ended,
    one Church triumphant one new song shall sing,
to praise his glory, risen and ascended,
    Christ over all, the everlasting King!

Timothy Dudley-Smith (b. 1926)

GOD THE HOLY SPIRIT, LIFE-GIVER

304

Omni die 87 87

Melody from Corner's
Gesangbuch (Nuremberg, 1631)

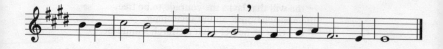

Waltham (Gott des Himmels) 87 87

Based on a chorale melody
by Heinrich Albert (1604–51)

THE OUTPOURING OF THE HOLY SPIRIT

1 Loving Spirit, loving Spirit,
   you have chosen me to be—
 you have drawn me to your wonder,
   you have set your sign on me.

2 Like a mother, you enfold me,
   hold my life within your own,
 feed me with your very body,
   form me of your flesh and bone.

3 Like a father, you protect me,
   teach me the discerning eye,
 hoist me up upon your shoulder,
   let me see the world from high.

4 Friend and lover, in your closeness
   I am known and held and blessed:
 in your promise is my comfort,
   in your presence I may rest.

5 Loving Spirit, loving Spirit,
   you have chosen me to be—
 you have drawn me to your wonder,
   you have set your sign on me.

Shirley Erena Murray (b. 1931)

305

Spiritus vitae   98 98

Mary Jane Hammond (1878–1964)

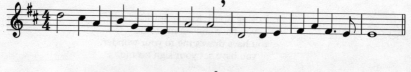
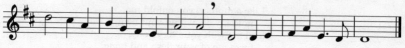

Alternative tune: 73 ST CLEMENT

1 O Breath of life, come sweeping through us,
      revive your Church with life and power.
   O Breath of life, come, cleanse, renew us,
      and fit your Church to meet this hour.

2 O Wind of God, come, bend us, break us,
      till humbly we confess our need;
   then in your tenderness re-make us,
      revive, restore, for this we plead.

3 O Breath of love, come breathe within us,
      renewing thought and will and heart;
   come, love of Christ, afresh to win us,
      revive your Church in every part.

4 Revive us, Lord! Is zeal abating
      while harvest fields are vast and white?
   Revive us, Lord, the world is waiting,
      equip your Church to spread the light.

Elizabeth (Betty) A. P. Head (1850–1936)

306

Illsley   88 88 (LM)   John Bishop (1665–1737)

* Later variant of this bar:

For the significance of the small notes above the stave, see the Musical Preface.

1 O Spirit of the living God,
    in all the fullness of your grace,
  wherever human feet have trod,
    descend upon our fallen race.

2 Give tongues of fire and hearts of love
    to preach the reconciling word;
  give power and wisdom from above
    whenever gospel truth is heard.

3 Let darkness turn to radiant light,
    confusion vanish from your path;
  those who are weak inspire with might:
    let mercy triumph over wrath.

4 O Spirit of our God, prepare
    the whole wide world the Lord to meet;
  breathe out new life, like morning air,
    till hearts of stone begin to beat.

5 Baptize the nations; far and near
    the triumphs of the cross record;
  till Christ in glory shall appear
    and every race declare him Lord.

James Montgomery (1771–1854) altd.
based on Acts 2: 3–4

307

St Cuthbert   88 88 (LM)

John Bacchus Dykes (1823–76)

1 Our great Redeemer, as he breathed
    his tender last farewell,
a guide, a Comforter, bequeathed
    with us to dwell.

2 He came in tongues of living flame
    to teach, convince, subdue;
unseen as rushing wind he came—
    as powerful too.

3 He comes his influence to impart,
    a gracious, willing guest,
when he can find one humble heart
    where he may rest.

4 And every virtue we possess,
    and every victory won,
and every thought of holiness
    are his alone.

5 Spirit of purity and grace,
    our weakness, pitying, see;
and make our hearts thy dwelling-place
    and worthier thee.

Harriet Auber (1773–1862) altd.

308

Steeple Ashton   66 86 (SM)   John Barnard (b. 1948)

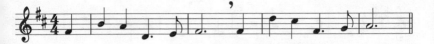

Alternative tunes: 370, 461i CARLISLE   485 FESTAL SONG

1 Revive your Church, O Lord,
    in grace and power draw near;
speak with the voice that wakes the dead,
    and make your people hear!

2 Revive your Church, O Lord,
    disturb the sleep of death;
give life to smouldering embers now
    by your almighty breath.

3 Revive your Church, O Lord,
    exalt your precious name;
and by your Holy Spirit come
    and set our love aflame.

4 Revive your Church, O Lord,
    give us a thirst for you,
a hunger for the bread of life
    our spirits to renew.

5 Revive your Church, O Lord,
    and let your power be shown;
the gifts and graces shall be ours,
    the glory yours alone!

Albert Midlane (1825–1909)

309

Limerick 66 86 66

Edward F. Darling (b. 1933)

Malone 66 86 66

Donald Davison (b. 1937)

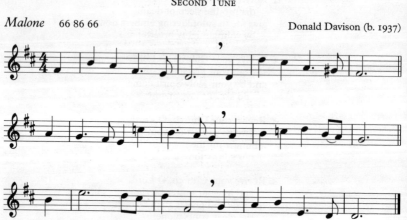

THE OUTPOURING OF THE HOLY SPIRIT

1 When God the Spirit came
   upon his Church outpoured
in sound of wind and sign of flame
   they spread his truth abroad,
      and filled with the Spirit
   proclaimed that Christ is Lord.

2 What courage, power and grace
   that youthful Church displayed!
To those of every tribe and race
   they witnessed unafraid,
      and filled with the Spirit
   they broke their bread and prayed.

3 They saw God's word prevail,
   his kingdom still increase,
no part of all his purpose fail,
   no promised blessing cease,
      and filled with the Spirit
   knew love and joy and peace.

4 Their theme was Christ alone,
   the Lord who lived and died,
who rose to his eternal throne
   at God the Father's side,
      and filled with the Spirit
   the Church was multiplied.

5 So to this present hour
   our task is still the same,
in pentecostal love and power
   his gospel to proclaim,
      and filled with the Spirit,
   rejoice in Jesus' name.

Timothy Dudley-Smith (b. 1926)
based on Acts 2: 1–11

310

Spirit of the living God   75 75 44 75

Words and music by
Daniel Iverson (1890–1972)

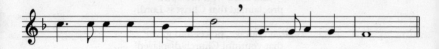

Spirit of the living God,
   fall afresh on me.
Spirit of the living God,
   fall afresh on me.
Break me, melt me,
   mould me, fill me.
Spirit of the living God,
   fall afresh on me.

Daniel Iverson (1890–1972)

311

Beechgrove   87 87

Donald Davison (b. 1937)

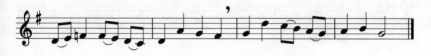

Alternative tune: 41 SHIPSTON

1 Fruitful trees, the Spirit's sowing,
    may we ripen and increase,
  fruit to life eternal growing,
    rich in love and joy and peace.

2 Laden branches freely bearing
    gifts the Giver loves to bless;
  here is fruit that grows by sharing,
    patience, kindness, gentleness.

3 Rooted deep in Christ our master,
    Christ our pattern and our goal,
  teach us, as the years fly faster,
    goodness, faith and self-control.

4 Fruitful trees, the Spirit's tending,
    may we grow till harvests cease;
  till we taste, in life unending,
    heaven's love and joy and peace.

Timothy Dudley-Smith (b. 1926)
based on Galatians 5: 22–23

312

FIRST TUNE

Charity   777 5   John Stainer (1840–1901)

SECOND TUNE

Guildford Cathedral   777 5   W. Grayston Ives (b. 1948)

1 Gracious Spirit, Holy Ghost,
   taught by thee, we covet most
   of thy gifts at Pentecost,
      holy, heavenly love.

*2 Faith that mountains could remove,
   tongues of earth or heaven above,
   knowledge, all things, empty prove
      if I have not love.

*3 Though I as a martyr bleed,
   give my goods the poor to feed,
   all is vain, if love I need;
      therefore give me love.

4 Love is kind and suffers long,
   love is meek and thinks no wrong,
   love than death itself more strong;
      therefore give us love.

5 Prophecy will fade away,
   melting in the light of day;
   love will ever with us stay;
      therefore give us love.

6 Faith and hope and love we see
   joining hand in hand agree;
   but the greatest of the three,
      and the best is love.

Christopher Wordsworth (1807–85)
based on 1 Corinthians 13

313

Day of rest   76 76 D   James William Elliott (1833–1915)

Alternative tune: 125, 204 CRÜGER

1 The Spirit came, as promised,
   in God's appointed hour;
and now to each believer
   he comes in love and power:
and by his Holy Spirit
   God seals us as his own,
and, through his Son and Spirit,
   makes access to his throne.

2 The Spirit makes our bodies
   the temple of the Lord;
he binds us all together
   in faith and true accord:
the Spirit in his greatness
   brings power from God above,
and, with the Son and Father,
   dwells in our hearts in love.

3 He bids us live together
   in unity and peace,
employ his gifts in blessing
   and let base passions cease:
we should not grieve the Spirit
   by open sin or shame,
nor let our words and actions
   deny his holy name.

4 The word, the Spirit's weapon,
   will bring all sin to light;
and prayer, by his directing,
   will add new joy and might:
be filled then with his Spirit,
   live out God's will and word;
rejoice with hymns and singing,
   make music to the Lord!

J. E. Seddon (1915–83)

314

Lauds   77 77

John W. Wilson (1905–92)

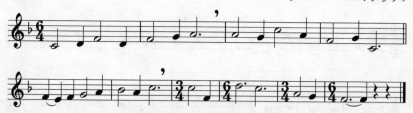

Alternative tune: 79i ORIENTIS PARTIBUS

1 There's a spirit in the air,
   telling Christians everywhere:
      'Praise the love that Christ revealed,
      living, working, in our world!'

2 Lose your shyness, find your tongue,
   tell the world what God has done:
      God in Christ has come to stay.
      Live tomorrow's life today!

3 When believers break the bread,
   when a hungry child is fed,
      praise the love that Christ revealed,
      living, working, in our world.

4 Still the Spirit gives us light,
   seeing wrong and setting right:
      God in Christ has come to stay.
      Live tomorrow's life today!

5 When a stranger's not alone,
   where the homeless find a home,
      praise the love that Christ revealed,
      living, working, in our world.

6 May the Spirit fill our praise,
   guide our thoughts and change our ways.
      God in Christ has come to stay.
      Live tomorrow's life today!

7 There's a Spirit in the air,
   calling people everywhere:
      praise the love that Christ revealed,
      living, working, in our world.

Brian Wren (b. 1936)

315

Emly   88 88 (LM)

Irish traditional melody

1 'This is my will,
my one command,
that love should dwell
among you all.
This is my will,
that you should love
as I have shown
that I love you.

2 'No greater love
can be than this:
to choose to die
to save one's friends.
You are my friends
if you obey
what I command
that you should do.

3 'I call you now
no longer slaves;
no slave knows all
the master does.
I call you friends,
for all I hear
my Father say
you hear from me.

4 'You chose not me,
but I chose you,
that you should go
and bear much fruit.
I chose you out
that you in me
should bear much fruit
that will abide.

5 'All that you ask
my Father dear
for my name's sake
you shall receive.
This is my will,
my one command,
that love should dwell
in each, in all.'

James Quinn (b. 1919)
based on John 15: 12–17

316

Laus Deo (Redhead no. 46)   87 87

Richard Redhead (1820–1901)
in *Church Hymn Tunes* (1853)
(based on a German original?)

1 Bright the vision[1] that delighted
    once the sight of Judah's seer;
sweet the countless tongues united
    to entrance the prophet's ear.

2 Round the Lord in glory seated
    cherubim and seraphim
filled his temple, and repeated
    each to each the alternate hymn:

3 'Lord, thy glory fills the heaven,
    earth is with thy fullness stored;
unto thee be glory given,
    holy, holy, holy Lord.'

4 Heaven is still with glory ringing,
    earth takes up the angels' cry,
'Holy, holy, holy', singing,
    'Lord of hosts, the Lord most high'.

5 With his seraph-train before him,
    with his holy Church below,
thus conspire we to adore him,
    bid we thus our anthem flow:

6 'Lord, thy glory fills the heaven,
    earth is with thy fullness stored;
unto thee be glory given,
    holy, holy, holy Lord.'

Richard Mant (1776–1848)
based on Isaiah 6: 1–3

[1] The vision referred to is that of the prophet Isaiah
('Judah's seer') described in Isaiah chapter 6.

317

Moredun   12 10 12 10

Henry Smart (1813–79)

Alternative tune: 196 WAS LEBET, WAS SCHWEBET

1 Father all-loving, you rule us in majesty,
    judgment is yours and condemns all our pride,
  stir up our rulers and peoples to penitence,
    sorrow for sins that for vengeance have cried.

2 Blessèd Lord Jesus, you came here in poverty,
    sharing a stable with beasts at your birth;
  stir us to work for your justice and charity,
    truly to care for the poor of the earth.

3 Come, Holy Spirit, create us in holiness,
    lift up our lives to your standard of right;
  stir every will to new ventures of faithfulness,
    flood the whole Church with your glorious light.

4 Holiest Trinity, perfect in unity,
    bind in your love every nation and race:
  may we adore you for time and eternity,
    Father, Redeemer, and Spirit of grace.

Patrick Appleford (b. 1925) altd.

318

Abbot's Leigh   87 87 D

Cyril V. Taylor (1907–91)

1 Father, Lord of all creation,
    ground of being, life and love;
height and depth beyond description
    only life in you can prove:
you are mortal life's dependence:
    thought, speech, sight are ours by grace;
yours is every hour's existence,
    sovereign Lord of time and space.

2 Jesus Christ, the Man for others,
    we, your people, make our prayer:
help us love—as sisters, brothers—
    all whose burdens we can share.
Where your name binds us together
    you, Lord Christ, will surely be;
where no selfishness can sever
    there your love the world may see.

3 Holy Spirit, rushing, burning
    wind and flame of Pentecost,
fire our hearts afresh with yearning
    to regain what we have lost.
May your love unite our action,
    nevermore to speak alone:
God, in us abolish faction,
    God, through us your love make known.

Stewart Cross (1928–89)

319

Rivaulx   88 88 (LM)

John Bacchus Dykes (1823–76)

1 Father, of heaven, whose love profound
  a ransom for our souls has found,
    before your throne we sinners bend;
    to us your pardoning love extend.

2 Almighty Son, incarnate Word,
  our prophet, priest, redeemer, Lord,
    before your throne we sinners bend;
    to us your saving grace extend.

3 Eternal Spirit, by whose breath
  the soul is raised from sin and death,
    before your throne we sinners bend;
    to us your quickening power extend.

4 Thrice holy, Father, Spirit, Son,
  mysterious Godhead, Three in One,
    before your throne we sinners bend;
    grace, pardon, life to us extend.

Edward Cooper (1770–1833) altd.

320

Halton Holgate   87 87

Later form of a melody by William Boyce (1711–79)
as given in S. S. Wesley's *European Psalmist* (1872)

Alternative tune: 41 SHIPSTON

1 Firmly I believe and truly
     God is Three, and God is One;
  and I next acknowledge duly
     manhood taken by the Son.

2 And I trust and hope most fully
     in that Manhood crucified;
  and each thought and deed unruly
     do to death, as he has died.

3 Simply to his grace and wholly
     light and life and strength belong,
  and I love supremely, solely,
     him the holy, him the strong.

4 And I hold in veneration,
     for the love of him alone,
  holy Church as his creation,
     and her teachings as his own.

5 Adoration ay be given,
     with and through the angelic host,
  to the God of earth and heaven,
     Father, Son, and Holy Ghost.

John Henry Newman (1801–90)
from The Dream of Gerontius
based on The Apostles' Creed

321

Nicaea 11 12 12 10

John Bacchus Dykes (1823–76)

1 Holy, holy, holy! Lord God almighty,
     early in the morning our song shall rise to thee;
   holy, holy, holy! merciful and mighty;
     God in Three Persons, blessèd Trinity!

2 Holy, holy, holy! all the saints adore thee,
     casting down their golden crowns around the glassy sea;
   cherubim and seraphim falling down before thee,
     God everlasting through eternity.

3 Holy, holy, holy! though the darkness hide thee,
     though the sinful human eye thy glory may not see,
   only thou art holy: there is none beside thee
     perfect in power, in love, and purity.

4 Holy, holy, holy! Lord God almighty,
     all thy works shall praise thy name in earth and sky and sea;
   holy, holy, holy! merciful and mighty;
     God in Three Persons, blessèd Trinity!

Reginald Heber (1783–1826) altd.
based on Revelation 4: 8–11;
Isaiah 6: 1–8

322

St Patrick's Breastplate
88 88 D (DLM)

Irish traditional hymn melodies
arr. Charles Villiers Stanford (1852–1924)

The Breastplate of St. Patrick
Atomriug indiú niurt trén togairm trinoit

1. I bind un - to___ my - self___ to - day___ the

strong___ name of___ the Tri - ni - ty, by

in - vo - ca - tion of the same,___ the___

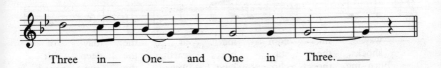

Three in___ One___ and One in Three.___

2. I bind this day to me for ev-er, by
4. I bind un-to my-self to-day the
7.* a-gainst all Sa-tan's spells and wiles, a-

pow'r of faith, Christ's in-car-na-tion, his bap-tism
vir-tues of the star-lit hea-ven, the glo-rious
-gainst false words of he-re-sy, a-gainst the

in the Jor-dan ri-ver, his death on cross for
sun's life-giv-ing ray, the white-ness of the
know-ledge that de-files, a-gainst the heart's i-

my sal-va-tion; his burst-ing from the
moon at e-ven, the flash-ing of the
-dol-a-try, a-gainst the wiz-ard's

spi-ced tomb, his ri-ding up the heav'n-ly
light-ning free, the whirl-ing wind's tem-pest-uous
e-vil craft, a-gainst the death-wound and the

way, his com-ing at the day of
shocks, the sta-ble earth, the deep salt
burn-ing, the cho-king wave, the poi-soned

doom, I bind un-to my-self to-day.
sea a-round the old e-ter-nal rocks.
shaft, pro-tect me, Christ, till thy re-turn-ing.

432

THE TRINITY

3. I bind un - to my - self the power of
5. I bind un - to my - self to - day the
6.* a - gainst the de - mon - snares of sin, the

the great love of che - ru - bim, the sweet 'Well
pow'r of God to hold and lead, his eye to
vice that gives temp - ta - tion force, the na - tu - ral

done' in judge - ment hour, the ser - vice of the
watch, his might to stay, his ear to heark - en
lusts that war with - in, the hos - tile foes that

se - ra - phim, con - fess - ors' faith, a -
to my need, the wis - dom of my
mar my course; or few or ma - ny,

- post - les' word, the pa - triarchs' prayers, the pro - phets'
God to teach, his hand to guide, his shield to
far or nigh, in ev - ery place, and in all

scrolls, all good deeds done un - to the
ward, the word of God to give me
hours, a - gainst their fierce hos - ti - li -

Lord, and pu - ri - ty of vir - gin souls.
speech, his heaven - ly host to be my guard:
- ty, I bind to me these ho - ly powers;

433

Gartan (2) 88 88

8. Christ be with me, Christ with-in me, Christ be-hind me,

Christ be-fore___ me,___ Christ be-side me,

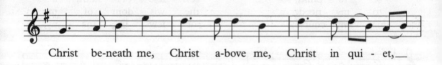

Christ to win me, Christ to com-fort and re-store me,

Christ be-neath me, Christ a-bove me, Christ in qui-et,___

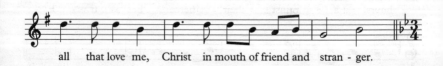

Christ in dan-ger,___ Christ in hearts of

all that love me, Christ in mouth of friend and stran-ger.

THE TRINITY

9. I bind un-to___ my-self___ the_ name, the

strong name of___ the Tri-ni-ty, by in-vo-

-ca-tion of the same, the_ Three in___ One_ and

One in Three;_____ of whom all na-ture_

hath cre-a-tion, e-ter-nal Fa-ther,

Spi-rit, Word. Praise to_____ the_ Lord_ of

my sal-va-tion: sal-va-tion is___ of Christ the

Lord._____ A - men._____

323

Leoni 66 84 D

Hebrew melody noted by Thomas Olivers (1725–99)
from the singing of Meyer Lyon of
the London Great Synagogue, adpt. *c.*1770

יִגְדַּל אֱלֹהִים חַי

Yigdal Elohim Chai

1 The God of Abraham praise,
    who reigns enthroned above;
ancient of everlasting days,
    and God of love;
to him uplift your voice,
    at whose supreme command
from earth we rise, and seek the joys
    at his right hand.

2 He by himself has sworn:
    I on his oath depend;
I shall, on eagle-wings upborne,
    to heaven ascend:
I shall behold his face,
    I shall his power adore,
and sing the wonders of his grace
    for evermore.

436

3 There dwells the Lord, our King,
    the Lord, our righteousness,
triumphant o'er the world of sin,
    the Prince of peace;
on Zion's sacred height
    his kingdom still maintains,
and glorious with his saints in light,
    for ever reigns.

4 The God who reigns on high
    the great archangels sing,
and 'Holy, holy, holy,' cry,
    'Almighty King,
who was, and is, the same,
    and evermore shall be:
Jehovah, Father, great I AM,
    we worship thee!'

5 The whole triumphant host
    give thanks to God on high;
'Hail, Father, Son, and Holy Ghost!'
    they ever cry.
Hail, Abraham's God and mine!
    I join the heavenly lays;
all might and majesty are thine,
    and endless praise.

Thomas Olivers (1725–99) altd.
based on the Jewish Yigdal

The 12th-century scholar Moses Maimonides drew up the thirteen articles of the Hebrew Creed, which were subsequently written in metrical form (the Yigdal).

324

Moscow   664 6664

adpt. from Felice Giardini (1716–96)

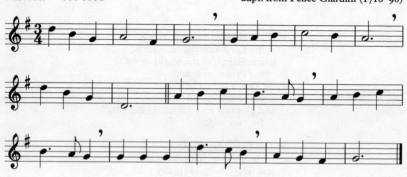

1 God, whose almighty word
   chaos and darkness heard,
      and took their flight:
   hear us, we humbly pray,
   and where the gospel-day
   sheds not its glorious ray,
      let there be light!

2 Saviour, who came to bring
   on your redeeming wing
      healing and sight,
   health to the sick in mind,
   sight to the inly blind:
   now to all humankind
      let there be light!

3 Spirit of truth and love,
   life-giving, holy dove,
      speed on your flight!
   Move on the water's face
   bearing the lamp of grace,
   and in earth's darkest place
      let there be light!

4 Holy and blessèd Three,
   glorious Trinity,
      wisdom, love, might:
   boundless as ocean's tide
   rolling in fullest pride,
   through the world, far and wide,
      let there be light!

John Marriott (1780–1825) altd.

THE LIFE OF FAITH

325

Be still

Dave Evans (b. 1957)

1 Be still, for the presence of the Lord, the Holy One, is here.
Come, bow before him now, with reverence and fear.
In him no sin is found, we stand on holy ground.
Be still, for the presence of the Lord, the Holy One, is here.

2 Be still, for the glory of the Lord is shining all around;
he burns with holy fire, with splendour he is crowned.
How awesome is the sight, our radiant King of light!
Be still, for the glory of the Lord is shining all around.

3 Be still, for the power of the Lord is moving in this place,
he comes to cleanse and heal, to minister his grace.
No work too hard for him, in faith receive from him;
be still, for the power of the Lord is moving in this place.

Dave Evans (b. 1957)
based on Exodus 3: 1–6

326

Westminster Abbey   87 87 87

FIRST TUNE

Adapted from the final section ('Hallelujah')
in the anthem 'O God, thou art my God'
by Henry Purcell (*c.*1659–1695)
for the tune *Belville* in *The Psalmist* (1843)

SECOND TUNE

Urbs beata   87 87 87

Plainsong melody, mode ii

A - men.

Alternative tune: 117 ORIEL

Urbs beata Ierusalem

*1 Blessèd city, heavenly Salem,
      vision dear of peace and love,
   who, of living stones upbuilded,
      are the joy of heaven above:
   we, with all thy holy people,
      glorious to thy glory move.

2 Christ is made the sure foundation,
      Christ the head and corner-stone,
   chosen of the Lord and precious,
      binding all the Church in one;
   holy Zion's help for ever,
      and her confidence alone.

3 All that dedicated city,
      dearly loved of God on high,
   in exultant jubilation
      pours perpetual melody,
   God, the One in Three, adoring
      in glad hymns eternally.

4 To this temple, where we call thee,
      come, O Lord of Hosts, today;
   with thy wonted loving-kindness
      hear thy servants as they pray,
   and thy fullest benediction
      shed within these walls alway.

5 Here vouchsafe to all thy servants
      what they ask of thee to gain,
   what they gain from thee, for ever ‿
      with the blessèd to retain,
   and hereafter in thy glory
      evermore with thee to reign.

6 Praise and honour to the Father,
      praise and honour to the Son,
   praise and honour to the Spirit,
      ever Three and ever One,
   one in might and one in glory,
      while eternal ages run.

Latin 7th cent.
tr. *John Mason Neale* (1818–66)
based on 1 Peter 2: 4–7; Ephesians 2: 20–22

327

Harewood   66 66 88   Samuel Sebastian Wesley (1810–76)

Angularis fundamentum lapis Christus missus est

1 Christ is our corner-stone,
   on him alone we build;
with his true saints alone
   the courts of heaven are filled:
      on his great love
      our hopes we place
      of present grace
   and joys above.

2 O then with hymns of praise
   these hallowed courts shall ring;
our voices we will raise
   the Three-in-One to sing,
      and so proclaim
      in joyful song,
      both loud and long,
   that glorious name.

3 Here, gracious God, come now,
   and evermore draw near;
accept each faithful vow
   and mark each earnest prayer;
      in copious shower
      on all who pray
      each holy day
   your blessings pour.

4 Here may we gain from heaven
   the grace which we implore;
and may that grace, once given,
   be with us evermore,
      until that day
      when all the blessed
      to endless rest
   are called away.

Anon. 7th- or 8th-century Latin
tr. *John Chandler* (1806–76) altd.

328

Come on and celebrate

Words and music by Dave Bankhead
and Trish Morgan

Come on and ce - le - brate! His gift of love we will ce - le - brate—
the Son of God who loved_ us_____ and gave us life._____
_ We'll shout your praise, O King: you give us joy no-thing
else can bring; we'll give to you our of - fer - ing_____ in ce - le - bra - tion

handclap:

praise._____ Come on and ce - le - brate,
ce - le - brate, ce - le - brate and sing, ce - le - brate and
sing to the King._____ Come on and sing to the King._____

329

Old 124th   10 10 10 10 10   Melody from *Genevan Psalter* (1551)

1 Father, again in Jesus' name we meet,
  and bow in penitence beneath your feet;
    again to you our feeble voices raise,
    to sue for mercy and to sing your praise.

2 Father we bless you for your ceaseless care,
  and all your work from day to day declare;
    is not our life with hourly mercies crowned?
    Does not your arm encircle us around?

3 We are unworthy of your boundless love,
  with careless feet from you we often rove;
    but now encouraged by your voice we come,
    returning sinners, to a Father's home.

4 O by that name in which all fullness dwells,
  O by that love which every love excels,
    O by that blood so freely shed for sin,
    open your mercy's gate and take us in.

Lucy Whitmore (1792–1840) altd.
based on Luke 15: 11–32

330

Blaenwern   87 87 D   William P. Rowlands (1860–1937)

Alternative tune: 318 ABBOT'S LEIGH (for which this hymn was written)

1 God is here! As we his people
    meet to offer praise and prayer,
  may we find in fuller measure
    what it is in Christ we share.
  Here, as in the world around us,
    all our varied skills and arts
  wait the coming of his Spirit
    into open minds and hearts.

2 Here are symbols to remind us
    of our lifelong need of grace;
  here are table, font and pulpit;
    here the cross has central place.
  Here in honesty of preaching,
    here in silence, as in speech,
  here, in newness and renewal,
    God the Spirit comes to each.

3 Here our children find a welcome
    in the Shepherd's flock and fold,
  here, as bread and wine are taken,
    Christ sustains us, as of old.
  Here the servants of the Servant
    seek in worship to explore
  what it means in daily living
    to believe and to adore.

4 Lord of all, of Church and Kingdom,
    in an age of change and doubt,
  keep us faithful to the gospel,
    help us work your purpose out.
  Here, in this day's dedication,
    all we have to give, receive:
  we, who cannot live without you,
    we adore you, we believe!

F. Pratt Green (b. 1903)

331

Arnsberg (Gott ist gegenwärtig)   668 D 33 66

Based on a melody by
Joachim Neander (1650–80)

Gott ist gegenwärtig

1 God reveals his presence;
    let us now adore him,
    and with awe appear before him;
God is in his temple;
    all within keep silence,
    prostrate lie with deepest reverence.
        Him alone‿
        God we own,
him our God and Saviour:
praise his name for ever.

2 God reveals his presence;
    hear the harps resounding,
    see the crowds the throne surrounding:
'Holy, holy, holy',
    hear the hymn ascending,
    angels, saints, their voices blending.
        Bow thine ear‿
        to us here;
hear, O Christ, the praises‿
that thy Church now raises.

3 O thou fount of blessing,
    purify my spirit,
    trusting only in thy merit;
like the holy angels
    who behold thy glory,
    may I ceaselessly adore thee;
        let thy will,
        ever still‿
rule thy Church terrestrial,
as the hosts celestial.

Gerhard Tersteegan (1697–1769)
tr. *Frederick W. Foster* (1760–1835)
and *William Mercer* (1811–73)

332

Nativity   86 86 (CM)   Henry Lahee (1826–1912)

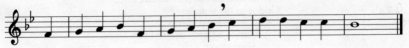

1 Come, let us join our cheerful songs
   with angels round the throne;
 ten thousand thousand are their tongues,
   but all their joys are one.

2 'Worthy the Lamb that died,' they cry,
   'to be exalted thus!'
 'Worthy the Lamb,' our lips reply,
   'for he was slain for us!'

3 Jesus is worthy to receive⌣
   all honour, power divine;
 and blessings more than we can give
   be, Lord, for ever thine.

*4 Let all who live above the sky,
   and air and earth and seas
 conspire to lift thy glories high
   and speak thine endless praise!

5 Let all creation join in one
   to bless the sacred name⌣
 of him that sits upon the throne,
   and to adore the Lamb.

Isaac Watts (1674–1748) altd.
based on Revelation 5

333

Harington (*Retirement*)   86 86 (CM)

From a 3-part glee by
Henry Harington (1727–1816)

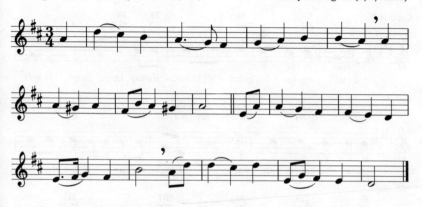

1 How lovely are thy dwellings fair!
   O Lord of hosts, how dear
  the pleasant tabernacles are,
   where thou dost dwell so near.

2 My soul doth long and almost die
   thy courts, O Lord, to see;
  my heart and flesh aloud do cry,
   O living God, for thee.

3 Happy who in thy house reside,
   where thee they ever praise;
  happy whose strength in thee doth bide,
   and in their hearts thy ways.

4 They journey on from strength to strength
   with joy and gladsome cheer,
  till all before our God at length
   in Zion do appear.

5 For God, the Lord, both sun and shield,
   gives grace and glory bright;
  no good from them shall be withheld
   whose ways are just and right.

John Milton (1608–74)
based on Psalm 84

451

334

I will enter

Words and music by Leona von Brethorst

based on Psalm 118: vv. 19 & 24

335

Jesus calls us   87 87 D

Scots Gaelic melody (from Lewis)
adpt. John L. Bell (b. 1949)
and Graham Maule (b. 1958)

OPTIONAL INTERLUDE

Alternative tune: 330, 634i BLAENWERN

1 Jesus calls us here to meet him
     as, through word and song and
          prayer,
   we affirm God's promised presence
     where his people live and care.
   Praise the God who keeps his promise;
     praise the Son who calls us friends;
   praise the Spirit who, among us,
     to our hopes and fears attends.

2 Jesus calls us to confess him
     Word of life and Lord of all,
   sharer of our flesh and frailness
     saving all who fail or fall.
   Tell his holy human story;
     tell his tales that all may hear;
   tell the world that Christ in glory
     came to earth to meet us here.

3 Jesus calls us to each other:
     vastly different though we are;
   Race and colour, class and gender
     neither limit nor debar.
   Join the hands of friend and stranger;
     join the hands of age and youth;
   join the faithful and the doubter
     in their common search for truth.

4 Jesus calls us to his table
     rooted firm in time and space,
   where the Church in earth and heaven
     finds a common meeting place.
   Share the bread and wine, his body;
     share the love of which we sing;
   share the feast for saints and sinners
     hosted by our Lord and King.

John L. Bell (b. 1949)
and *Graham Maule* (b. 1958)

If this song is being sung during worship where there is no
celebration of the eucharist, the last verse may be omitted.

336

Warrington   88 88 (LM)   Ralph Harrison (1748–1810)

1 Jesus, where'er thy people meet,
  there they behold thy mercy-seat;
      where'er they seek thee, thou art found,
      and every place is hallowed ground.

2 For thou, within no walls confined,
  inhabitest the humble mind;
      such ever bring thee where they come,
      and going, take thee to their home.

3 Dear Shepherd of thy chosen few,
  thy former mercies here renew;
      here to our waiting hearts proclaim
      the sweetness of thy saving name.

4 Here may we prove the power of prayer
  to strengthen faith and sweeten care,
      to teach our faint desires to rise,
      and bring all heaven before our eyes.

*5 Lord, we are few but thou art near;
  nor short thine arm, nor deaf thine ear;
      O rend the heavens, come quickly down,
      and make a thousand hearts thine own!

William Cowper (1731–1800)

454

337

Lift up your heads

Michelle Stoodley

based on Psalm 24

338

St Barnabas 65 65   John Bacchus Dykes (1823–76)

1 Jesus, stand among us
   in your risen power;
   let this time of worship
   be a hallowed hour.

2 Breathe your Holy Spirit
   into every heart;
   bid the fears and sorrows
   from each soul depart.

3 Thus with quickened footsteps
   we will go our way,
   watching for the dawning
   of the eternal day.

William Pennefather (1816–73) altd.
based on John 20: 19–23

339

St Columbanus   87 87 87   Walter Newport (1839–??)

1 Saviour, send a blessing to us,
   send a blessing from above;
  all your truth and mercy show us,
   come to us in power and love;
     grant your presence,
     grant your presence,
  be it ours your grace to prove.

2 Nothing have we, Lord, without you,
   but your promise is our stay;
  and your people must not doubt you;
   Saviour, now your power display;
     and let gladness,
     and let gladness
  fill your people's hearts today.

Thomas Kelly (1769–1854) altd.

457

340

John L. Bell (b. 1949)
and Graham Maule (b. 1958)

Campsie   96 10 7

1 Sing and be glad, for this is God's house!
    Christ is the cornerstone:
  worship and praise which the Spirit inspires
    we offer to God alone.

2 This sanctuary of fabric and faith
    grew both from prayer and skill:
  built on the promise of God, let it stay
    a sign of God's worth and will.

3 Here in our worship, witness and care,
    here in our work and word,
  may God enable each life to declare
    that Jesus is love and Lord.

4 Here may the lost and lonely be found;
    here may the sick be healed;
  here may the doubtful be summoned to serve
    and here may Christ be revealed.

5 All that we are and all that is here,
    all that is yet to be:
  these are the gifts we present to the Lord
    both now and eternally.

John L. Bell (b. 1949)
and *Graham Maule* (b. 1958)

341

Rochester   86 86 (CM)   C. Hylton Stewart (1884–1932)

Alternative tune: 439ii TALLIS'S ORDINAL

1 Spirit divine, attend our prayers
   and make this house your home,
   descend with all your gracious power:
   O come, great Spirit, come.

2 Come as the light: to us reveal
   our emptiness and woe;
   and lead us in those paths of life
   where all the righteous go.

3 Come as the fire: and purge our hearts
   like sacrificial flame;
   let our whole life an offering be
   to our Redeemer's name.

4 Come as the dove: and spread your wings,
   the wings of peaceful love,
   and let your Church on earth become
   blessed as the Church above.

5 Come as the wind, with rushing sound
   and pentecostal grace,
   that all of women born may see
   the glory of your face.

6 Spirit divine, attend our prayers,
   make this lost world your home;
   descend with all your gracious power:
   O come, great Spirit, come.

Andrew Reed (1787–1862) altd.

342

Duci cruento martyrum   88 88 (LM)   Theodore Edward Aylward (1844–1933)

1 Sweet is the solemn voice that calls
    the Christian to the house of prayer;
I love to stand within its walls,
    for Christ the Lord is present there.

2 I love to tread the hallowed courts
    where two or three for worship meet,
for there the Christ himself resorts,
    and makes the little band complete.

3 'Tis sweet to raise the common song,
    to join in holy praise and love,
and imitate the blessèd throng
    that mingle hearts and songs above.

4 Within these walls may peace abound;
    may all our hearts in one agree;
where Christians meet, where Christ is found,
    may peace and concord ever be.

Henry Francis Lyte (1793–1847) altd.

343

Quam dilecta   66 66   Henry L. Jenner (1820–98)

1 We love the place, O God,
     in which your honour dwells,
 the joy of your abode
     all earthly joy excels.

2 It is the house of prayer,
     where we your people meet,
 and you, our Lord are there
     your chosen flock to greet.

3 We love the font, for there
     new life in Christ begins;
 it speaks of your great care,
     of cleansing from our sins.

4 We love the word of life,
     the word that tells of peace,
 of comfort in the strife
     and joys that never cease.

5 We love your table, Lord—
     no place on earth so dear;
 for there, in faith adored,
     we find your presence near.

6 We love to sing below
     of mercies freely given;
 but O we long to know
     the triumph-song of heaven.

7 Lord Jesus, give us grace
     on earth to love you more,
 in heaven to see your face
     and with your saints adore.

William Bullock (1798–1874)
and *Henry Williams Baker* (1821–77) altd.
based on Psalm 26: 8

344

FIRST TUNE

Laudes Domini   666 D

Joseph Barnby (1838–96)

Alternative tune: 301 LUDGATE (composed for these words)

Je - sus Christ be prais - ed:

may Je - sus Christ be prais - ed.

Beim frühen Morgenlicht

1 When morning gilds the skies,
my heart awaking cries,
 may Jesus Christ be praised:
alike at work and prayer
to Jesus I repair;
 may Jesus Christ be praised.

*2 Whene'er the clear church bell
peals over hill and dell,
 may Jesus Christ be praised:
O hark to what it sings,
as joyously it rings,
 may Jesus Christ be praised.

*3 My tongue shall never tire
of chanting with the choir,
 may Jesus Christ be praised:
this song of sacred joy,
it never seems to cloy,
 may Jesus Christ be praised.

4 The night becomes as day,
when from the heart we say,
 may Jesus Christ be praised:
the powers of darkness fear,
when this glad song they hear,
 may Jesus Christ be praised.

5 In heaven's eternal bliss
the loveliest strain is this,
 may Jesus Christ be praised:
let earth, and sea, and sky
from depth to height reply,
 may Jesus Christ be praised.

6 Be this, while life is mine,
my canticle divine,
 may Jesus Christ be praised:
be this the eternal song
through ages all along,
 may Jesus Christ be praised.

19th-century German
tr. *Edward Caswall* (1814–78) altd.
based on Psalm 5: 3

463

345

Adoramus te, Domine

Jacques Berthier (1923–94)
for the Taizé Community

OSTINATO REFRAIN

(hum) A - do - ra - mus te, Do - mi - ne.

Alternative:

(hum) We a - dore you, Lord Je - sus Christ.

VERSES *(Cantor)*

1. With the an - gels and arch - an - gels:

2. With the pa - tri - archs and pro - phets:

3. With the a - pos - tles and e - van - gel - ists:

4. With all the mar - tyrs of Christ:

* Choose either part.

The refrain is sung by all as a continuous chorale, while a cantor sings the verses.

464

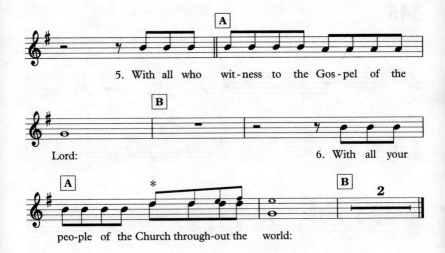

5. With all who wit-ness to the Gos-pel of the

Lord:

6. With all your

peo-ple of the Church through-out the world:

Adoramus te, Domine.

or

We adore you, Lord Jesus Christ.

1 With the angels and archangels:

2 With the patriarchs and prophets:

3 With the apostles and evangelists:

4 With all the martyrs of Christ:

5 With all who witness to the Gospel of the Lord:

6 With all your people of the Church throughout the world:

Taizé Community

346

Angel voices   85 85 843

E. G. Monk (1819–1900)

Alternative tune: 453 ARTHOG (composed for these words)

1 Angel voices, ever singing
   round thy throne of light;
angel harps, for ever ringing,
   rest not day nor night;
thousands only live to bless thee,
and confess thee,
   Lord of might.

2 Yea, we know that thou rejoicest
   o'er each work of thine;
thou didst ears and hands and voices
   for thy praise design;
craftsman's art and music's measure
for thy pleasure
   all combine.

3 In thy house, great God, we offer
   of thine own to thee;
and for thine acceptance proffer,
   all unworthily,
hearts and minds, and hands and voices,
in our choicest
   psalmody.

4 Honour, glory, might, and merit,
   thine shall ever be,
Father, Son, and Holy Spirit,
   blessèd Trinity.
Of the best that thou hast given,
earth and heaven
   render thee.

Francis Pott (1832–1909)

347

Children's praise   77 77 with Refrain   Curwen's *Tune Book* (1842)

Hark, hark, hark! while child-ren's voi-ces sing,

hark, hark, hark! while child-ren's voi-ces sing,   loud   ho-san-nas,

loud   ho-san-nas,   loud   ho-san - nas___ to   our   king.

1 Children of Jerusalem
   sang the praise of Jesus' name:
      children, too, of modern days,
      join to sing the Saviour's praise.

   Hark, hark, hark! while children's voices sing,
   hark, hark, hark! while children's voices sing,
      loud hosannas, loud hosannas,
      loud hosannas to our king.

2 We are taught to love the Lord,
   we are taught to read his word,
      we are taught the way to heaven:
      praise for all to God be given.

3 Parents, teachers, old and young,
   all unite to swell the song;
      higher let our praises rise
      till hosannas fill the skies.

John Henley (1800–1842) altd.
based on Mark 11: 1–11

348

Father, we love you

Music and words by Donna Adkins (b. 1940)

1. Fa - ther,
2. Je - sus, we love you, we wor - ship and a - dore you,
3. Spi - rit,

glo - ri - fy your name in all the earth.

Glo - ri - fy your name, glo - ri - fy your name,

glo - ri - fy your name in all the earth.

1 Father, we love you, we worship and adore you,
   glorify your name in all the earth.

   Glorify your name, glorify your name,
   glorify your name in all the earth.

2 Jesus, we love you, we worship and adore you,
   glorify your name in all the earth.

3 Spirit, we love you, we worship and adore you,
   glorify your name in all the earth.

Donna Adkins (b. 1940)

349

Richmond   86 86 (CM)   Thomas Haweis (1734–1820) adpt.

1 Fill thou my life, O Lord my God,
   in every part with praise,
that my whole being may proclaim
   thy being and thy ways.

2 Not for the lip of praise alone
   nor ev'n the praising heart
I ask, but for a life made up
   of praise in every part:

3 praise in the common things of life,
   its goings out and in;
praise in each duty and each deed,
   however small and mean.

4 Fill every part of me with praise:
   let all my being speak
of thee and of thy love, O Lord,
   poor though I be and weak.

5 So shall no part of day or night
   from sacredness be free;
but all my life, in every step,
   be fellowship with thee.

Horatius Bonar (1808–89)

350

Lucerna Laudoniae   77 77 with Refrain

David Evans (1874–1948)

REFRAIN

Christ our_ God, to thee we raise this our sac - ri - fice of praise.

SECOND TUNE

England's Lane   77 77 with Refrain

English traditional melody
adpt. Geoffrey Shaw (1879–1943)

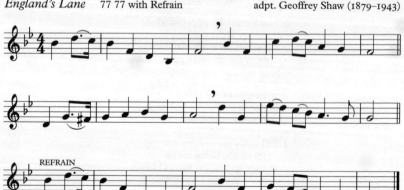

REFRAIN

Christ our_ God, to thee we raise this our sac - ri - fice of praise.

1 For the beauty of the earth,
    for the glory of the skies,
  for the love which from our birth
    over and around us lies,

        Christ our God, to thee we raise
        this our sacrifice of praise.

2 For the wonder of each hour
    of the day and of the night,
  hill and vale, and tree and flower,
    sun and moon, and stars of light,

3 For the joy of ear and eye,
    for the heart and mind's delight,
  for the mystic harmony
    linking sense to sound and sight,

4 For the joy of human love,
    brother, sister, parent, child,
  friends on earth, and friends above,
    pleasures pure and undefiled,

5 For each perfect gift of thine
    to the world so freely given,
  graces human and divine,
    flowers of earth and buds of heaven,

6 For thy Church for evermore
    lifting holy hands above,
  offering up on every shore
    her pure sacrifice of love,

Folliott Sandford Pierpoint (1835–1917) altd.

351

FIRST TUNE
Adpt. from a chorus in the oratorio *Samson* by
G. F. Handel (1685–1759)

Samson   88 88 (LM)

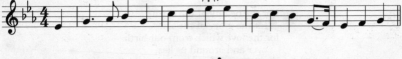

Llangollen (*Lledrod*)   88 88 (LM)   Welsh hymn melody (18th century)

1 From all that dwell below the skies
  let the Creator's praise arise;
      let the Redeemer's name be sung
      through every land, by every tongue.

2 Eternal are your mercies, Lord;
  Eternal truth attends your word:
      your praise shall sound from shore to shore,
      till suns shall rise and set no more.

Isaac Watts (1674–1748) adpt.
based on Psalm 117

352

Give thanks with a grateful heart

Words and music by Henry Smith

353

Worcester (Birstal)   88 88 (LM)   Accepted Widdup (*c.*1750–1801)

Alternative tunes: 97ii RIMINGTON   519 DUNEDIN

PRAISE AND THANKSGIVING

1 Give to our God immortal praise,
mercy and truth are all his ways;
    wonders of grace to God belong;
    repeat his mercies in your song.

2 Give to the Lord of lords renown;
the King of kings with glory crown:
    his mercies ever shall endure,
    when lords and kings are known no more.

3 He built the earth, he spread the sky,
and fixed the starry lights on high:
    wonders of grace to God belong;
    repeat his mercies in your song.

4 He fills the sun with morning light,
he bids the moon direct the night:
    his mercies ever shall endure,
    when suns and moons shall shine no more.

5 He sent his Son with power to save
from guilt, and darkness, and the grave:
    wonders of grace to God belong;
    repeat his mercies in your song.

6 Through this vain world he guides our feet,
and leads us to his heavenly seat;
    his mercies ever shall endure,
    when this vain world shall be no more.

Isaac Watts (1674–1748)
based on Psalm 136

354

Great is the Lord

Words and music by Steve McEwen

Great_____ is the Lord__ and most wor-thy of

praise, in the ci-ty of our God, the ho-ly place, the

joy of the__ whole earth.

Great_____ is the Lord, in whom we have the vic-to-ry—

__ he aids us a-gainst the e-ne-my, we

bow down on__ our knees. And

PRAISE AND THANKSGIVING

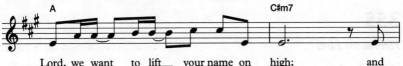

Lord, we want to lift__ your name on high; and

Lord, we want to thank you for the works you've done in our lives; and

Lord, we trust in your un - fail - ing love: for

you a - lone are God e - ter - nal, through-out earth and hea - ven a -

- bove._____

Great is the Lord and most worthy of praise,
in the city of our God, the holy place,
the joy of the whole earth.
Great is the Lord, in whom we have the victory—
he aids us against the enemy,
we bow down on our knees.
And Lord, we want to lift your name on high;
and Lord, we want to thank you for the works you've done in our lives;
and Lord, we trust in your unfailing love:
for you alone are God eternal, throughout earth and heaven above.

Steve McEwan
based on Psalm 48

477

355

Holy is the Lord

Anon.

1 Holy, holy, holy is the Lord;
 holy is the Lord God almighty!
 Holy, holy, holy is the Lord;
 holy is the Lord God almighty!
 who was, and is, and is to come:
 holy, holy, holy is the Lord!

2 Jesus, Jesus, Jesus is the Lord;
 Jesus is the Lord God almighty.
 Jesus, Jesus, Jesus is the Lord;
 Jesus is the Lord God almighty.
 who was, and is, and is to come:
 Jesus, Jesus, Jesus is the Lord!

3 Worthy, worthy, worthy is the Lord;
 worthy is the Lord God almighty!
 Worthy, worthy, worthy is the Lord;
 worthy is the Lord God almighty!
 who was, and is, and is to come:
 worthy, worthy, worthy is the Lord!

4 Glory, glory, glory to the Lord;
 glory to the Lord God almighty,
 Glory, glory, glory to the Lord;
 glory to the Lord God almighty,
 who was, and is, and is to come:
 glory, glory, glory to the Lord!

Based on Revelation 4: 8, 11

356

I will sing

Words and music by Max Dyer (1973)

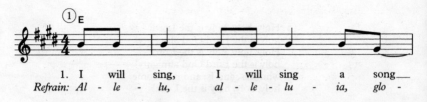

1. I will sing, I will sing a song___
Refrain: Al - le - lu, al - le - lu - ia, glo -

___ un - to the Lord, I will sing, I will sing a song
- ry to the Lord, al - le - lu, al - le - lu - ia, glo -

___ un - to the Lord, I will sing, I will sing a song
- ry to the Lord, al - le - lu, al - le - lu - ia, glo -

___ un-to the Lord, al - le - lu - ia, glo - ry to the Lord:
- ry to the Lord, al - le - lu - ia, glo - ry to the Lord.

If possible, part or all of this song should be sung unaccompanied or with guitar only.
Hand-clapping in various rhythms is effective.

Verses 3 and 5 are irregular, and are sung as follows:

3. If the Son, if the Son shall make___ you_ free, *(3 times)*

you_ shall be free___ in - deed:

5. Ev-ery knee__ shall bow and ev - ery tongue con-fess *(3 times)*

that_ Je - sus Christ_ is_ Lord:

1 I will sing, I will sing a song unto the Lord, *(3 times)*
alleluia, glory to the Lord:

> *Allelu, alleluia, glory to the Lord,*
> *allelu, alleluia, glory to the Lord,*
> *allelu, alleluia, glory to the Lord,*
> *alleluia, glory to the Lord.*

2 We will come, we will come as one before the Lord, *(3 times)*
alleluia, glory to the Lord:

3 If the Son, if the Son shall make you free, *(3 times)*
you shall be free indeed:

4 They that sow, they that sow in tears shall reap in joy, *(3 times)*
alleluia, glory to the Lord:

5 Every knee shall bow and every tongue confess *(3 times)*
that Jesus Christ is Lord:

6 In his name, in his name we have the victory. *(3 times)*
Alleluia, glory to the Lord.

Max Dyer, 1973
v. 4 based on Psalm 126: 6
v. 5 based on Philippians 2: 10–11

357

Monmouth 888 888

FIRST TUNE

Melody by Gabriel Davis (*c.*1768–1824)
in *Sacred Music* (*c.*1800)

Monmouth 888 888

SECOND TUNE

Ascendit Deus 888 888   Melody by Johann Gottfried Schicht (1753–1823)

PRAISE AND THANKSGIVING

1 I'll praise my maker while I've breath,
   and when my voice is lost in death,
      praise shall employ my nobler powers:
   my days of praise shall ne'er be past,
   while life and thought and being last,
      or immortality endures.

2 Happy are they whose hopes rely
   on Israel's God! He made the sky,
      and earth and sea, with all their train:
   his truth for ever stands secure:
   he saves the oppressed; he feeds the poor,
      and none shall find his promise vain.

3 The Lord pours eyesight on the blind;
   the Lord supports the fainting mind;
      he sends the labouring conscience peace;
   he helps the stranger in distress,
   the widow and the fatherless,
      and grants the prisoner sure release.

4 I'll praise him while he lends me breath;
   and when my voice is lost in death,
      praise shall employ my nobler powers:
   my days of praise shall ne'er be past,
   while life and thought and being last,
      or immortality endures.

Isaac Watts (1674–1748) altd.
based on Psalm 146: 1–2, 5–9

358

Gwalchmai   74 74 D

Joseph David Jones (1827–70)

Redland   74 74 D

Malcolm Archer (b. 1952)

1 King of glory, King of peace,
   I will love thee;
and, that love may never cease,
   I will move thee.
Thou hast granted my request,
   thou hast heard me;
thou didst note my working breast,
   thou hast spared me.

2 Wherefore with my utmost art
   I will sing thee,
and the cream of all my heart
   I will bring thee.
Though my sins against me cried,
   thou didst clear me,
and alone, when they replied,
   thou didst hear me.

3 Seven whole days, not one in seven,
   I will praise thee;
in my heart, though not in heaven,
   I can raise thee.
Small it is, in this poor sort,
   to enrol thee;
e'en eternity's too short
   to extol thee.

George Herbert (1593–1633)

359

Laudate Dominum

Jacques Berthier (1923–94)
for the Taizé Community

OSTINATO CHORALE

Lau - da - te Do - mi - num, Lau - da - te Do - mi - num,

om - nes gen - tes, Al - le - lu - ia. Al - le - lu - ia.

VERSES *(Cantor or Choir Sopranos)*

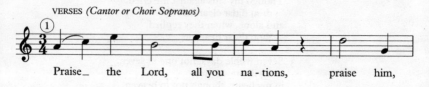

Praise_ the Lord, all you na - tions, praise him,

all you_ peo - ples. Al - le - lu - ia.

Strong is his love and mer - cy, he is faith - ful for

ev - er. Al - le - lu - ia. Al - le - lu -

The refrain is sung by all as a continuous chorale, while a cantor or group of Sopranos sings the verses.

PRAISE AND THANKSGIVING

- ia, al - le - lu - ia. Let ev - ery-thing liv - ing give

1. praise to the Lord. Al - le - **2.** praise to the Lord.

The verses of this psalm are sung by one or more solo voices over the repeating refrain 'Laudate Dominum'.

> [1]*Laudate Dominum, Laudate Dominum,
> omnes gentes, Alleluia.
> Laudate Dominum, Laudate Dominum,
> omnes gentes, Alleluia.*

1 Praise the Lord, all you nations,
   praise him, all you peoples.
      Alleluia.

2 Strong is his love and mercy,
   he is faithful for ever.
      Alleluia.

3 Alleluia, alleluia.
   Let everything living give praise to the Lord.
   (*repeat*)

The Taizé Community
based on Psalm 117

[1] Verse 1 is a translation of the Latin refrain.

360

Luckington   10 4 66 66 10 4   Basil Harwood (1859–1949)

1 *Let all the world in every corner sing*
    'My God and King!'
        The heav'ns are not too high,
        his praise may thither fly:
            the earth is not too low,
            his praises there may grow.
    Let all the world in every corner sing
    'My God and King!'

2 *Let all the world in every corner sing*
    'My God and King!'
        The Church with psalms must shout,
        no door can keep them out;
            but above all the heart
            must bear the longest part.
    Let all the world in every corner sing
    'My God and King!'

                                        George Herbert (1593–1633)

361

Nun danket   67 67 66 66

Later form of melody from Johann Crüger's
Praxis Pietatis Melica (Berlin, 1647 edn.)

Nun danket alle Gott

1 Now thank we all our God,
    with hearts and hands and voices,
who wondrous things hath done,
    in whom his world rejoices;
who, from our mother's arms
    hath blessed us on our way
with countless gifts of love,
    and still is ours today.

2 O may this bounteous God
    through all our life be near us,
with ever joyful hearts
    and blessèd peace to cheer us;
and keep us in his grace,
    and guide us when perplexed,
and free us from all ills
    in this world and the next.

3 All praise and thanks to God
    the Father now be given,
the Son, and him who reigns
    with them in highest heaven;
the one eternal God,
    whom earth and heaven adore;
for thus it was, is now,
    and shall be evermore.

Martin Rinkart (1586–1649)
tr. *Catherine Winkworth* (1829–78)

362

Thaxted   13 13 13 13 13 13   Gustav Holst (1874–1934)

1 O God beyond all praising,
     we worship you today
   and sing the love amazing
     that songs cannot repay;
   for we can only wonder
     at every gift you send,
   at blessings without number
     and mercies without end:
   we lift our hearts before you
     and wait upon your word,
   we honour and adore you,
     our great and mighty Lord.

2 Then hear, O gracious Saviour,
     accept the love we bring,
   that we who know your favour
     may serve you as our King;
   and whether our tomorrows
     be filled with good or ill,
   we'll triumph through our sorrows
     and rise to bless you still:
   to marvel at your beauty
     and glory in your ways,
   and make a joyful duty
     our sacrifice of praise!

Michael Perry (1942–96)

363

Almsgiving   888 4

John Bacchus Dykes (1823–76)

1 O Lord of heaven and earth and sea,
   to you all praise and glory be,
   who loved us from eternity
      and gave us all.

2 The golden sunshine, gentle air,
   sweet flowers and fruit, your love declare;
   when harvests ripen you are there—
      you give us all.

3 For peaceful homes and healthful days,
   for all the blessings earth displays,
   we owe you thankfulness and praise—
      you give us all.

4 Freely you gave your only Son,
   who on the cross salvation won;
   and in the life through him begun
      you give us all.

5 You sent your Spirit from above
   as wind and fire and gentle dove;
   and in his gifts of power and love
      you gave us all.

6 For souls redeemed, for sins forgiven,
   for means of grace and hopes of heaven,
   to you, O Lord, what can be given?
      You give us all.

7 We lose what on ourselves we spend;
   we have as treasure without end
   whatever, Lord, to you we lend—
      you give us all.

8 Father, from whom we all derive
   our life, our gifts, our power to give:
   O may we ever with you live;
      you give us all.

Christopher Wordsworth (1807–85)

364

Praise him on the trumpet

Words (from Psalm 150) and music
by John Kennett

Praise him on the trum - pet,_ the psal - tery and harp.

Praise him on the tim - brel and the dance,___ praise him

with stringed in - stru-ments too._____

Praise him on the loud cym-bals, praise him on the loud

cym-bals. Let ev - ery-thing that has breath praise the

Lord. Al - le - lu - ia, praise the Lord,

al - le - lu - ia, praise the Lord._ Let ev - ery-thing that has

1. breath praise the Lord._____ 2. breath praise the Lord.___

365

Lobe den Herren   14 14 47 8

Melody from Joachim Neander's
Alpha and Omega (1680)

Lobe den Herren, den mächtigen König der Ehren

1 Praise to the Lord, the Almighty, the King of creation!
O my soul, praise him, for he is thy health and salvation!
All ye who hear
now to his temple draw near,
joining in glad adoration.

2 Praise to the Lord, who o'er all things so wondrously reigneth,
shieldeth thee gently from harm, or when fainting sustaineth;
hast thou not seen
how thy heart's wishes have been
granted in what he ordaineth?

3 Praise to the Lord, who doth prosper thy work and defend thee;
surely his goodness and mercy shall daily attend thee;
ponder anew
what the Almighty can do,
who with his love doth befriend thee.

4 Praise to the Lord! O let all that is in me adore him!
All that hath life and breath, come now with praises before him!
Let the Amen
sound from his people again:
gladly for aye we adore him.

Joachim Neander (1650–80)
tr. *Catherine Winkworth* (1827–78)

366

Praise, my soul 87 87 87

Music by John Goss (1800–80)

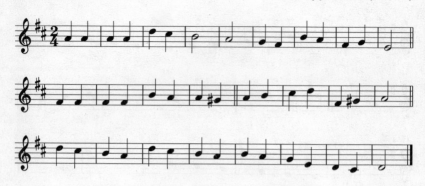

1 Praise, my soul, the King of heaven;
   to his feet thy tribute bring.
Ransomed, healed, restored, forgiven,
   who like me his praise should sing?
      Praise him! Praise him!
      Praise the everlasting King!

2 Praise him for his grace and favour
   to his people in distress;
praise him, still the same for ever,
   slow to chide and swift to bless:
      Praise him! Praise him,
      glorious in his faithfulness.

upper voices only ad lib.
3 Father-like, he tends and spares us;
   well our feeble frame he knows;
in his hands he gently bears us,
   rescues us from all our foes.
      Praise him! Praise him,
      widely as his mercy flows!

4 Angels, help us to adore him;
   ye behold him face to face;
sun and moon bow down before him,
   dwellers all in time and space.
      Praise him! Praise him!
      Praise with us the God of grace.

Henry Francis Lyte (1793–1847) altd.
based on Psalm 103

367

Praise him   10 6 10 6

Melody (source unknown) from *Child Songs* (1908)
ed. Carey Bonner (1859–1938)

God is love,   God is love.

God is love,   God is love.

The original rhythm of the last bar was:

1 Praise him, praise him, everybody praise him!
   God is love, God is love.
   Praise him, praise him, everybody praise him!
   God is love, God is love.

2 Thank him, thank him, everybody thank him!
   God is love, God is love.
   Thank him, thank him, everybody thank him!
   God is love, God is love.

3 Love him, love him, everybody love him!
   God is love, God is love.
   Love him, love him, everybody love him!
   God is love, God is love.

4 Serve him, serve him, everybody serve him!
   God is love, God is love.
   Serve him, serve him, everybody serve him!
   God is love, God is love.

Anon. (19th cent.) altd.

368

Sing of the Lord's goodness

Words and music by Ernest Sands

1. Sing of the Lord's good-ness,
2. Pow-er he has wield-ed,
3. Cour-age in our dark-ness,
4. Praise him with your sing-ing,

Fa-ther of all wis-dom, come to him and bless his
hon-our is his gar-ment, ris-en from the snares of
com-fort in our sor-row— Spi-rit of our God most
praise him with the trum-pet, praise God with the lute and

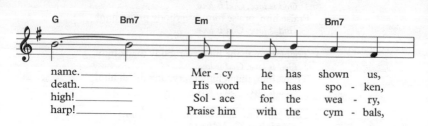

name._____ Mer-cy he has shown us,
death._____ His word he has spo-ken,
high!_____ Sol-ace for the wea-ry,
harp!_____ Praise him with the cym-bals,

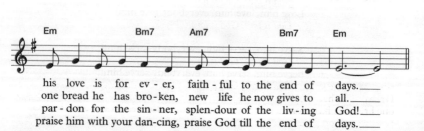

his love is for ev-er, faith-ful to the end of days.____
one bread he has bro-ken, new life he now gives to all.____
par-don for the sin-ner, splen-dour of the liv-ing God!____
praise him with your dan-cing, praise God till the end of days.____

Published by OCP Publications, 5336 NE Hassalo, Portland OR 97213, USA.

PRAISE AND THANKSGIVING

REFRAIN

Come then all you na-tions, sing of your Lord's good-ness, me-lo-dies of praise and

thanks to God; ring out the Lord's glo-ry, praise him with your mu-sic,

wor-ship him and bless his name.

1 Sing of the Lord's goodness,
Father of all wisdom,
come to him and bless his name.
Mercy he has shown us,
his love is for ever,
faithful to the end of days.

Come then all you nations,
sing of your Lord's goodness,
melodies of praise and thanks to God;
ring out the Lord's glory,
praise him with your music,
worship him and bless his name.

2 Power he has wielded,
honour is his garment,
risen from the snares of death.
His word he has spoken,
one bread he has broken,
new life he now gives to all.

3 Courage in our darkness,
comfort in our sorrow—
Spirit of our God most high!
Solace for the weary,
pardon for the sinner,
splendour of the living God!

4 Praise him with your singing,
praise him with the trumpet,
praise God with the lute and harp!
Praise him with the cymbals,
praise him with your dancing,
praise God till the end of days.

Ernest Sands

497

369

Northampton   77 77

C. J. King (1859–1934)

Alternative tune: 314 LAUDS

1 Songs of praise the angels sang,
heaven with alleluias rang,
  when creation was begun,
  when God spoke and it was done.

2 Songs of praise awoke the morn
when the Prince of Peace was born;
  songs of praise arose when he
  captive led captivity.

3 Heaven and earth must pass away,
songs of praise shall crown that day;
  God will make new heavens, new earth,
  songs of praise shall hail their birth.

4 And shall we alone be dumb
till that glorious kingdom come?
  No! The Church delights to raise
  psalms and hymns and songs of praise.

5 Saints below, with heart and voice,
still in songs of praise rejoice,
  learning here, by faith and love,
  songs of praise to sing above.

6 Borne upon their final breath,
songs of praise shall conquer death;
  then, amidst eternal joy,
  songs of praise their powers employ.

James Montgomery (1771–1854) altd.

370

Carlisle 66 86 (SM) Charles Lockhart (1745–1815)

1 Stand up, and bless the Lord,
    you people of his choice;
  stand up, and bless the Lord your God
    with heart and soul and voice.

2 Though high above all praise,
    above all blessing high,
  who would not fear his holy name,
    and praise and magnify?

3 O for the living flame
    from his own altar brought,
  to touch our lips, our minds inspire,
    and wing to heaven our thought!

4 God is our strength and song,
    and his salvation ours;
  then be his love in Christ proclaimed
    with all our ransomed powers.

5 Stand up, and bless the Lord,
    the Lord your God adore;
  stand up, and bless his glorious name
    both now and evermore.

James Montgomery (1771–1854) altd.
based on Nehemiah 9: 5

371

Les Commandemens de Dieu   98 98

Melody from *La Forme des Prières et Chants Ecclésiastiques* (Strasbourg, 1545) composed or adpt. by Louis Bourgeois (*c.*1510–*c.*1561)

For an explanation of the small notes above the stave, see the Musical Preface.
Alternative tune: 305 SPIRITUS VITAE

1 Thank you, O Lord, of earth and heaven,
    thank you for all your love has planned;
  thank you for food and daily blessings,
    gifts from your ever-gracious hand.

2 Thank you for such a great salvation,
    mercy as boundless as the sea;
  thank you for love which died to save us,
    love which gave all to set us free.

3 Thank you for means of grace and guidance,
    gifts of your Spirit, strength divine;
  thank you for word and prayer and symbol,
    food for our souls in bread and wine.

4 Thank you for that blessed hope of glory,
    great day when Christ shall come again,
  day when, in perfect love and justice,
    he in his majesty shall reign.

5 Grant us, because of all your mercies,
    lips which proclaim our thanks and praise;
  lives which, in loving glad surrender,
    serve and adore you all their days.

6 Glory to God our heavenly Father,
    glory to Jesus, God the Son,
  glory to God the Holy Spirit,
    glory to God the Three-in-One.

James E. Seddon (1915–83)
based on A General Thanksgiving (BCP)
by *Edward Reynolds* (1599–1676)

372

Wiltshire   86 86 (CM)

George T. Smart (1776–1867)
from his *Collection of Sacred Music* (1863)
(originally set to Psalm 48 in 1795)

* Alternative: minim E

1 Through all the changing scenes of life,
   in trouble and in joy,
   the praises of my God shall still
   my heart and tongue employ.

2 O magnify the Lord with me,
   with me exalt his name;
   when in distress to him I called,
   he to my rescue came.

3 The hosts of God encamp around
   the dwellings of the just;
   deliverance he affords to all
   who on his succour trust.

4 O make but trial of his love,
   experience will decide
   how blessed are they, and only they,
   who in his truth confide.

5 Fear him, ye saints, and you will then
   have nothing else to fear;
   make you his service your delight,
   your wants shall be his care.

6 To Father, Son and Holy Ghost,
   the God whom we adore,
   be glory, as it was, is now,
   and shall be evermore.

Nahum Tate (1652–1715)
and *Nicholas Brady* (1659–1726)
New Version, 1696
based on Psalm 34

373

To God be the glory 11 11 11 11 with Refrain

William Howard Doane
(1832–1915)

Praise the Lord! Praise the Lord! Let the earth hear his voice! Praise the Lord! Praise the Lord! Let the peo - ple re - joice!

This tune is often sung with dotted quaver rhythm throughout.

O come to the Fa-ther, through Je-sus the Son: and

give him the glo-ry! Great things he has done!

1 To God be the glory! Great things he has done!
So loved he the world that he gave us his Son;
who yielded his life an atonement for sin,
and opened the life-gate that all may go in.

Praise the Lord! Praise the Lord!
   Let the earth hear his voice!
Praise the Lord! Praise the Lord!
   Let the people rejoice!
O come to the Father, through Jesus the Son:
and give him the glory! Great things he has done!

2 O perfect redemption, the purchase of blood!
to every believer the promise of God;
   the vilest offender who truly believes,
   that moment from Jesus a pardon receives.

3 Great things he has taught us, great things he has done,
and great our rejoicing through Jesus the Son;
   but purer, and higher, and greater will be
   our wonder, our rapture, when Jesus we see.

Fanny J. Crosby [Frances J. van Alstyne] (1820–1915)
based on Revelation 15: 3–4

374

Contemplation   86 86 (CM)   Frederick A. Gore Ouseley (1825–89)

This tune was written for these words.

SECOND TUNE

St Fulbert   86 86 (CM)   Henry J. Gauntlett (1805–76)

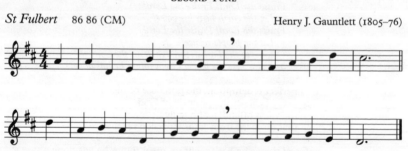

Alternative tune: 229i BELGRAVE

1 When all thy mercies, O my God,
    my rising soul surveys,
transported with the view, I'm lost ⏝
    in wonder, love, and praise.

2 When worn with sickness, oft hast thou ⏝
    with health renewed my face;
and when in sins and sorrows sunk,
    revived my soul with grace.

3 Ten thousand thousand precious gifts
    my daily thanks employ;
nor is the least a cheerful heart,
    that tastes those gifts with joy.

4 Through every period of my life
    thy goodness I'll pursue;
and after death, in distant worlds,
    the glorious theme renew.

5 When nature fails, and day and night
    divide thy works no more,
my ever-grateful heart, O Lord,
    thy mercy shall adore.

6 Through all eternity, to thee ⏝
    a joyful song I'll raise;
for O eternity's too short ⏝
    to utter all thy praise!

signed 'C' in The Spectator (9 Aug. 1712)
attrib. *Joseph Addison* (1672–1719)
based on Psalm 103

375

Count your blessings 11 11 11 11 with Refrain

Edwin Excell
(1851–1921)

REFRAIN

Count   your   bless-ings, name them   one   by   one;

count   your   bless-ings, see what   God   has   done!

Count   your   bless-ings,   name them one   by   one;

and   it   will   sur - prise you what the   Lord   has   done.

OPTIONAL INTERLUDE

1 When upon life's billows you are tempest-tossed,
when you are discouraged, thinking all is lost,
    count your many blessings, name them one by one,
    and it will surprise you what the Lord has done.

    Count your blessings, name them one by one;
    count your blessings, see what God has done!
    Count your blessings, name them one by one;
    and it will surprise you what the Lord has done.

2 Are you ever burdened with a load of care?
Does the cross seem heavy you are called to bear?
    Count your many blessings, ev'ry doubt will fly,
    and you will keep singing as the days go by.

3 When you look at others with their lands and gold,
think that Christ has promised you his wealth untold;
    count your many blessings, wealth can never buy
    your reward in heaven, nor your home on high.

4 So, amid the conflict, whether great or small,
do not be disheartened, God is over all;
    count your many blessings, angels will attend,
    help and comfort give you to your journey's end.

J. Oatman altd.

376

Darwall's 148th   66 66 44 44   John Darwall (1731–1789)

1 Ye holy angels bright,
      who wait at God's right hand,
   or through the realms of light
   fly at your Lord's command,
      assist our song,
         or else the theme
         too high doth seem
      for mortal tongue.

2 Ye blessèd souls at rest,
      who ran this earthly race,
   and now, from sin released,
   behold your Saviour's face,
      his praises sound,
         as in his sight
         with sweet delight
      ye do abound.

3 Ye saints, who toil below,
      adore your heavenly King,
   and onward as ye go
      some joyful anthem sing;
      take what he gives
         and praise him still,
         through good and ill,
      who ever lives!

4 My soul, bear thou thy part,
      triumph in God above,
   and with a well-tuned heart
      sing thou the songs of love!
      Let all thy days
         till life shall end,
         whate'er he send,
      be filled with praise.

Richard Baxter (1615–91)
v. 3 by John Hampden Gurney (1802–62)

377

You shall go out with joy

Words and music by Stuart Dauermann (b. 1944)
and Steffi Geiser Rubin

You shall go out with joy___ and be led forth with peace,

___ and the moun-tains and the hills shall break forth be -

- fore you. There'll be shouts of joy___ and the trees of the

field shall___ clap, shall clap their hands,

and the trees of the field shall clap their hands,

___ and the trees of the field shall clap their hands,

___ and the trees of the field shall clap their hands,

___ and you'll go out with joy.___

based on Isaiah 55: 12

378

St Stephen   86 86 (CM)

Melody by William Jones (1726–1800)
in *Ten Church Pieces for the Organ* (Nayland, 1789)

1 Almighty God, your word is cast
   like seed upon the ground;
O may it grow in humble hearts,
   and righteous fruits abound.

2 Let not the universal foe
   this holy seed remove;
but give it root in every heart
   to bring forth fruits of love.

3 Let not the world's deceitful cares
   the rising plant destroy;
but let it yield a hundredfold
   the fruits of peace and joy.

4 Great God, come down and on your word
   your mighty power bestow,
that all who hear the joyful sound,
   your saving grace may know.

John Cawood (1775–1852) altd.
based on Mark 4: 1–20

379

Bread of life   64 64 D   William F Sherwin (1826–88)

1 Break thou the bread of life,
    dear Lord to me,
  as thou didst break the loaves
    beside the sea;
  beyond the sacred page
    I seek thee, Lord,
  my spirit longs for thee,
    O living Word.

2 Bless thou the truth, dear Lord,
    to me, to me,
  as thou didst bless the bread
    by Galilee;
  then shall all bondage cease,
    all fetters fall,
  and I shall find my peace,
    my all in all.

Mary Artemisia Lathbury (1841–1913)

380

God has spoken

Israeli folk melody

God has spoken to his people, alleluia!
And his words are words of wisdom, alleluia!
God has spoken to his people, alleluia!
And his words are words of wisdom, alleluia!

1 Open your ears, O Christian people,
open your ears and hear good news.
Open your hearts, O royal priesthood,
God has come to you. *(twice)*

2 They who have ears to hear his message,
they who have ears, then let them hear.
They who would learn the way of wisdom,
let them hear God's word. *(twice)*

3 Israël comes to greet the Saviour,
Judah is glad to see his day.
From east and west the peoples travel,
he will show the way. *(twice)*

Willard Francis Jabusch (b. 1930)

381

Würzburg   87 87 D

Melody from *Andächtige und auserlesene
Gesänger* (Würzburg, 1705)

Alternative tune: 268, 398ii, 456, 493 HYFRYDOL

1 God has spoken—by his prophets,
    spoken his unchanging word,
  each from age to age proclaiming
    God, the one, the righteous Lord;
  in the world's despair and turmoil
    one firm anchor still holds fast:
  God is King, his throne eternal,
    God the first and God the last.

2 God has spoken—by Christ Jesus,
    Christ, the everlasting Son,
  brightness of the Father's glory,
    with the Father ever one:
  spoken by the Word incarnate,
    Life, before all time began,
  Light of light to earth descending,
    God revealed as Son of Man.

3 God is speaking—by his Spirit
    speaking to our hearts again;
  in the age-long word expounding
    God's own message, now as then.
  Through the rise and fall of nations
    one sure faith is standing fast:
  God abides, his word unchanging,
    God the first and God the last.

George W. Briggs (1875–1959)
based on Hebrews 1: 1–2

382

Dominica   66 86 (SM)

H. S. Oakeley (1830–1903)

Alternative tunes: 302ii DONCASTER   393 WINDERMERE   601, 650 SANDYS

1 Help us, O Lord, to learn
    the truths your word imparts:
  to study that your laws may be
    inscribed upon our hearts.

2 Help us, O Lord, to live
    the faith which we proclaim,
  that all our thoughts and words and deeds
    may glorify your name.

3 Help us, O Lord, to teach
    the beauty of your ways,
  that all who seek may find the Christ,
    and sing aloud his praise.

William Watkins Reid, Jnr. (b. 1923) altd.

383

Lawes' Psalm 32   66 66

Henry Lawes (1596–1662)

For the significance of the small notes above and below the staves, see the Musical Preface.

SECOND TUNE

Ibstone   66 66

Maria Tiddeman (1837–1915)

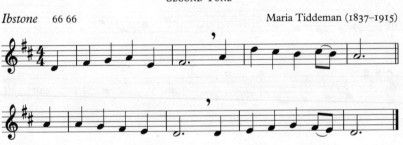

Alternative tune: 64, 343 QUAM DILECTA

1 Lord, be thy word my rule;
   in it may I rejoice:
 thy glory be my aim,
   thy holy will my choice;

2 thy promises my hope;
   thy providence my guard;
 thine arm my strong support;
   thyself my great reward.

Christopher Wordsworth (1807–85)

384

Ravenshaw 66 66

FIRST TUNE

Melody from M. Weisse's *Ein Neu Gesangbüchlen*
(Behmen, 1531) adpt. William Henry Monk (1823–89)

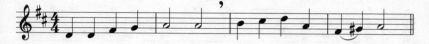

SECOND TUNE

St Cyprian 66 66

Richard Robert Chope (1830–1928)

1 Lord, thy word abideth,
  and our footsteps guideth;
    who its truth believeth,
    light and joy receiveth.

2 When our foes are near us,
  then thy word doth cheer us,
    word of consolation,
    message of salvation.

3 When the storms are o'er us,
  and dark clouds before us,
    then its light directeth,
    and our way protecteth.

4 Who can tell the pleasure,
  who recount the treasure,
    by thy word imparted
    to the simple-hearted?

5 Word of mercy, giving
  succour to the living;
    word of life, supplying
    comfort to the dying.

6 O that we, discerning
  its most holy learning,
    Lord, may love and fear thee,
    evermore be near thee!

Henry Williams Baker (1821–77)

385

Sussex 87 87

English traditional melody

1 Rise and hear! The Lord is speaking,
  as the gospel words unfold;
  we, in all our age-long seeking,
  find no firmer truth to hold.

2 Word of goodness, truth, and beauty,
  heard by simple folk and wise,
  word of freedom, word of duty,
  word of life beyond our eyes.

3 Word of God's forgiveness granted
  to the wild or guilty soul,
  word of love that works undaunted,
  changes, heals, and makes us whole.

4 Speak to us, O Lord, believing,
  as we hear, the sower sows;
  may our hearts, your word receiving,
  be the good ground where it grows.

H. C. A. Gaunt (1902–83)
based on Mark 4: 1–20

386

Skye Boat Song   86 86 (CM) with Refrain   Scottish traditional melody

Spirit of God, unseen as the wind,
    gentle as is the dove;
teach us the truth and help us believe,
    show us the Saviour's love.

1 You spoke to us long, long ago,
    gave us the written word;
we read it still, needing its truth,
    through it God's voice is heard.

2 Without your help we fail our Lord,
    we cannot live his way;
we need your power, we need your strength,
    following Christ each day.

Margaret Old (b. 1932)
based on Acts 2: 2

387

Kingley Vale   87 87 47   H. P. Allen (1869–1946)

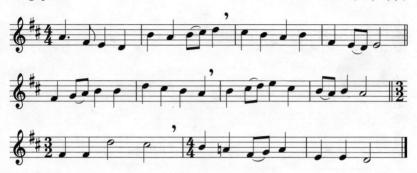

Alternative tunes: this hymn may be sung to any suitable 87 87 87 tune by repeating the penultimate line of each verse, e.g. 431i ST HELEN   431ii REGENT SQUARE

1 Thanks to God whose Word was spoken
   in the deed that made the earth;
his the voice that called a nation,
   his the fires that tried her worth.
     God has spoken:
   praise him for his open Word.

2 Thanks to God whose Word
    incarnate
  human flesh has glorified,
who by life and death and rising
grace abundant has supplied.
   God has spoken:
  praise him for his open Word.

3 Thanks to God whose Word was
    written
  in the Bible's sacred page,
record of the revelation
showing God to every age.
   God has spoken:
  praise him for his open Word.

4 Thanks to God whose Word is published
   in the tongues of every race.
See its glory undiminished
   by the change of time or place.
     God has spoken:
   praise him for his open Word.

5 Thanks to God whose Word is answered
   by the Spirit's voice within.
Here we drink of joy unmeasured,
   life redeemed from death and sin.
     God is speaking:
   praise him for his open Word.

R. T. Brooks (1918–85)

388

Diademata   66 86 D (DSM)   George J. Elvey (1816–93)

1 Word of the living God,
    lighting the souls of men,
with heavenly wisdom from on high
    inspiring lips and pen!
Their hearts athirst for truth
    with truth did God inspire;
in human words God spoke the word,
    his word a burning fire.

2 Ages and empires passed;
    the word was still the same;
still from the ancient beacon-fires
    was caught the living flame;
unchanged the truth of God,
    unchanged his righteousness,
his hand stretched out to judge the world,
    his arms outstretched to bless.

3 Still burns the fire of God,
    from age to following age;
new mornings break, new light is thrown
    upon the hallowed page;
still sounds the trumpet-call,
    still speaks the living word;
rings out, as in the ancient days,
    the cry, 'Thus saith the Lord'.

George W. Briggs (1875–1959)

389

Mit Freuden zart   87 87 887

Later form of a melody in the Bohemian
Brethren's *Kirchengesang* (Berlin, 1566)

SECOND TUNE

Luther's Hymn (Nun freut euch)
87 87 887

Chorale Melody
'Nun freut euch, lieben Christen g'mein'
by Martin Luther (1483–1546)
in Klug's *Geistliche Lieder* (Wittemberg, 1535)

Emhver som tror og bliver döbt

1 All who believe and are baptized
   shall see the Lord's salvation;
   baptized into the death of Christ,
      they are a new creation.
   Through Christ's redemption they
         shall stand
   among the glorious heavenly band
      of every tribe and nation.

2 With one accord, O God, we pray:
   grant us your Holy Spirit,
   cleanse and forgive us day by day
      through Jesus' blood and merit.
   O keep us in baptismal grace,
   until at last we take our place
      with all who life inherit.

Thomas Hansen Kingo (1634–1703)
tr. *George Alfred Taylor Rygh (1860–1943) altd.*
based on Romans 6: 3–4

390

O dass ich tausend   98 98 88   Cornelius Dretzel (1731)

Ich bin getauft auf deinem Namen

1 Baptized into your name most holy,
    O Father, Son, and Holy Ghost,
 I claim a place, though weak and lowly,
    among your seed, your chosen host.
 Buried with Christ and dead to sin,
    your Spirit now shall live within.

2 My loving Father, here you take me
    to be henceforth your child and heir;
 my faithful Saviour, now you make me
    the fruit of all your sorrows share;
 my Comforter will strengthen me
    when darkest clouds around I see.

3 My faithful God, who fails me never;
    your cov'nant surely will abide.
 O cast me not away for ever,
    should I transgress it on my side!
 Have mercy when I come defiled;
    forgive, lift up, restore your child.

4 All that I am and love most dearly,
    to you I offer now the whole.
 O let me make my vows sincerely,
    take full possession of my soul!
 Let nothing that I am or own
    serve any will but yours alone.

Johann J. Rambach (1693–1735)
tr. *Catherine Winkworth* (1827–78) altd.

391

Glenfinlas   65 65   Kenneth George Finlay (1882–1974)

1 Father, now behold us
    and this child, we pray:
in your love enfold us,
    wash our sins away.

2 Christ's eternal blessing
    for this life we claim:
faith, by ours, professing;
    signed in Jesus' Name.

3 By the Spirit tended,
    childhood grow to youth;
from all ill defended,
    full of grace and truth.

4 God of all creation,
    stoop from heaven's throne,
and by Christ's salvation
    make this child your own.

Timothy Dudley-Smith (b. 1926)

392

Christchurch   66 66 88   Charles Steggall (1826–1905)

1 Now is eternal life,
     if ris'n with Christ we stand,
in him to life reborn,
     and held within his hand;
no more we fear death's ancient dread,
in Christ arisen from the dead.

2 For God, the living God,
     stooped down to share our state;
by death destroying death,
     Christ opened wide life's gate.
He lives, who died; he reigns on high;
who lives in him shall never die.

3 Unfathomed love divine,
     reign thou within my heart;
from thee nor depth nor height,
     nor life nor death can part;
my life is hid in God with thee,
now and through all eternity.

George W. Briggs (1875–1959) altd.

393

Windermere   66 86 (SM)   Arthur Somervell (1863–1937)

Alternative tune: 601 SANDYS

1 This child from God above,
    the Father's gift divine,
  to this new life of light and love
    we give his seal and sign;

2 to bear the eternal name,
    to walk the Master's way,
  the Father's covenant to claim,
    the Spirit's will obey;

3 to take the Saviour's cross,
    in faith to hold it fast;
  and for it reckon all things loss
    as long as life shall last;

4 to tell his truth abroad,
    to tread the path he trod,
  with all who love and serve the Lord,
    the family of God.

                Timothy Dudley-Smith (b. 1926)

394

Crucis victoria   86 86 (CM)   Myles B. Foster (1851–1922)

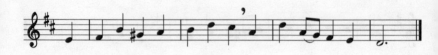

Alternative tune: 292 ST FULBERT

1 We praise you, Lord, for Jesus Christ
 who died and rose again;
he lives to break the power of sin,
 and over death to reign.

2 We praise you that this child now shares
 the freedom Christ can give,
has died to sin with Christ, and now
 with Christ is raised to live.

3 We praise you, Lord, that now this child
 is grafted to the vine,
is made a member of your house
 and bears the cross as sign.

4 We praise you, Lord, for Jesus Christ;
 he loves this child we bring:
he frees, forgives and heals us all,
 he lives and reigns as King.

Judith Beatrice O'Neill (b. 1930)

395

Surrey (Carey's)   88 88 88   Henry Carey (1687–1743)

Alternative tune: 176 SUSSEX CAROL

1 When Jesus taught by Galilee
    he called disciples to his side,
his friends and followers to be,
    to spread his gospel far and wide:
the word of life we still proclaim,
    baptizing in the threefold Name.

2 That Name declares a Father's love,
    a covenant of grace and care,
an everlasting home above,
    a family on earth to share,
beloved and precious in his sight,
    who walk as children of the light.

3 The Name of Christ becomes our own,
    our sovereign Lord and Saviour now,
to follow him, and him alone,
    whose sign is printed on our brow;
his service share, his cause defend,
    and so continue to the end.

4 We bear the Holy Spirit's Name,
    who life and truth and power imparts,
who comes, as once in wind and flame,
    to make his home within our hearts;
and daily in our lives increase
    his fruit of love, and joy and peace.

5 So in the threefold Name today
    baptized in faith from all our sins,
we turn to Christ, our Truth and Way,
    the Life in whom our life begins;
to Christ who saves and sets us free,
    his followers and friends to be.

Timothy Dudley-Smith (b. 1926)

396

FIRST TUNE

Gloucester (Farrant)   86 86 (CM)

Adapted from the anthem 'Lord, for thy tender
mercy's sake' of the school of Richard Farrant
attributed to his pupil John Hilton (*c.*1560–1608)

SECOND TUNE

Bangor   86 86 (CM)

Melody from William Tans'ur's
Harmony of Zion (1735)

Alternative tune: 435 ST FLAVIAN

1 According to thy gracious word,
   in meek humility,
 this will I do, my dying Lord,
   I will remember thee.

2 Thy body, broken for my sake,
   my bread from heaven shall be;
 thy testamental cup I take,
   and thus remember thee.

3 Gethsemane can I forget?
   or there thy conflict see,
 thine agony and bloody sweat,
   and not remember thee?

4 When to the cross I turn mine eyes,
   and rest on Calvary,
 O Lamb of God, my sacrifice,
   I must remember thee;

5 remember thee, and all thy pains,
   and all thy love to me;
 yea, while a breath, a pulse remains,
   will I remember thee.

6 And when these failing lips grow dumb,
   and mind and memory flee,
 when thou shalt in thy kingdom come,
   Jesus, remember me.

James Montgomery (1771–1854)

397

Post Green

Music by Sherrell Prebble
Words by Sherrell Prebble and Howard Clark

398

FIRST TUNE

Alleluia 87 87 D

S. S. Wesley (1810–76)

SECOND TUNE

Hyfrydol 87 87 D

Rowland Hugh Pritchard (1811–87)

1 Alleluia! sing to Jesus,
      his the sceptre, his the throne;
   alleluia! his the triumph,
      his the victory alone:
   hark the songs of holy Zion
      thunder like a mighty flood;
   Jesus, out of every nation,
      hath redeemed us by his blood.

2 Alleluia! not as orphans ⌣
      are we left in sorrow now;
   alleluia! he is near us,
      faith believes, nor questions how;
   though the cloud from sight received him
      when the forty days were o'er,
   shall our hearts forget his promise,
      'I am with you evermore'?

3 Alleluia! bread of heaven,
      thou on earth our food, our stay;
   alleluia! here the sinful ⌣
      flee to thee from day to day;
   intercessor, friend of sinners,
      earth's Redeemer, plead for me,
   where the songs of all the sinless ⌣
      sweep across the crystal sea.

*4 Alleluia! King eternal,
      thee the Lord of lords we own;
   alleluia! born of Mary,
      earth thy footstool, heaven thy throne;
   thou within the veil hast entered,
      robed in flesh our great high priest;
   here proclaimed as priest and victim
      in the eucharistic feast.

William Chatterton Dix (1837–98) altd.
based on Acts 1: 3–11

* At non-eucharistic services verse 1 may be repeated in place of verse 4

399

Folksong   98 98   English traditional melody (Somerset)

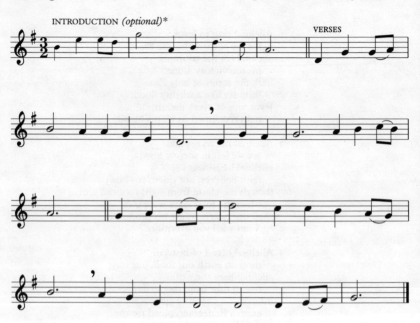

* The introduction may be played before verses 1 and 4.

The words were written for this tune.

EUCHARIST

1 An Upper Room did our Lord prepare
    for those he loved until the end:
and his disciples still gather there
    to celebrate their Risen Friend.

2 A lasting gift Jesus gave his own:
    to share his bread, his loving cup.
Whatever burdens may bow us down,
    he by his Cross shall lift us up.

3 And after Supper he washed their feet
    for service, too, is sacrament.
In him our joy shall be made complete—
    sent out to serve, as he was sent.

4 No end there is! We depart in peace,
    he loves beyond our uttermost:
in every room in our Father's house
    he will be there, as Lord and host.

F. Pratt Green (b. 1903)
based on Mark 14: 12–16, 22–24
& John 13: 3–5

400

FIRST TUNE

Song 1   10 10 10 10 10 10

Orlando Gibbons (1583–1625)

SECOND TUNE

Unde et memores   10 10 10 10 10 10

William Henry Monk (1823–89)

Alternative tune: 409 SONG 24

EUCHARIST

1 And now, O Father, mindful of the love
    that bought us, once for all, on Calvary's tree,
and having with us him that pleads above,
    we here present, we here spread forth to thee
that only offering perfect in thine eyes,
    the one true, pure, immortal sacrifice.

2 Look, Father, look on his anointed face,
    and only look on us as found in him;
look not on our misusings of thy grace,
    our prayer so languid, and our faith so dim:
for lo! between our sins and their reward
    we set the passion of thy Son our Lord.

*3 And then for those, our dearest and our best,
    by this prevailing presence we appeal;
O fold them closer to thy mercy's breast,
    O do thine utmost for their souls' true weal;
from tainting mischief keep them white and clear,
    and crown thy gifts with strength to persevere.

4 And so we come; O draw us to thy feet,
    most patient Saviour, who canst love us still;
and by this food, so aweful[1] and so sweet,
    deliver us from every touch of ill:
in thine own service make us glad and free,
    and grant us never more to part with thee.

William Bright (1824–1901)

---

[1] 'aweful' is an old spelling for 'awful' and is used here in
    the poetic sense meaning 'inspiring awe'.

401

Land of rest   86 86 (CM)   North American folk hymn melody

Alternative tune: 235ii AYRSHIRE

1 Be known to us in breaking bread,
    but do not then depart;
  Saviour, abide with us, and spread
    your table in our heart.

2 There sup with us in love divine;
    your body and your blood,
  that living bread, that heavenly wine,
    be our immortal food.

James Montgomery (1771–1854) altd.
based on Luke 24: 29–33

402

John L. Bell (b. 1949)
and Graham Maule (b. 1958)

Laying down   10 10 10 4

1 Before I take the body of my Lord,
   before I share his life in bread and wine,
   I recognise the sorry things within—
       these I lay down.

2 The words of hope I often failed to give,
   the prayers of kindness buried by my pride,
   the signs of care I argued out of sight:
       these I lay down.

3 The narrowness of vision and of mind,
   the need for other folk to serve my will,
   and every word and silence meant to hurt:
       these I lay down.

4 Of those around in whom I meet my Lord,
   I ask their pardon and I grant them mine,
   that every contradiction to Christ's peace
       might be laid down.

5 Lord Jesus Christ, companion at this feast,
   I empty now my heart and stretch my hands,
   and ask to meet you here in bread and wine
       which you lay down.

John L. Bell (b. 1949)
and *Graham Maule* (b. 1958)

403

Sanctuary   98 98

Charles John Dickinson (1822–83)

This tune is sung twice.

Bread of the world, in mercy broken,
  wine of the soul, in mercy shed,
by whom the words of life were spoken,
  and in whose death our sins are dead;
look on the heart by sorrow broken,
  look on the tears by sinners shed;
and be your feast to us the token
  that by your grace our souls are fed.

Reginald Heber (1783–1826)
based on John 6: 58

EUCHARIST

SECOND TUNE

Rendez à Dieu 98 98 D

Psalm 118 in the *Genevan Psalter* (1545)
adpt. or composed by Louis Bourgeois (*c.*1510–61)

Bread of the world, in mer - cy bro - ken,
wine of the soul, in mer - cy shed,
by whom the words of life were spo - ken,
and in whose death our sins are dead;
look on the heart by sor - row bro - ken,
look on the tears by sin - ners shed;
and be your feast to us the to - ken
that by your grace our souls are fed.

Alternative tune: 371, 413 LES COMMANDEMENS DE DIEU

404

Broken for me   Janet Lunt (b. 1954)

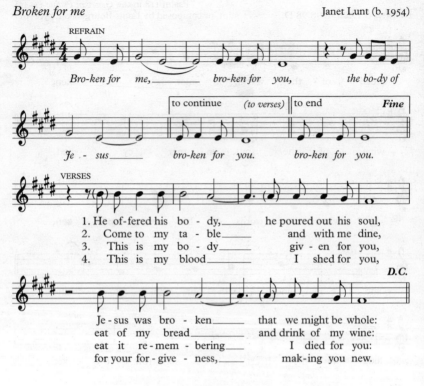

REFRAIN

Bro-ken for me,_____ bro-ken for you,   the bo-dy of

to continue (*to verses*) | *to end* | **Fine**

Je - sus_____ bro-ken for you.   bro-ken for you.

VERSES

1. He of-fered his bo - dy,____ he poured out his soul,
2. Come to my ta - ble____ and with me dine,
3. This is my bo - dy____ giv - en for you,
4. This is my blood_____ I shed for you,

D.C.

Je - sus was bro - ken____ that we might be whole:
eat of my bread____ and drink of my wine:
eat it re - mem - bering____ I died for you:
for your for - give - ness,____ mak-ing you new.

Broken for me, broken for you,
the body of Jesus broken for you.

1 He offered his body, he poured out his soul,
Jesus was broken that we might be whole:

2 Come to my table and with me dine,
eat of my bread and drink of my wine:

3 This is my body given for you,
eat it remembering I died for you:

4 This is my blood I shed for you,
for your forgiveness, making you new.

Janet Lunt (b. 1954)
based on 1 Corinthians 11: 24

405

Portland   888 4   Cyril V. Taylor (1907–91)

1 By Christ redeemed, in Christ restored,
   we keep the memory adored,
   and show the death of our dear Lord,
      until he come.

2 His body slain upon the tree,
   his life-blood, shed for us, we see;
   thus faith shall read the mystery
      until he come.

3 And thus his dark betrayal night
   with his last advent we unite
   by one blessed chain of loving rite,
      until he come:

4 until the trump of God be heard,
   until the ancient graves be stirred,
   and with the great commanding word,
      the Lord shall come.

5 O blessèd hope! With this elate,
   let not our hearts be desolate,
   but, strong in faith, in patience wait
      until he come.

George Rawson (1807–89)

406

Alleluia, dulce carmen   87 87 87

Melody from
An Essay on the Church Plain Chant (1782)
probably by Samuel Webbe the elder (1740–1816)

1 Christians, lift your hearts and voices,
    let your praises be outpoured;
  come with joy and exultation
    to the table of the Lord;
  come believing, come expectant,
    in obedience to his word.

2 See, presiding at his table,
    Jesus Christ our great high priest;
  where he summons all his people,
    none is greatest, none is least;
  graciously he bids them welcome
    to the eucharistic feast.

3 Lord, we offer in thanksgiving
    life and work for you to bless;
  yet unworthy is the offering,
    marred by pride and carelessness;
  so, Lord, pardon our transgressions,
    plant in us true holiness.

4 On the evening of his passion
    Jesus gave the wine and bread,
  so that all who love and serve him
    shall for evermore be fed.
  Taste and see the Lord is gracious,
    feed upon the living bread.

John E. Bowers (b. 1923)
based on Luke 22: 14–23

407

Soll's sein   86 86 D (DCM)

Melody from D. G. Corner's
Geistliche Nachtigal (1649)

SECOND TUNE

Jackson (Byzantium)   86 86 (CM)

Thomas Jackson (1715–81)
from *Twelve Psalm Tunes* (1780)

This tune is sung twice for each verse.

1 Christ is the heavenly food that gives
      to every famished soul
   new life and strength, new joy and hope,
      and faith to make them whole.
   We all are made for God alone,
      without him we are dead;
   no food suffices for the soul
      but Christ, the living bread.

2 Christ is the unity that binds
      in one the near and far;
   for we who share his life divine
      his living body are:
   on earth, and in the realms beyond,
      one fellowship are we;
   and at his altar we are knit
      in mystic unity.

Timothy Rees (1874–1939)

408

Farley Castle   10 10 10 10   Henry Lawes (1596–1662)

1 Come, risen Lord, and deign to be our guest;
       nay, let us be thy guests: the feast is thine;
   thyself at thine own board make manifest
       in thine own sacrament of bread and wine.

2 We meet, as in that upper room they met;
       thou at the table, blessing, yet dost stand;
   'This is my body'; so thou givest yet;
       faith still receives the cup as from thy hand.

3 One body we, one Body who partake,
       one Church united in communion blessed;
   one name we bear, one bread of life we break,
       with all thy saints on earth and saints at rest.

4 One with each other, Lord, for one in thee,
       who art one Saviour and one living Head;
   then open thou our eyes, that we may see;
       be known to us in breaking of the bread.

George W. Briggs (1875–1959)
based on Luke 22: 14–23

409

Song 24 (1)   10 10 10 10 10 10   Orlando Gibbons (1583–1625)

Alternative tune: 400ii, 438 SONG 1

1 Dear Lord, to you again our gifts we bring,
   this bread our toil, this wine our ecstasy,
   poor and imperfect though they both must be;
yet you will take a heart-free offering.
Yours is the bounty, ours the unfettered will
to make or mar, to fashion good or ill.

2 Yes, you will take and bless, and grace impart
   to make again what once your goodness gave,
   what we half crave, and half refuse to have,
a sturdier will, a more repentant heart.
You have on earth no hands, no hearts but ours;
bless them as yours, ourselves, our will, our powers.

3 Break bread, O Lord, break down our wayward wills,
   break down our prized possessions, break them down;
   let them be freely given as your own
to all who need our gifts to heal their ills.
Break this, the bread we bring, that all may share
in your one living body, everywhere.

4 Our lips receive your wine, our hands your bread;
   you give us back the selves we offered you,
   won by the cross, by Calvary made new,
a heart enriched, a life raised from the dead.
Grant us to take and guard your treasure well,
that we in you, and you in us may dwell.

H. C. A. Gaunt (1902–83)

410

Liebster Jesu   78 78 88   Johann Rudolph Ahle (1625–73)

Liebster Jesu, wir sind hier

Part 1: At the Ministry of the Word

1 Dearest Jesus, at your word
    we are gathered here to hear you;
let our hearts and minds be stirred
    now to seek and love and fear you;
by your gospel pure and holy
teach us, Lord, to love you solely.

2 All our knowledge, sense and sight
    lie in deepest darkness shrouded.
till your Spirit breaks our night
    with your beams of truth unclouded;
you alone to God can win us,
you must work all good within us.

3 Glorious Lord, yourself impart,
    light of light from God proceeding;
open lips and ears and heart,
    help us by your Spirit's leading;
hear the cry your Church now raises;
Lord, accept our prayers and praises.

Part 2: At the Ministry of the Sacrament

4 Dearest Jesus, we are here,
    at your call, your presence owning;
pleading now in holy fear
    that great sacrifice atoning:
Word incarnate, much in wonder
on this mystery deep we ponder.

5 Jesus, strong to save—the same
    yesterday, today, for ever—
make us fear and love your name,
    serving you with best endeavour:
in this life, O ne'er forsake us,
but to bliss hereafter take us.

Tobias Clausnitzer (1619–84)
Part 1 tr. *Catherine Winkworth* (1827–78) altd.
Part 2 tr. *George R. Woodward* (1848–1934) altd.
v. 5 based on Hebrews 13: 8

411

Lammas   10 10   Arthur Henry Brown (1830–1929)

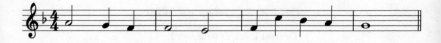

St Sechnall   10 10 10 10   Irish traditional melody

This tune covers two verses at a time.

Alternative tune: 548, 675i SONG 46

Sancti venite, Christi Corpus sumite

1 Draw near and take the body of the Lord,
  and drink by faith the blood for you outpoured.

2 Saved by his body, hallowed by his blood,
  with souls refreshed we render thanks to God.

3 Salvation's giver, Christ the only Son,
  by his dear cross and blood the victory won.

4 Offered was he for greatest and for least,
  himself the victim and himself the priest.

*5 Victims were offered by the law of old,
  which, in a type, celestial mysteries told.

*6 Lord of all life and Saviour of our race,
  Christ has restored our hope and brings us grace.

7 Therefore approach with faithful hearts sincere,
  and take the pledges of salvation here.

8 He, that in this world all his saints defends,
  gives to believers life that never ends.

9 He feeds the hungry with the bread of heaven,
  and living streams to those who thirst are given.

10 Alpha and Omega,[1] to whom shall bow ⏝
   all at the Judgment Day, is with us now.

> From the 7th-century Latin Bangor Antiphonary
> tr. *John Mason Neale* (1818–66) altd.

[1] Alpha and Omega, the first and last letters of
the Greek alphabet, are a reference to Jesus
Christ as the beginning and the ending of all
things (see Revelation 1: 8; 21: 6; 22: 13).

412

Fáilte romhat   88 87 with Refrain   Irish traditional hymn melody

REFRAIN

Glóir   don   Ath-air don
To   the   Fa - ther,

Mhac's don Naomh Sprid,   glóir   go   deo   is   mo - ladh   síor.
Son   and   Spi - rit,   praise   and   glo - ry   ev - er   be.

* The metrical variants indicated by small notes refer only to the Irish text: the English text is regular.

1 Fáilte romhat, a Rí na nAingeal,
   t'réis do ghlactha, a choirp an Rí;
   fáilte romhat, a Rí na bhflaitheas,
   fóir, a Chríost, gach duine dínn.

   *Glóir don Athair don Mhac's don
      Naomh Sprid,
   glóir go deo is moladh síor.*

2 Dia do bheatha, a Thiarna Dia,
   dia is duine thú, a Íosa Chríost;
   dia do bheatha, 'bhláth is gile,
   tusa beatha cháich go fíor.

3 Dia do bheatha, 'bhláth na lile,
   'AonMhic Mhuire, a ghin gan smál;
   dia do bheatha, 'chroí 's glaine,
   d'fhuascail sinn led' chrois led' pháis.

Aoingas Fionn Ó Dálaigh

1 *You are welcome, King of angels,
   as your body we now receive;
   you are welcome, King of heaven,
   help, O Christ, to each one bring.*

   *To the Father, Son and Spirit,
   praise and glory ever be.*

2 *You are welcome, Lord almighty,
   O Christ Jesus, both God and man;
   you are welcome, fairest flower,
   truly you are life of all.*

3 *Welcome, you the Lily's Flower,
   you of Mary the sinless Son;
   welcome, you of hearts the purest,
   who redeemed us through your cross.*

tr. *Donald A. R. Caird* (b. 1925)
and *Gary Hastings* (b. 1956)
Versified *Donald Davison* (b. 1937)

413

Les Commandemens de Dieu   98 98

Melody from *La Forme des Prières et Chants Ecclésiastiques* (Strasbourg, 1545) composed or adpt. by Louis Bourgeois (*c.*1510–*c.*1561)

For an explanation of the small notes above the stave, see the Musical Preface.

Εὐχαριστοῦμέν σοι, πάτερ ἅγιε

1 Father, we thank thee who hast planted
    thy holy name within our hearts.
  Knowledge and faith and life immortal
    Jesus thy Son to us imparts.

2 Thou, Lord, didst make all for thy pleasure,
    didst give us food for all our days,
  giving in Christ the bread eternal;
    thine is the power, be thine the praise.

3 Watch o'er thy Church, O Lord, in mercy,
    save it from evil, guard it still,
  perfect it in thy love, unite it,
    cleansed and conformed unto thy will.

4 As grain, once scattered on the hillsides,
    was in this broken bread made one,
  so from all lands thy Church be gathered
    into thy kingdom by thy Son.

Francis Bland Tucker (1895–1984) altd.
from the Greek *Didache* (*c.*110)

414

Charing   88 87   Stanley Leslie L. Russell (1901–78)

Alternative tune: 585 QUEM PASTORES

1 God whose love is all around us,
   who in Jesus sought and found us,
who to freedom new unbound us,
   keep our hearts with joy aflame.

2 For the sacramental breaking,
   for the honour of partaking,
for your life, our lives remaking,
   young and old, we praise your name.

3 From the service of this table
   lead us to a life more stable,
for our witness make us able;
   blessing on our work we claim.

4 Through our calling closely knitted,
   daily to your praise committed,
for a life of service fitted,
   let us now your love proclaim.

Fred Kaan (b. 1929)

415

Omni die   87 87

Melody from Corner's
Gesangbuch (Nuremberg, 1631)

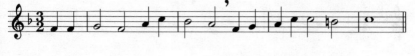

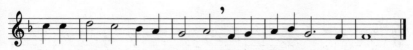

Wraysbury   87 87

Edward John Hopkins (1818–1901)

1 For the bread which you have broken,
   for the wine which you have poured,
for the words which you have spoken,
   now we give you thanks, O Lord.

2 By these pledges that you love us,
   by your gift of peace restored,
by your call to heaven above us,
   hallow all our lives, O Lord.

3 In your service, Lord, defend us,
   in our hearts keep watch and ward;
in the world to which you send us
   let your kingdom come, O Lord.

Louis Fitzgerald Benson (1855–1930)

416

Ryburn   88 88 88   Norman Cocker (1889–1953)

Alternative tune: 395 SURREY (CAREY'S)

1 Great God, your love has called us here,
   as we, by love for love were made.
   Your living likeness still we bear,
   though marred, dishonoured, disobeyed.
   We come, with all our heart and mind
   your call to hear, your love to find.

2 We come with self-inflicted pains
   of broken trust and chosen wrong,
   half-free, half-bound by inner chains,
   by social forces swept along,
   by powers and systems close confined,
   yet seeking hope for humankind.

3 Great God, in Christ you call our name
   and then receive us as your own,
   not through some merit, right or claim,
   but by your gracious love alone.
   We strain to glimpse your mercy-seat
   and find you kneeling at our feet.

4 Then take the towel, and break the bread,
   and humble us, and call us friends.
   Suffer and serve till all are fed,
   and show how grandly love intends ⌣
   to work till all creation sings,
   to fill all worlds, to crown all things.

5 Great God, in Christ you set us free
   your life to live, your joy to share.
   Give us your Spirit's liberty
   to turn from guilt and dull despair
   and offer all that faith can do
   while love is making all things new.

Brian Wren (b. 1936)

Words: © 1975, 1995 Stainer & Bell Ltd

417

St Matthew 86 86 D (DCM)

Later form of a tune in
A Supplement to the New Version (1708)
probably by William Croft (1678–1727)

Alternative tune: 468 COE FEN

1 He gave his life in selfless love,
   for sinners once he came;
   he had no stain of sin himself,
   but bore our guilt and shame:
   he took the cup of pain and death,
   his blood was freely shed;
   we see his body on the cross,
   we share the living bread.

2 He did not come to call the good
   but sinners to repent;
   it was the lame, the deaf, the blind
   for whom his life was spent:
   to heal the sick, to find the lost—
   it was for such he came,
   and round his table all may come
   to praise his holy name.

3 They heard him call his Father's name—
   then 'Finished!' was his cry;
   like them we have forsaken him
   and left him there to die:
   the sins that crucified him then
   are sins his blood has cured;
   the love that bound him to a cross
   our freedom has ensured.

4 His body broken once for us
   is glorious now above;
   the cup of blessing we receive,
   a sharing of his love:
   as in his presence we partake,
   his dying we proclaim
   until the hour of majesty
   when Jesus comes again.

Christopher Porteous (b. 1935)
v. 3 based on John 19: 30

Words: © C. Porteous/Jubilate Hymns

418

Song 24 (2) 10 10 10 10

Orlando Gibbons (1583–1625)

SECOND TUNE

St Agnes 10 10 10 10

James Langran (1835–1909) altd.

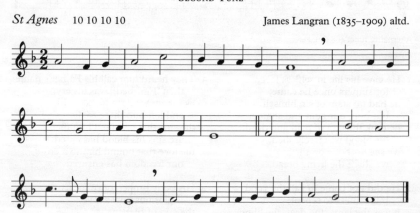

Alternative tune: 444 ANIMA CHRISTI

1 Here, O my Lord, I see thee face to face;
    here faith can touch and handle things unseen;
  here would I grasp with firmer hand thy grace;
    and all my weariness upon thee lean.

2 Here would I feed upon the bread of God;
    here drink with thee the royal wine of heaven;
  here would I lay aside each earthly load;
    here taste afresh the calm of sin forgiven.

3 I have no help but thine; nor do I need
    another arm save thine to lean upon;
  it is enough, my Lord, enough indeed;
    my strength is in thy might, thy might alone.

4 Mine is the sin, but thine the righteousness;
    mine is the guilt, but thine the cleansing blood;
  here is my robe, my refuge, and my peace—
    thy blood, thy righteousness, O Lord my God.

*5 This is the hour of banquet and of song;
    this is the heavenly table spread for me;
  here let me feast, and, feasting, still proclaim
    the hallowed hour of fellowship with thee.

Horatius Bonar (1809–89)

419

Leicester   86 86 (CM)

William Hurst (1849–1934)

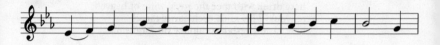

Alternative tune: 396ii BANGOR

1   I am not worthy, holy Lord,
     that you should come to me;
  but speak the word; one gracious word
     can set the sinner free.

2   I am not worthy—cold and bare
     the lodging of my soul;
  how can you stoop to enter there?
     Lord, speak and make me whole.

3   I am not worthy; yet, my God,
     shall I turn you away
  when you have giv'n your flesh and blood
     my ransom-price to pay?

4   O come! in this appointed hour
     feed me with food divine;
  and fill with all your love and power
     this worthless heart of mine.

Henry Williams Baker (1821–77) altd.
based on Matthew 8: 8

420

I am the bread of life

Words and music Suzanne Toolan (b. 1927)
based on John 6

EUCHARIST

raise____ them up, and I will raise____ them

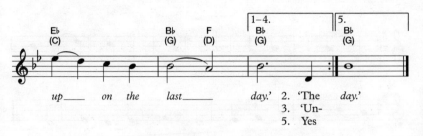

up____ on the last____ day.' 2. 'The day.'
3. 'Un-
5. Yes

1 'I am the bread of life.
They who come to me shall not hunger;
they who believe in me shall not thirst.
No-one can come to me
unless drawn by the Father.

'And I will raise them up,
and I will raise them up,
and I will raise them up on the last day.'

2 'The bread that I will give
is my flesh for the life of the world,
and they who eat of this bread,
they shall live for ever,
they shall live for ever.'

3 'Unless you eat
of the flesh of the Son of Man,
and drink of his blood,
and drink of his blood,
you shall not have life within you.'

4 'I am the Resurrection,
I am the Life.
They who believe in me,
even if they die,
they shall live for ever.'

5 Yes Lord, we believe
that you are the Christ,
the Son of God
who has come
into the world.

Suzanne Toolin (b. 1927)
based on John 6, 35–59; 11: 25–26

421

St Botolph   86 86 (CM)   Gordon Slater (1896–1979)

Alternative tunes: 401 LAND OF REST   462ii THIS ENDRIS NYGHT

1 I come with joy, a child of God,
   forgiven, loved, and free,
   the life of Jesus to recall
   in love laid down for me.

2 I come with Christians far and near
   to find, as all are fed,
   the new community of love
   in Christ's communion bread.

3 As Christ breaks bread, and bids us share,
   each proud division ends.
   The love that made us, makes us one,
   and strangers now are friends.

4 The Spirit of the risen Christ,
   unseen, but ever near,
   is in such friendship better known,
   alive among us here.

5 Together met, together bound,
   we'll go our different ways,
   and, as his people in the world,
   we'll live and speak his praise.

Brian Wren (b. 1936)

422

Halton Holgate   87 87

Later form of a melody by William Boyce (1711–79)
as given in S. S. Wesley's *European Psalmist* (1872)

1 In the quiet consecration
   of this glad communion hour,
  here we rest in you, Lord Jesus,
   taste your love and touch your power.

2 Here we learn through sacred symbol
   all your grace can be and do,
  by this wonderful indwelling—
   you in us, and we in you.

3 Christ the living bread from heaven,
   Christ whose blood is drink indeed,
  here by faith and with thanksgiving
   in our hearts on you we feed.

4 By your death for sin atoning,
   by your resurrection-life,
  hold us fast in joyful union,
   strengthen us to face the strife.

5 While afar in solemn radiance
   shines the feast that is to come—
  after conflict, heaven's glory,
   your great feast of love and home.

Constance Coote (1844–1936)

423

Slane (2)   10 11 11 12   Irish traditional melody

1 Jesus, our Master, on the night that they came
   to take you to prison, to death and to shame,
      you called to your table the friends that you knew,
      and asked them to do this in remembrance of you.

2 Still through the ages your new friends draw near,
   and know when they do so that you will be here;
      we know you are present, though just out of view,
      to meet those who gather in remembrance of you.

3 When it is over, and all gone away,
   come back to our thoughts for the rest of the day,
      and stay with us always, who met here to do
      the thing you commanded, in remembrance of you.

Michael Hewlett (1916–2000)
based on Luke 22: 14–20

424

Jesus, stand among us

Graham Kendrick (b. 1950)

O Je-sus, we love you, so we ga-ther here, join our hearts in u-ni-ty___ and take a-way___ our fear.___ our fear.___

1 Jesus, stand among us
  at the meeting of our lives,
  be our sweet agreement
  at the meeting of our eyes;

  O Jesus, we love you,
  so we gather here,
  join our hearts in unity
  and take away our fear.

2 So to you we're gathering
  out of each and every land,
  Christ the love between us
  at the joining of our hands;

*3 Jesus, stand among us
  at the breaking of the bread,
  join us as one body
  as we worship you, our head.

Graham Kendrick (b. 1950)
based on Matthew 18: 20

425

FIRST TUNE

Exultet caelum laudibus   88 88 (LM)   Plainsong melody, mode ii

A - men.

SECOND TUNE

Maryton   88 88 (LM)   Henry Percy Smith (1825–98)

Jesu, dulcedo cordium

1 Jesus, thou joy of loving hearts;
    thou fount of life, our lives sustain;
   from the best bliss that earth imparts
    we turn unfilled to thee again.

2 Thy truth unchanged hath ever stood;
    thou savest those that on thee call;
   to them that seek thee, thou art good,
    to them that find thee, all in all.

3 We taste thee, O thou living bread,
    and long to feast upon thee still;
   we drink of thee, the fountain-head,
    and thirst our souls from thee to fill.

4 Our restless spirits yearn for thee,
    where'er our changeful lot is cast;
   glad when thy gracious smile we see,
    blessed when our faith can hold thee fast.

5 O Jesus, ever with us stay,
    make all our moments calm and bright;
   chase the dark night of sin away,
    shed o'er the world thy holy light.

12th-century Latin
Attrib. *Bernard of Clairvaux* (1091–1153)
tr. *Ray Palmer* (1808–87) altd.

426

St Philip   777

William Henry Monk (1823–89)

SECOND TUNE

Tyholland   777

German trad. carol melody
'Wir wollen alle fröhlich sein'
adpt. David F. R. Wilson (1871–1957)

1 Jesus, to your table led,
now let every heart be fed,
with the true and living bread.

2 While in penitence we kneel,
your sweet presence let us feel,
all your wondrous love reveal.

3 While on your dear Cross we gaze,
mourning all our sinful ways,
turn our sadness into praise.

4 When we taste the mystic wine,
of your outpoured blood the sign,
fill our hearts with love divine.

5 Draw us to your wounded side,
whence there flowed the healing tide,
there our sins and sorrows hide.

6 From the bonds of sin release,
cold and wavering faith increase;
Lamb of God, grant us your peace.

Robert Hall Baynes (1831–95) altd.

427

Picardy 87 87 87

French traditional carol melody

Σιγησάτω πᾶσα σὰρξ βροτεία

1 Let all mortal flesh keep silence
   and with fear and trembling stand;
   ponder nothing earthly-minded,
   for with blessing in his hand
   Christ our God to earth descendeth,
   our full homage to demand.

2 King of kings, yet born of Mary,
   as of old on earth he stood,
   Lord of lords, in human vesture—
   in the body and the blood—
   he will give to all the faithful
   his own self for heavenly food.

3 Rank on rank the host of heaven
   spreads its vanguard on the way,
   as the Light of light descendeth
   from the realms of endless day,
   that the powers of hell may vanish
   as the darkness clears away.

4 At his feet the six-winged seraph;
   cherubim with sleepless eye
   veil their faces to the Presence,
   as with ceaseless voice they cry,
   alleluia, alleluia,
   alleluia, Lord most high.

From the Liturgy of St. James
tr. *Gerard Moultrie* (1829–85)
based on Isaiah 6: 1–3

428

Let us break bread

North American folk hymn melody

1 Let us break bread together, we are one;
let us break bread together, we are one:

> *We are one as we stand[1]*
> *with our face to the risen Son;*
> *O Lord, have mercy on us.*

2 Let us drink wine together, we are one;
let us drink wine together, we are one:

3 Let us praise God together, we are one;
let us praise God together, we are one:

based on a North American traditional folk hymn

[1] The word 'kneel' may be substituted
for 'stand' when appropriate.

429

Living Lord

Patrick Appleford (b. 1925)

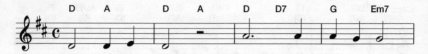

1 Lord Jesus Christ,
  you have come to us,
  you are one with us,
      Mary's son
  cleansing our souls from all their sin,
  pouring your love and goodness in;
  Jesus, our love for you we sing,
      living Lord.

2 Lord Jesus Christ,
  now and every day
  teach us how to pray,
      Son of God.
  You have commanded us to do
  this, in remembrance, Lord of you;
  into our lives your power breaks
          through,
      living Lord.

3 Lord Jesus Christ,
  you have come to us,
  born as one of us,
      Mary's son—
  led out to die on Calvary,
  risen from death to set us free;
  living Lord Jesus, help us see
      you are Lord.

4 Lord Jesus Christ,
  we would come to you,
  live our lives for you,
      Son of God;
  all your commands we know are true;
  your many gifts will make us new;
  into our lives your power breaks
          through,
      living Lord.

Patrick Appleford (b. 1925)

430

School House   11 10 11 10   Thomas Wood (1892–1950)

Alternative tune: 70 STRENGTH AND STAY

1 Lord, as the grain which once on upland acres
    scattered abroad, was gathered into one
  in this one loaf whereof we are partakers,
    in the blessed fellowship of your dear Son:

2 so may your Church dispersed through all creation,
    seed of the living bread, your holy Son,
  broken for us and humankind's salvation,
    from the world's ends be gathered into one.

George Seaver (1890–1976) altd.
adapted from the Greek Didache (*c.*110)

431

FIRST TUNE

St Helen   87 87 87   George C. Martin (1844–1916)

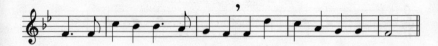

SECOND TUNE

Regent Square   87 87 87   Henry Smart (1813–79)

EUCHARIST

1 Lord, enthroned in heavenly splendour,
   first-begotten from the dead,
thou alone, our strong defender,
   liftest up thy people's head.
      Alleluia, alleluia,
   Jesus, true and living bread.

2 Here for faith's descernment praying
   lest we fail to know thee now,
here our deepest homage paying,
   we in loving reverence bow;
      alleluia, alleluia,
   thou art here, we ask not how.

3 Now though lowliest form do veil thee
   as of old in Bethlehem,
angels in thy mystery hail thee;
   we in worship join with them.
      Alleluia, alleluia,
   branch and flower of Jesse's stem.

4 Paschal Lamb, thine offering finished ⏝
   once for all when thou wast slain,
in its fulness undiminished
   shall for evermore remain,
      alleluia, alleluia,
   cleansing souls from every stain.

*5 Great High Priest of our profession,
   through the veil thou wentest in,
by thy mighty intercession
   grace and peace for us to win;
      alleluia, alleluia,
   only sacrifice for sin.

6 Life-imparting, heavenly manna,
   stricken rock with streaming side,
heaven and earth with one hosanna,
   worship thee, the Lamb that died,
      alleluia, alleluia,
   risen, ascended, glorified!

George Hugh Bourne (1840–1925)

432

Cresswell 88 97 with Refrain Anthony Milner (b. 1925)

REFRAIN

Rich-er than gold is the love of my Lord, *bet-ter than splen-dour and wealth.*

1 Love is his word, love is his way,
  feasting with friends, fasting alone,
  living and dying, rising again,
  love, only love is his way:

  Richer than gold is the love of my Lord,
  better than splendour and wealth.

2 Love is his way, love is his mark,
  sharing his last Passover feast.
  Christ at his table, host to the twelve,
  love, only love, is his mark:

3 Love is his mark, love is his sign,
  bread for our strength, wine for our joy,
  'This is my body, this is my blood'—
  love, only love, is his sign:

4 Love is his sign, love is his news,
  'Do this,' he said, 'lest you forget
  all my deep sorrow, all my dear blood'—
  love, only love, is his news:

5 Love is his news, love is his name,
  we are his own, chosen and called,
  sisters and brothers, parents and kin,
  love, only love, is his name:

6 Love is his name, love is his law,
  hear his command, all who are his:
  'Love one another, I have loved you'—
  love, only love, is his law:

7 Love is his law, love is his word:
  love of the Lord, Father and Word,
  love of the Spirit, God ever one,
  love, only love, is his word:

Luke Connaughton (1917–79)

433

Rockingham 88 88 (LM)

Adapted by Edward Miller (1731–1807)
from a melody in *A Second Supplement
to Psalmody in Miniature* (*c.*1780)

Bromley 88 88 (LM)

Jeremiah Clarke (*c.*1673–1707)

1 My God, your table here is spread,
    your cup with love still overflows;
  may we your loved ones now be fed
    as Christ his peace and mercy shows.

2 This sacred feast, which Jesus makes
    a banquet of his flesh and blood—
  how glad each one who here partakes
    that sacred drink, that heavenly food!

3 So let your table honoured be,
    a place of love for joyful guests;
  and may each soul salvation see,
    who here its sacred pledges tastes.

Philip Doddridge (1702–51) altd.

434

Nu wol Gott   88 88 (LM)

Melody from Johann Leisentritt's
Catholicum Hymnologium Germanicum
(Cologne, 1584)

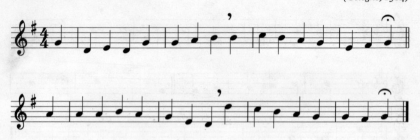

Aus Lieb' verwund'ter, Jesu mein

1 My Jesus, pierced for love of me,
  thankful enough how can I be?
    O blessèd Saviour, if I might
    thine everlasting love requite!

2 In mystic wise thou dost me feed
  with thy true flesh and blood indeed;
    most highest, yet thou stoopest low;
    what greater boon might God bestow?

3 I pray thee, hither come to me;
  revive me of thy charity:
    for thee my spirit yearneth sore;
    would I were worthy of thee more!

4 As harts, athirst upon the chase,
  speed to the water-brooks apace,
    so longeth sore mine heart for thee:
    O Jesus, Jesus, haste to me.

from the Paderborn Gesangbuch
tr. *George R. Woodward* (1849–1934)
verse 4 based on Psalm 42: 1

435

Day's *Psalter* (1562)
adpt. Richard Redhead (1820–1901)

St Flavian (Old 132nd)   86 86 (CM)

For the significance of the small notes above the stave, see the Musical Preface.

1 O God, unseen, yet ever near,
    thy presence may we feel;
  and thus, inspired with holy fear,
    before thy table kneel.

2 Here may thy faithful people know
    the blessings of thy love;
  the streams that through the desert flow,
    the manna from above.

3 We come, obedient to thy word,
    to feast on heavenly food;
  our meat, the body of the Lord,
    our drink, his precious blood.

4 Thus would we all thy words obey,
    for we, O God, are thine;
  and go rejoicing on our way,
    renewed with strength divine.

Edward Osler (1798–1863)

436

Niagara   88 88 (LM)   Robert Jackson (1840–1914)

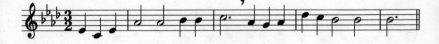

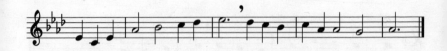

Solothurn   88 88 (LM)   Swiss traditional melody

EUCHARIST

1 Now let us from this table rise
    renewed in body, mind and soul;
with Christ we die and live again,
    his selfless love has made us whole.

2 With minds alert, upheld by grace,
    to spread the Word in speech and deed,
we follow in the steps of Christ,
    at one with all in hope and need.

3 To fill each human house with love,
    it is the sacrament of care;
the work that Christ began to do
    we humbly pledge ourselves to share.

4 Then grant us grace, Companion God,
    to choose again the pilgrim way
and help us to accept with joy
    the challenge of tomorrow's day.

Fred Kaan (b. 1929)

437

Pange lingua   87 87 87

Plainsong melody (Sarum form), mode iii

A - men.

SECOND TUNE

French *Tantum ergo* melody in
Chants Ordinaires de l'Office Divin (Paris, 1881)

Grafton   87 87 87

When this tune is sung in unison, all ♫♫ groups may be alternatively be sung ♫♫, as in the second half of the penultimate bar.

Part 1
Pange, lingua, gloriosi corporis mysterium

1 Now, my tongue, the mystery telling
  of the glorious body sing,
and the blood, all price excelling,
  which the whole world's Lord and King,
in a virgin's womb once dwelling,
  shed for this world's ransoming.

2 Given for us, and condescending
  to be born for us below,
he, with us in converse blending,
  dwelt, the seed of truth to sow;
till he closed with wondrous ending
  his most patient life of woe.

3 That last night at supper lying,
  'mid the twelve, his chosen band,
Jesus, with the law complying,
  keeps the feast its rites demand;
then, more precious food supplying,
  gives himself with his own hand.

4 Word made flesh! by word he maketh
  very bread his flesh to be,
wine his blood, which whoso taketh
  must from carnal thoughts be free:
faith alone, though sight forsaketh,
  shows true hearts the mystery.

Part 2
Tantum ergo sacramentum

5 Therefore we, before him bending,
  this great sacrament revere:
types and shadows have their ending,
  for the newer rite is here;
faith, our outward sense befriending,
  makes our inward vision clear.

6 Glory let us give and blessing
  to the Father and the Son,
honour, might, and praise addressing,
  while eternal ages run;
ever too his love confessing,
  who, from both, with both is one.

Thomas Aquinas (c.1227–74)
tr. Edward Caswall (1814–78)
and John Mason Neale (1818–66) altd.

438

Song 1   10 10 10 10 10 10   Orlando Gibbons (1583–1625)

Alternative tune: 409 SONG 24

1 O thou, who at thy eucharist didst pray
    that all thy Church might be for ever one,
   grant us at every eucharist to say
    with longing heart and soul, 'Thy will be done'.
   O may we all one bread, one body be,
   one through this sacrament of unity.

2 For all thy Church, O Lord, we intercede;
    make thou our sad divisions soon to cease;
   draw us the nearer each to each, we plead,
    by drawing all to thee, O Prince of Peace:
   thus may we all one bread, one body be,
   one through this sacrament of unity.

3 We pray thee too for wanderers from thy fold;
    O bring them back, Good Shepherd of the sheep,
   back to the faith which saints believed of old,
    back to the Church which still that faith doth keep:
   soon may we all one bread, one body be,
   one through this sacrament of unity.

4 So, Lord, at length when sacraments shall cease,
    may we be one with all thy Church above,
   one with thy saints in one unbroken peace,
    one with thy saints in one unbounded love:
   more blessèd still, in peace and love to be
   one with the Trinity in Unity.

William Henry Turton (1856–1938)

439 First Tune

Albano   86 86 (CM)   Vincent Novello (1781–1861)

Second Tune

Tallis's Ordinal   86 86 (CM)   Thomas Tallis (c.1505–1585)

1 Once, only once, and once for all,
   his precious life he gave;
   before the Cross in faith we fall,
   and own it strong to save.

2 'One offering, single and complete,'
   with lips and heart we say;
   but what he never can repeat
   he shows forth day by day.

3 For, as the priest of Aaron's line
   within the holiest stood,
   and sprinkled all the mercy-shrine
   with sacrificial blood;

4 so he, who once atonement wrought,
   our Priest of endless power,
   presents himself for those he bought
   in that dark noontide hour.

5 His manhood pleads where now it lives
   on heaven's eternal throne,
   and where in mystic rite he gives
   its presence to his own.

6 We know, when we approach thy board,
   that thou thyself art here;
   and thus we show thy death, O Lord,
   till thou again appear.

William Bright (1824–1901) altd.

440

One bread, one body

John B. Foley (b. 1939)

EUCHARIST

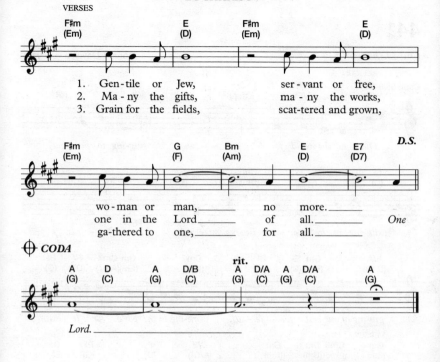

VERSES

1. Gen-tile or Jew, ser-vant or free,
2. Ma-ny the gifts, ma-ny the works,
3. Grain for the fields, scat-tered and grown,

wo-man or man,_____ no more._____
one in the Lord_____ of all._____ *One*
ga-thered to one,_____ for all._____

CODA

Lord._____

One bread, one body, one Lord of all,
one cup of blessing which we bless;
and we, though many, throughout the earth,
we are one body in this one Lord.

1 Gentile or Jew,
   servant or free,
   woman or man,
   no more.

2 Many the gifts,
   many the works,
   one in the Lord
   of all.

3 Grain for the fields,
   scattered and grown,
   gathered to one,
   for all.

John B. Foley (b. 1939)
based on 1 Corinthians 10: 16–17; 12: 4;
Galatians 3: 28; The Didache, 9

441

Out to the world

Donald Davison (b. 1937)

Out to the world for Jesus,
singing to his name, walking in his love,
living every day for Jesus,
giving of our best for Jesus,
working in the world for Jesus.

1 Round the table we meet him,
   sharing the wine and the bread;
   now we're one in his body;
   by him our souls are fed.

2 Kneeling here in his presence,
   peace and forgiveness we know;
   now he calls us to serve him
   and help his kingdom grow.

3 Round the world others gather,
   guests of their Saviour adored;
   now we're sisters and brothers—
   one family, one Lord.

Donald Davison (b. 1937)

442

Evangelists (Alles ist an Gottes segen)   887 D

Adapted from J. S. Bach's setting
of a chorale by J. Löhner (1691)
and others

1 Praise the Lord, rise up rejoicing,
  worship, thanks, devotion voicing:
      glory be to God on high!
  Christ, your cross and passion sharing,
  by this Eucharist declaring
      yours the eternal victory.

2 Scattered flock, one Shepherd sharing,
  lost and lonely, one voice hearing,
      ears are open to your word;
  by your blood new life receiving,
  in your body firm, believing,
      we are yours, and you the Lord.

3 Send us forth alert and living,
  sins forgiven, wrongs forgiving,
      in your Spirit strong and free.
  Finding love in all creation,
  bringing peace in every nation,
      may we faithful followers be.

H. C. A. Gaunt (1902–83)

443

The Ash Grove   12 11 12 11 D   Welsh traditional melody

Alternative tune: 469ii WAS LEBET, WAS SCHWEBET (sung twice for each verse)

1 Sent forth by God's blessing, our true faith confessing,
   the people of God from his table take leave.
   The supper is ended; O now be extended
   the fruits of his service in all who believe.
   The seed of his teaching, our hungry souls reaching,
   shall blossom in action for God and for all.
   His grace shall incite us, his love shall unite us
   to further God's kingdom and answer his call.

2 With praise and thanksgiving to God ever living,
   the tasks of our everyday life we will face.
   Our faith ever sharing, in love ever caring,
   we claim as our neighbours the whole human race.
   One bread that has fed us, one light that has led us,
   unite us as one in his life that we share.
   Then may all the living, with praise and thanksgiving,
   give honour to Christ and his name that we bear.

Omer Westendorf (b. 1916) altd.

444

Anima Christi   10 10 10 10   William Maher (1823–77)

Anima Christi

1 Soul of my Saviour, sanctify my breast,
  Body of Christ, be thou my saving guest,
    Blood of my Saviour, bathe me in thy tide,
    wash me with water flowing from thy side.

2 Strength and protection may thy passion be,
  O blessèd Jesu, hear and answer me;
    deep in thy wounds, Lord, hide and shelter me,
    so shall I never, never part from thee.

3 Guard and defend me from the foe malign,
  in death's dread moments make me only thine;
    call me, and bid me come to thee on high,
    where I may praise thee with thy saints for ay.

14th-century Latin
tr. Anon.

445

Schmücke dich   88 88 D

Melody by Johann Crüger (1598–1662)
in his *Geistliche Kirchen-Melodien* (Berlin, 1649)

EUCHARIST

Schmücke dich

1 Soul, array thyself with gladness,
   leave the gloomy haunts of sadness;
       come into the daylight's splendour,
       there with joy thy praises render
   unto him whose grace unbounded
   hath this wondrous banquet founded:
       high o'er all the heavens he reigneth,
       yet to dwell with thee he deigneth.

*2 Now I sink before thee lowly,
    filled with joy most deep and holy,
        as with trembling awe and wonder
        on thy mighty works I ponder:
    how, by mystery surrounded,
    depths no mortal e'er hath sounded,
        none may dare to pierce unbidden
        secrets that with thee are hidden.

*3 Sun, who all my life dost brighten,
    Light, who dost my soul enlighten;
        Joy, the best my heart e'er knoweth,
        Fount, whence all my being floweth,
    at thy feet I cry, my Maker—
    let me be a fit partaker
        of this blessèd food from heaven,
        for our good, thy glory, given.

4 Jesus, Bread of life, I pray thee,
   let me gladly here obey thee;
       never to my hurt invited,
       be thy love with love requited:
   from this banquet let me measure,
   Lord, how vast and deep its treasure;
       through the gifts thou here dost give me,
       as thy guest in heaven receive me.

after *Johann Franck* (1618–77)
tr. *Catherine Winkworth* (1827–78) altd.

446

FIRST TUNE

Ach Gott und Herr   87 87

Melody from Christoph Peter's
Andachts Zymbeln (Freiburg, 1655)
adpt. J. S. Bach (1685–1750)

SECOND TUNE

Jacob's Well   87 87 (Iambic)

Barry Rose (b. 1934)

Alternative tune: 20ii ST COLUMBA

بﻨﻴﻠﺍ ﻏﻦٍ ﺇﻧﻴﺍ ﺫﻫﺸﺖ

Hayyēl Māran 'īdhē daphshaṭ

1 Strengthen for service, Lord, the hands
   that holy things have taken;
   let ears that now have heard thy songs
   to clamour never waken.

2 Lord, may the tongues which 'Holy' sang
   keep free from all deceiving;
   the eyes which saw thy love be bright,
   thy blessèd hope perceiving.

3 The feet that tread thy holy courts
   from light do thou not banish;
   the bodies by thy Body fed
   with thy new life replenish.

from The Liturgy of Malabar
Attrib. *Ephraim the Syrian* (*c.*306–73)
tr. *Charles William Humphries* (1840–1921)
and *Percy Dearmer* (1867–1936) altd.

447

Winton   10 10 10 10   George Dyson (1883–1964)

Alternative tune: 712 WOODLANDS

1 The Lord is here—he finds us as we seek
 to learn his will and follow in his way.
He gives himself just as he gave his Word,
 the God of promise greets us every day.

2 The Lord is here—he meets us as we share—
 this is the life he calls us now to live;
in offered peace, in shared-out bread and wine,
 our God is gift and calls us now to give.

3 The Lord is here—inviting us to go
 and share the news with people everywhere.
He waits outside in need and help alike,
 the Spirit moves through deed as well as prayer.

4 So let us go, intent to seek and find,
 living this hope that God is always near.
Sharing and trusting, let us live his love,
 that all the world may say—'The Lord is here'.

Christopher Ellis (b. 1949)

448

The feast is ready

Words and music by Graham Kendrick (b. 1950)

1. The trum-pets sound, the an - gels sing,
2. Ta - bles are la - den with good things:
3. The hun - gry heart he sa - tis - fies,

the feast is rea - dy to__ be - gin; the gates of
O taste the peace and joy__ he brings! He'll fill you
of - fers the poor his pa - ra - dise. Now hear, all

repeat 1st time only

heaven are o - pen wide, and Je - sus wel-comes you_ in - side.
up with love di - vine, he'll turn your wa - ter in - to wine.
heaven and earth ap-plaud the a - maz - ing good-ness of__ the Lord!

Sing with thank-ful-ness songs of pure de-light, come and re - vel in

hea-ven's love and light; take your place at the ta - ble of__ the King—

EUCHARIST

the feast is rea-dy to__ be-gin, the feast is rea-dy to__ be-gin.

1 The trumpets sound, the angels sing,
   the feast is ready to begin;
      the gates of heaven are open wide,
      and Jesus welcomes you inside.

   Sing with thankfulness songs of pure delight,
   come and revel in heaven's love and light;
      take your place at the table of the King—
      the feast is ready to begin,
      the feast is ready to begin.

2 Tables are laden with good things:
   O taste the peace and joy he brings!
   He'll fill you up with love divine,
   he'll turn your water into wine.

3 The hungry heart he satisfies,
   offers the poor his paradise.
      Now hear, all heaven and earth applaud
      the amazing goodness of the Lord!

Graham Kendrick (b. 1950)

449

FIRST TUNE

Adoro te devote   10 10 10 10

Plainsong melody, mode v
as given in *Paris Processional* (1697)

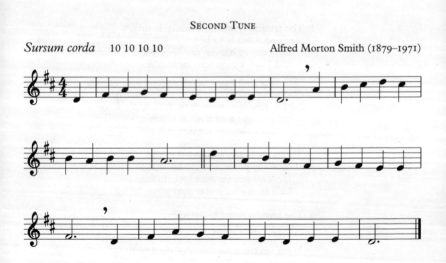

SECOND TUNE

Sursum corda   10 10 10 10

Alfred Morton Smith (1879–1971)

Adoro te devote, latens Deitas

1 Thee we adore, O hidden Saviour, thee,
  who in thy sacrament dost deign to be;
    both flesh and spirit at thy presence fail,
    yet here thy presence we devoutly hail.

2 O blessed memorial of our dying Lord,
  who living bread to all doth here afford!
    O may our souls for ever feed on thee,
    and thou, O Christ, for ever precious be.

3 Fountain of goodness, Jesus, Lord and God,
  cleanse us, unclean, with thy most cleansing blood;
    increase our faith and love, that we may know
    the hope and peace which from thy presence flow.

4 O Christ, whom now beneath a veil we see,
  may what we thirst for soon our portion be,
    to gaze on thee unveiled, and see thy face,
    the vision of thy glory and thy grace.

Thomas Aquinas (c.1225–74)
tr. James R. Woodford (1820–85) altd.

450

Ely   88 88 (LM)   Thomas Turton (1780–1864)

Alternative tune: 497 BROCKHAM

1 Upon thy table, Lord, we place
    these symbols of our work and thine,
life's food won only by thy grace,
    who givest all, the bread and wine.

2 Within these simple things there lie
    the height and depth of human life,
the thoughts we own, our tears and toil,
    our hopes, our fears, our joy and strife.

3 The faith that sows, the care that tends,
    the ceaseless work of farm and field,
have wrought these elemental things
    that they in turn our wealth should yield.

4 Accept them, Lord; from thee they come;
    we but surrender to thy hand
these gifts of thine to higher use
    obedient to thine own command.

5 All life is thine, O give us faith
    to know thee in the broken bread,
and drink with thee the wine of life,
    thou Lord supreme of quick and dead.

6 To thee we come, refresh us, thou,
    with food from thy most holy board,
until the kingdoms of this world
    become the kingdoms of the Lord.

7 And let this feast, so simply spread,
    assure us that we all are one
whate'er our colour or our race
    within the kingdom of God's Son.

Maurice F. C. Willson (1884–1944)

451

King's Lynn   76 76 D   English traditional melody

Alternative tune: 528 AURELIA

1 We come as guests invited
    when Jesus bids us dine,
  his friends on earth united
    to share the bread and wine;
  the bread of life is broken,
    the wine is freely poured
  for us, in solemn token
    of Christ our dying Lord.

2 We eat and drink, receiving
    from Christ the grace we need,
  and in our hearts believing
    on him by faith we feed;
  with wonder and thanksgiving
    for love that knows no end,
  we find in Jesus living
    our ever-present friend.

3 One bread is ours for sharing,
    one single fruitful vine,
  our fellowship declaring
    renewed in bread and wine:
  renewed, sustained and given
    by token, sign and word,
  the pledge and seal of heaven,
    the love of Christ our Lord.

Timothy Dudley-Smith (b. 1926)

452

Gift of finest wheat   86 86 (CM) with Refrain   Robert E. Kreutz (b. 1922)

You satisfy the hungry heart with gift of finest wheat; come, give to us, O saving Lord, the bread of life to eat. 1. As when the shepherd calls his sheep, they know and heed his voice; so when you call your family, Lord, we follow and rejoice.

You satisfy the hungry heart
with gift of finest wheat;
come, give to us, O saving Lord,
the bread of life to eat.

1 As when the shepherd calls his sheep,
   they know and heed his voice;
so when you call your family, Lord,
   we follow and rejoice.

2 With joyful lips we sing to you
   our praise and gratitude,
that you should count us worthy, Lord,
   to share this heav'nly food.

3 Is not the cup we bless and share
   the blood of Christ outpoured?
Do not one cup, one loaf declare
   our oneness in the Lord?

4 The myst'ry of your presence, Lord,
   no mortal tongue can tell:
whom all the world cannot contain
   comes in our hearts to dwell.

5 You give yourself to us, O Lord;
   then selfless let us be,
to serve each other in your name
   in truth and charity.

Omer Westendorf (b. 1916)

453

Arthog   85 85 843   George Thalben-Ball (1896–1987)

Alternative tune: 346 ANGEL VOICES

1 Come to us, creative Spirit,
   in our Father's house;
  every human talent hallow,
   hidden skills arouse,
  that within your earthly temple,
  wise and simple‿
   may rejoice.

2 Poet, painter, music-maker,
   all your treasures bring;
  craftsman, actor, graceful dancer,
   make your offering;
  join your hands in celebration:
  let creation‿
   shout and sing!

3 Word from God eternal springing
   fill our minds, we pray;
  and in all artistic vision
   give integrity:
  may the flame within us burning
  kindle yearning‿
   day by day.

4 In all places and forever
   glory be expressed
  to the Son, with God the Father
   and the Spirit blessed:
  in our worship and our living
  keep us striving‿
   for the best.

David Mowbray (b. 1938)

454

Duke Street   88 88 (LM)

Melody from H. Boyds' *Psalm and Hymn Tunes* (1793)
later attrib. John L. Hatton (d. 1793)

1 Forth in the peace of Christ we go;
   Christ to the world with joy we bring;
 Christ in our minds, Christ on our lips,
   Christ in our hearts, the world's true King.

2 King of our hearts, Christ makes us kings;
   kingship with him his servants gain;
 with Christ, the Servant-Lord of all,
   Christ's world we serve to share Christ's reign.

3 Priests of the world, Christ sends us forth
   this world of time to consecrate,
 our world of sin by grace to heal,
   Christ's world in Christ to re-create.

4 Prophets of Christ, we hear his word:
   he claims our minds, to search his ways,
 he claims our lips, to speak his truth,
   he claims our hearts, to sing his praise.

5 We are his Church, he makes us one:
   here is one hearth for all to find,
 here is one flock, one Shepherd-King,
   here is one faith, one heart, one mind.

James Quinn (b. 1919)

455

Magda   11 10 10 10   R. Vaughan Williams (1872–1958)

Alternative tune: 712 WOODLANDS (omitting slur in bar 3, for vv. 1–4)

1 Go forth for God; go forth to the world in peace;
   be of good courage, armed with heavenly grace,
 in God's good Spirit daily to increase,
   till in his kingdom we behold his face.

2 Go forth for God; go forth to the world in strength;
   hold fast the good, be urgent for the right,
 render to no one evil; Christ at length
   shall overcome all darkness with his light.

3 Go forth for God; go forth to the world in love;
   strengthen the faint, give courage to the weak,
 help the afflicted; richly from above
   his love supplies the grace and power we seek.

4 Go forth for God; go forth to the world in joy,
   to serve God's people every day and hour,
 and serving Christ, our every gift employ,
   rejoicing in the Holy Spirit's power.

5 Sing praise to him who brought us on our way,
   sing praise to him who bought us with his blood,
 sing praise to him who sanctifies each day,
   sing praise to him who reigns one Lord and God.

J. R. Peacey (1896–1971)
based on a Confirmation Blessing

456

Hyfrydol   87 87 D   Rowland Hugh Pritchard (1811–87)

with___ the   Spi - rit's   gifts___ em - power_____ us

for   the   work___ of   mi - nis - try.

Alternative tune: 527i EVERTON

1 Lord, you give the great commission:
    'Heal the sick and preach the word'.
  Lest the Church neglect its mission
    and the gospel go unheard,
  help us witness to your purpose
    with renewed integrity;
  with the Spirit's gifts empower us
    for the work of ministry.

2 Lord, you call us to your service:
    'In my name baptize and teach'.
  That the world may trust your promise,
    life abundant meant for each,
  give us all new fervour, draw us
    closer in community;
  with the Spirit's gifts empower us
    for the work of ministry.

3 Lord, you make the common holy:
    'This my body, this my blood'.
  Let us all, for earth's true glory
    daily lift life heavenward,
  asking that the world around us
    share your children's liberty;
  with the Spirit's gifts empower us
    for the work of ministry.

4 Lord, you show us love's true measure:
    'Father, what they do, forgive'.
  Yet we hoard as private treasure
    all that you so freely give.
  May your care and mercy lead us
    to a just society;
  with the Spirit's gifts empower us
    for the work of ministry.

5 Lord, you bless with words assuring:
    'I am with you to the end'.
  Faith and hope and love restoring,
    may we serve as you intend,
  and, amid the cares that claim us,
    hold in mind eternity;
  with the Spirit's gifts empower us
    for the work of ministry.

Jeffery Rowthorn (b. 1934)

457

Warrington   88 88 (LM)   Ralph Harrison (1748–1810)

1 Pour out thy Spirit from on high,
     Lord, thine ordainèd servants bless;
  graces and gifts to each supply,
     and clothe thy priests with righteousness.

2 Within thy temple when they stand,
     to teach the truth as taught by thee,
  Saviour, like stars in thy right hand,
     let all thy Church's pastors be.

3 Wisdom and zeal and faith impart,
     firmness and meekness, from above,
  to bear thy people on their heart,
     and love the souls whom thou dost love;

4 to watch and pray and never faint,
     by day and night their guard to keep,
  to warn the sinner, cheer the saint,
     to feed thy lambs and tend thy sheep.

5 Then, when their work is finished here,
     in humble hope their charge resign;
  when the chief Shepherd shall appear,
     may they with crowns of glory shine.

James Montgomery (1771–1854)

458

Engelberg   10 10 10 with Alleluia   Charles Villiers Stanford (1852–1924)

Al - le - lu - ia!___

1 When, in our music, God is glorified,
   and adoration leaves no room for pride,
   it is as though the whole creation cried:
      Alleluia!

2 How often, making music, we have found
   a new dimension in the world of sound,
   as worship moved us to a more profound
      Alleluia!

3 So has the Church, in liturgy and song,
   in faith and love, through centuries of wrong,
   borne witness to the truth in every tongue:
      Alleluia!

4 And did not Jesus sing a psalm that night
   when utmost evil strove against the Light?
   Then let us sing, for whom he won the fight:
      Alleluia!

5 Let every instrument be tuned for praise!
   Let all rejoice who have a voice to raise!
   And may God give us faith to sing always:
      Alleluia!

                                    F. Pratt Green (b. 1903)

459

Sine nomine   10 10 10 with Alleluias   R. Vaughan Williams (1872–1958)

1. For all the saints, who from their la-bours rest, who
2. Thou wast their rock, their fort-ress, and their might;
3. O may thy sol - diers, faith-ful, true and bold,
7. But lo! there breaks a yet more glo-rious day; the
8. From earth's wide bounds, from o - cean's far-thest coast, through

thee___ by faith be - fore the world con - fessed, thy
thou, Lord, their cap - tain in the well-fought fight;
fight as the saints who no - bly fought of old, and
saints___ tri - um - phant rise in bright ar - ray; the
gates___ of pearl streams in the count-less host,

Name, O Je - su, be for ev - er___ blessed.
thou, in the dark - ness, still their one_ true Light.
win, with them, the vic-tor's crown of___ gold. *Al* -
King of glo - ry pass - es on_ his_ way.
sing - ing to Fa - ther, Son and Ho - ly___ Ghost

- le - lu - ia! *Al* - le - lu - ia!

4. O blest com - mu - nion, fel - low-ship di - vine!
5. And when the strife is fierce, the war-fare long,
6. The gold - en even - ing bright-ens in the west;

We fee - bly strug - gle, they in glo - ry shine; yet
steals on the ear the dis - tant tri - umph - song, and
soon, soon to faith - ful war-riors comes their rest;___

Alternative tune: 458 ENGELBERG (also written for these words)

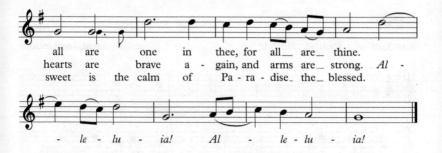

all are one in thee, for all__ are__ thine.
hearts are brave a - gain, and arms are__ strong. *Al* -
sweet is the calm of Pa - ra - dise__ the__ blessed.

- *le* - *lu* - *ia!* *Al* - *le* - *lu* - *ia!*

1 For all the saints, who from their labours rest,
who thee by faith before the world confessed,
thy Name, O Jesu, be for ever blessed.
Alleluia!

2 Thou wast their rock, their fortress, and their might;
thou, Lord, their captain in the well-fought fight;
thou, in the darkness, still their one true Light.
Alleluia!

3 O may thy soldiers, faithful, true and bold,
fight as the saints who nobly fought of old,
and win, with them, the victor's crown of gold.
Alleluia!

4 O blest communion, fellowship divine!
We feebly struggle, they in glory shine;
yet all are one in thee, for all are thine.
Alleluia!

5 And when the strife is fierce, the warfare long,
steals on the ear the distant triumph-song,
and hearts are brave again, and arms are strong.
Alleluia!

6 The golden evening brightens in the west;
soon, soon to faithful warriors comes their rest;
sweet is the calm of Paradise the blessed.
Alleluia!

7 But lo! there breaks a yet more glorious day:
the saints triumphant rise in bright array;
the King of glory passes on his way.
Alleluia!

8 From earth's wide bounds, from ocean's farthest coast,
through gates of pearl streams in the countless host,
singing to Father, Son and Holy Ghost
Alleluia!

W. Walsham How (1823–97)

609

460

The Star (An Réalt)   76 76 D   Irish traditional melody

Alternative tunes: 125, 204 CRUGER   522i CLONMEL   706i OFFERTORIUM

Composite hymn for a Saint's day

*The first and last stanzas should always be used, and the special stanza
of the day should be used as the second stanza.*

1   For all your saints in glory, for all your saints at rest,
    to you, our Lord and Saviour, all praises be addressed;
       apostles, martyrs, prophets, who served you in their day,
       have left us their example of following your way.

THE CONVERSION OF ST. PAUL—JANUARY 25

2a When travelling to Damascus, Paul heard your voice with awe,
    the dazzling blaze of glory the persecutor saw.
       The light of his conversion, the brightening Spirit's ray,
       brings hope to us in darkness and blesses us today.

ST. BRIGID—FEBRUARY I

2b Lord, for your servant Brigid, a woman good and true,
    we offer thanks and glory and joyful praise to you.
       Your Church's life she strengthened, and founded in Kildare
       a place of truth and learning, of holiness and prayer.

THE COMMUNION OF SAINTS

ST. PATRICK—MARCH 17

2c To Ireland came Saint Patrick, your called and chosen one;
he taught of God, the Father, the Spirit and the Son.
    He led the Irish people from darkness into light,
    and showed them how to trust you in all your power and might.

ST. MARK—APRIL 25

2d For Mark who told your story, we offer thanks and praise;
the news of our redemption still speaks through all our days;
    it comforts us in sadness, in weakness makes us strong,
    for this your holy gospel we sing our grateful song.

SS. PHILIP & JAMES—MAY 1

2e All praise for your apostles, for James and Philip too,
whose lives inspired their people to serve their Lord anew.
    They saw you as their leader—the Way, the Truth, the Life—
    who guards us in temptation and strengthens us in strife.

ST. MATTHIAS—MAY 14

2f Today for Saint Matthias we praise you and rejoice,
for in the place of Judas did he become your choice.
    Your Church from false disciples, we pray you, Lord, defend,
    and, by your parting promise, be with us to the end.

ST. COLUMBA—JUNE 9

2g Your chosen priest, Columba, sailed from his native land,
and reached the shores of Scotland with his companion band;
    he preached the saving gospel to those who never knew
    your love and your compassion, your power to make lives new.

ST. BARNABAS—JUNE 11

2h The 'Son of Consolation' was Barnabas by fame,
his loving care and mercy brought honour to your name.
    Grant us his sense of caring, and help us all to give
    encouragement to neighbours that they may fully live.

THE BIRTH OF ST. JOHN THE BAPTIST—JUNE 24

2i We praise you for the Baptist, Forerunner of the Word—
'Make straight in preparation a highway for the Lord'.
    Of prophets last and greatest, he urged us to repent—
    'Be ready for God's kingdom and him whom God will send'.

ST. PETER—JUNE 29

2j We praise you, Lord, for Peter, the eager and the bold;
   three times though he had failed you, you charged him feed your fold.
   He recognised your kingship, proclaimed 'You are the Christ';
   he overcame his weakness, his faith in you sufficed.

ST. THOMAS—JULY 3

2k Your lonely servant, Thomas, had doubts and could not prove ⌣
   that you yourself had risen, the perfect proof of love.
   On all who doubt your presence, grant them your peace, good Lord,
   and give them faith to know you and own you 'Lord and God'.

ST. MARY MAGDALENE—JULY 22

2l Dear Mary of Magdala, her sins were washed away
   when on your feet, Lord Jesus, her tears and ointment lay.
   She who on black Good Friday stood stricken at your pain,
   amazed, on Easter morning, beheld you risen again.

ST. JAMES—JULY 25

2m The fisherman apostle was slain by Herod's sword;
   he drank your cup of suffering and so fulfilled your word.
   Like James may we be loyal and serve you to the end,
   and trust in you, Lord Jesus, our Saviour and our friend.

ST. BARTHOLOMEW—AUGUST 24

2n Beneath the shading fig-tree Bartholomew you knew,
   and saw him, Lord, as guileless, as one to follow you.
   Like him may we now follow in every word and deed,
   and serve you in obedience, and from our sins be freed.

THE BIRTH OF THE BLESSED VIRGIN MARY—SEPTEMBER 8

2o We celebrate the birthday of Mary, chosen one
   to be the virgin mother of God's incarnate Son.
   She loved you and she raised you as God's great plan unfurled,
   then saw you die on Calv'ry as Saviour of the world.

ST. MATTHEW—SEPTEMBER 21

2p Praise, Lord, for him whose gospel your human life declared,
   who, worldly gains forsaking, your path of suffering shared.
   From all false love of riches, like Matthew, Lord, we pray
   that we may be delivered, and follow you today.

ST. LUKE—OCTOBER 18

2q For Luke, beloved physician, all praise, whose gospel shows ⌣
the healer of the nations, the sharer of our woes.
> Your healing love, dear Saviour, on troubled lives now pour,
> and with your Spirit's unction anoint us evermore.

SS. SIMON & JUDE—OCTOBER 28

2r Praise, Lord, for your apostles, who sealed their faith today:
one love, one zeal impelled them to tread the sacred way.
> May we, like Jude and Simon, our faith in you maintain,
> and, bound in love, one fam'ly, at length your rest attain.

ST. ANDREW—NOVEMBER 30

2s Lord, your disciple, Andrew, was first to welcome you,
and first to lead his brother for faith and life anew.
> With hearts for you made ready, may we throughout the year
> be first to witness always to your own Advent here.

ST. STEPHEN—DECEMBER 26

2t For Stephen, your first martyr, your name shall be adored;
he suffered persecution for trusting in his Lord;
> he prayed for those who killed him, when by them he was stoned,
> and asked for their forgiveness from you, the Lord enthroned.

ST. JOHN THE EVANGELIST—DECEMBER 27

2u Lord, your beloved disciple a faithful record bore,
that we might be believers, the 'Word made flesh' adore,
> that we might know you, Jesus, the Son of God by name,
> and through that name have true life, and glory in the same.

THE HOLY INNOCENTS—DECEMBER 28

2v Praise, Lord, for infant martyrs, who with your tender love
you called from earthly living to share your rest above.
> O Rachel, cease your weeping, they rest from pains and cares:
> Lord, grant us hearts as innocent, and crowns as bright as theirs.

————————

3 All praise to God the Father, all praise to God the Son,
and God the Holy Spirit, eternal Three in One;
> till all the ransomed number fall down before the throne,
> and honour, power, and glory ascribe to God alone.

Edward F. Darling (b. 1933)
v. 2l *Edith Newman-Devlin* (b. 1926)
based on a hymn by *Horatio Bolton Nelson* (1823–1913)
in the Sarum Hymnal (1868)

461

FIRST TUNE

Carlisle   66 86 (SM)   Charles Lockhart (1745–1815)

SECOND TUNE

Mount Ephraim   66 86 (SM)   Benjamin Milgrove (1731–1810)

1 For all thy saints, O Lord,
   who strove in thee to live,
who followed thee, obeyed, adored,
   our grateful hymn receive.

2 For all thy saints, O Lord,
   accept our thankful cry,
who counted thee their great reward,
   and strove in thee to die.

3 They all, in life and death,
   with thee their Lord in view,
learned from thy Holy Spirit's breath
   to suffer and to do.

4 Thine earthly members fit
   to join thy saints above,
in one communion ever knit,
   one fellowship of love.

5 Jesu, thy name we bless,
   and humbly pray that we
may follow them in holiness,
   and live and die in thee.

Richard Mant (1776–1848)

462

St Botolph   86 86 (CM)   Gordon Slater (1896–1979)

This endris nyght   86 86 (CM)   English 15th-century carol melody

1 For Mary, mother of our Lord,
    God's holy name be praised,
who first the Son of God adored,
    as on her child she gazed.

2 The angel Gabriel brought the word
    she should Christ's mother be;
and Mary, handmaid of the Lord,
    made answer willingly:

3 in meek obedience she believed,
    though hard the task assigned,
and by the Spirit she conceived
    the Saviour of mankind.

4 She gave her body as God's shrine,
    her heart to piercing pain;
she knew the cost of love divine,
    when Jesus Christ was slain.

5 From Mary's gentle lowliness
    and home in Galilee
there comes a joy and holiness
    to every family.

6 Give thanks for Mary, filled with grace,
    above all women blessed,
and blessed her Son, whom her embrace
    in birth and death confessed.

J. R. Peacey (1896–1971) altd.
based on Luke 1: 26–38

463

Song 67   86 86 (CM)

Orlando Gibbons (1583–1625)
from E. Prys's *Llyfr y Psalmau* (1621)

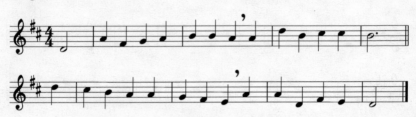

Second Tune

San Rocco   86 86 (CM)

Derek Williams (b. 1945)

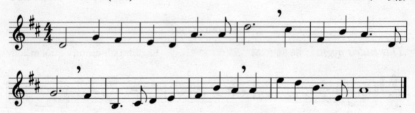

1 Give us the wings of faith to rise
  within the veil, and see
the saints above, how great their joys,
  how bright their glories be.

2 Once they were mourning here below,
  their couch was wet with tears;
they wrestled hard, as we do now,
  with sins and doubts and fears.

3 We ask them whence their victory came;
  they, with united breath,
ascribe their conquest to the Lamb,
  their triumph to his death.

4 They marked the footsteps that he trod,
  his zeal inspired their breast,
and, following their incarnate God,
  possess the promised rest.

5 Our glorious Leader claims our praise
  for his own pattern given,
while the long cloud of witnesses
  show the same path to heaven.

Isaac Watts (1674–1748) altd.
v. 5 based on Hebrews 12: 1–2

464

Westminster Abbey   87 87 87

Adapted from the final section ('Hallelujah')
in the anthem 'O God, thou art my God'
by Henry Purcell (*c.*1659–1695)
for the tune *Belville* in *The Psalmist* (1843)

1 God, whose city's sure foundation
   stands upon his holy hill,
 by his mighty inspiration
   chose of old and chooses still
 people out of every nation
   his good pleasure to fulfil.

2 Here in Ireland through the ages,
   while the Christian years went by,
 saints, confessors, martyrs, sages,
   strong to live and strong to die,
 wrote their name upon the pages
   of God's blessèd company.

3 Some there were like lamps of learning
   shining in a faithless night,
 some on fire with love, and burning
   with a flaming zeal for right,
 some by simple goodness turning
   souls from darkness into light.

4 As we now with high thanksgiving
   their triumphant names record,
 grant that we, like them, believing
   in the promise of your word,
 may, like them, in all good living
   praise and magnify the Lord.

Cyril A. Alington (1872–1956) altd.

465

Pilgrims   11 10 11 10 9 11   Henry T. Smart (1813–79)

An - gels of Je - sus, an - gels of light, sing-ing to wel - come the pil-grims of the night.

ST. MICHAEL AND ALL ANGELS
SEPTEMBER 29

1 Hark, hark, my soul, angelic songs are swelling
   o'er earth's green fields and ocean's wave-beat shore!
 How sweet the truth those blessèd strains are telling
   of that new life when sin shall be no more!

   *Angels of Jesus, angels of light,
   singing to welcome the pilgrims of the night.*

2 Onward we go, for still we hear them singing,
   come, weary souls, for Jesus bids you come;
 and through the dark, its echoes sweetly ringing,
   the music of the gospel leads us home:

*3 Far, far away, like bells at evening pealing,
   the voice of Jesus sounds o'er land and sea;
 and laden souls, by thousands meekly stealing,
   kind Shepherd, turn their weary steps to thee:

4 Rest comes at length; though life be long and dreary,
   the day must dawn, and darksome night be past;
 faith's journey ends in welcome to the weary,
   and heaven, the heart's true home, will come at last.

5 Angels, sing on, your faithful watches keeping,
   sing us sweet fragments of the songs above;
 till morning's joy shall end the night of weeping,
   and life's long shadows break in cloudless love.

Frederick W. Faber (1814–63)

466

O quanta qualia   11 10 11 10

Adaptation of a melody from
François de la Feillée's
Méthode du Plainchant (1808)

1 Here from all nations, all tongues, and all peoples,
　　countless the crowd but their voices are one;
　vast is the sight and majestic their singing—
　　'God has the victory: he reigns from the throne!'

2 These have come out of the hardest oppression;
　　now they may stand in the presence of God,
　serving their Lord day and night in his temple,
　　ransomed and cleansed by the Lamb's precious blood.

3 Gone is their thirst and no more shall they hunger,
　　God is their shelter, his power at their side:
　sun shall not pain them, no burning will torture;
　　Jesus the Lamb is their shepherd and guide.

4 He will go with them to clear living water
　　flowing from springs which his mercy supplies:
　gone is their grief, and their trials are over;
　　God wipes away every tear from their eyes.

5 Blessing and glory and wisdom and power
　　be to the Saviour again and again;
　might and thanksgiving and honour for ever
　　be to our God: Alleluia! Amen.

Christopher Idle (b. 1938)
based on Revelation 7: 9–17

467

Beatitudo   86 86 (CM)   John Bacchus Dykes (1823–76)

This tune was composed for these words

SECOND TUNE

Crediton   86 86 (CM)   Thomas Clark (1775–1859)

Alternative tune: 522i BALLERMA

1 How bright those glorious spirits shine!
  Whence all their white array?
How came they to the blissful seats
  of everlasting day?

2 Lo! these are they from sufferings great
  who came to realms of light,
and in the blood of Christ have washed
  those robes which shine so white.

3 Now with triumphal palms they stand,
  before the throne on high;
and serve the God they love, amidst
  the glories of the sky.

4 Hunger and thirst are felt no more,
  nor suns with scorching ray;
God is their sun, whose cheering
      beams
  diffuse eternal day.

5 The Lamb, who dwells amidst the
      throne,
  shall o'er them still preside;
feed them with nourishment divine,
  and all their footsteps guide.

6 In pastures green he'll lead his flock
  where living streams appear;
and God the Lord from every eye
  shall wipe off every tear.

Isaac Watts (1674–1748)
and *William Cameron* (1751–1811) altd.
based on Revelation 7: 13–17

468

Coe Fen   86 86 D (DCM)   Kenneth Naylor (1931–1991)

Alternative tune: 407i SOLL'S SEIN

1 How shall I sing that majesty
     which angels do admire?
   Let dust in dust and silence lie;
     sing, sing, ye heavenly choir.
   Thousands of thousands stand around
     thy throne, O God most high;
   ten thousand times ten thousand sound
     thy praise; but who am I?

2 Thy brightness unto them appears,
     whilst I thy footsteps trace;
   a sound of God comes to my ears,
     but they behold thy face.
   They sing because thou art their Sun;
     Lord, send a beam on me;
   for where heav'n is but once begun,
     there alleluias be.

3 How great a being, Lord, is thine,
     which doth all beings keep!
   Thy knowledge is the only line
     to sound so vast a deep.
   Thou art a sea without a shore,
     a sun without a sphere;
   thy time is now and evermore,
     thy place is everywhere.

John Mason (c.1645–94)

469

St Catherine's Court   12 11 12 11   Richard Strutt (1848–1927)

Was lebet, was schwebet (2)   12 11 12 11   Melody from the *Rheinhardt MS* (Üttingen, 1754)

THE COMMUNION OF SAINTS

1 In our day of thanksgiving one psalm let us offer
    for the saints who before us have found their reward;
  when the shadow of death fell upon them, we sorrowed,
    but now we rejoice that they rest in the Lord.

*2 In the morning of life, and at noon, and at even,
    he called them away from our worship below;
  but not till his love, at the font and the altar,
    had girt them with grace for the way they should go.

3 These stones that have echoed their praises are holy,
    and dear is the ground where their feet have once trod;
  yet here they confessed they were strangers and pilgrims,
    and still they were seeking the city of God.

4 Sing praise, then, for all who here sought and here found him,
    whose journey is ended, whose perils are past;
  they believed in the light; and its glory is round them,
    where the clouds of earth's sorrows are lifted at last.

William H. Draper (1855–1933)

470

Cymer   87 87 87

Mode ii melody from
Mount Saint Bernard Abbey, Leicester

Alternative tunes: 193 ALLELUIA, DULCE CARMEN   652 MANNHEIM

THE COMMUNION OF SAINTS

1 Let God's people join in worship
on the Virgin Mary's feast,
and entreat the gracious favour
of the child she carried then,
whom Elizabeth, discerning,
welcomed as the coming Christ.

2 As the infant leapt with gladness
at the presence of the Word,
so Elizabeth, believing,
knew the mother of the Lord,
and in awe proclaimed her blessèd
in the wonder of her child.

3 'How should God's unworthy servant
now be giv'n so rich a grace:
salutation from the mother
of the king of all the world?
For the prophet child within me
leapt in sign of holy joy.'

4 Then the Virgin, God acknowledged,
pouring forth her praise in song,
glorified with adoration
him who saved her by his grace,
that in every generation
all the world should call her blessed.

5 Holy Father, Son, and Spirit,
reigning in eternal power,
with your loving grace and favour
keep us safe for evermore,
and our earthly course completed,
bring us to eternal life.

The Community of the Holy Name, Derby altd.
based on Luke 1, 39–45

471

Old 104th   10 10 11 11

Melody from Thomas Ravenscroft's
Psalmes (1621)

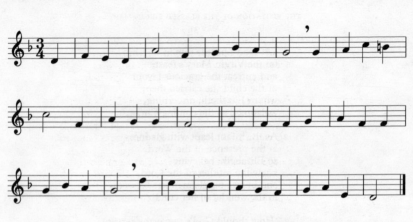

Darwall's 149th   10 10 11 11

John Darwall (1731–89)

1 Rejoice in God's saints, today and all days!
A world without saints forgets how to praise.
  Their faith in acquiring the habit of prayer,
  their depth of adoring, Lord, help us to share.

2 Some march with events to turn them God's way;
some need to withdraw, the better to pray;
  some carry the gospel through fire and through flood:
  our world is their parish; their purpose is God.

3 Rejoice in those saints, unpraised and unknown,
who bear someone's cross or shoulder their own;
  they shame our complaining, our comforts, our cares:
  what patience in caring, what courage, is theirs!

4 Rejoice in God's saints, today and all days!
A world without saints forgets how to praise.
  In loving, in living, they prove it is true:
  the way of self-giving, Lord, leads us to you.

F. Pratt Green (b. 1903)

472

Laudes Mariae 87 87 D

Henri F. Hémy (1818–88)

Alternative tune: 3, 38, 318 ABBOT'S LEIGH

1 Sing we of the blessèd mother
    who received the angel's word,
and obedient to his summons
    bore in love the infant Lord;
sing we of the joys of Mary
    at whose breast that child was fed,
who is Son of God eternal
    and the everlasting Bread.

2 Sing we, too, of Mary's sorrows,
    of the sword that pierced her through,
when beneath the cross of Jesus
    she his weight of suffering knew,
looked upon her Son and Saviour
    reigning high on Calvary's tree,
saw the price of our redemption
    paid to set the sinner free

3 Sing again the joys of Mary
    when she saw the risen Lord,
and in prayer with Christ's apostles,
    waited on his promised word:
from on high the blazing glory
    of the Spirit's presence came,
heavenly breath of God's own being,
    manifest through wind and flame.

4 Sing the chiefest joy of Mary
    when on earth her work was done,
and the Lord of all creation
    brought her to his heavenly home:
where, raised high with saints and angels,
    in Jerusalem above,
she beholds her Son and Saviour
    reigning as the Lord of love.

George B. Timms (1910–97) altd.

473

Síormholadh is glóir duit (St Patrick)
11 11 11 11 66 11

Modified form of a melody by
Henri F. Hémy (1818–88)

SAINT PATRICK
MARCH 17

1 Síormholadh is glóir duit, a Athair shíoraí,
   a gheall dúinn an tsíocháin leat féin i do ríocht,
   is d'Aonmhac nuair d'fhuascail Síol Éabh' lena bhás,
   gur réitigh an ród dúinn chun aontacht is páirt.
       Ón gcroí gabhaimid buíochas
       as ucht do dhea-scéal dúinn
   is Pádraig a chraol é fá ghríosadh do ghrá.

2 An ghlóir atá i ndán dúinn id' bhriathar is léir
   "T'réis m'ardú ón talamh tarraingeoidh mé gach n-aon."
   Go raibh muid, a Dhia dhil, 'nár scáth-an go deo.
   Díot féin le grá's páirt, ar nós Pádraig fadó.
       Aon anró níor bhrí leis
       ach briathar Dé 'chraoladh
   is míorúilt ghrá Dé do-ghní chuile ní nua.

Tadhg Ó Sé
verse 2 based on John 12: 32

1 *All glory and praise to you, Father, above,*
   who promised us peace in your kingdom of love;
       and praise to your Son who has freed humankind
       to walk in true fellowship, oneness of mind.
           Our hearts ever grateful
           give thanks for your gospel,
       and Patrick who told of the joy we can find.

2 *Your word tells us clearly of glory to be:*
   'When raised from the earth I will draw all to me.'
       Like Patrick, may we be as mirrors for you,
       and show loving kindness in all that we do;
           all hardship disdaining,
           this message proclaiming—
       'God's wonderful love can make everything new!'

tr. *Donald A. R. Caird* (b. 1925)
and *Gary Hastings* (b. 1956)
Versified *Donald Davison* (b. 1937)

474

Ecclesia   87 87 D with Refrain   Richard R. Terry (1865–1938)

REFRAIN

A - men! A - men! Al - le - lu - ia! Glo - ry, hon-our, might and praise,

to the God of earth and hea - ven let the whole cre - a - tion raise!

1 Such a host as none can number,
    every tribe and every race,
robed before the Lamb in glory,
    gather at the throne of grace.
'To our God ascribe salvation;
    glory to the Lamb belongs!'
All the saints in one communion,
    join the glad triumphal song:

    Amen! Amen! Alleluia!
    Glory, honour, might and praise,
    to the God of earth and heaven
    let the whole creation raise!

2 Those who suffered great injustice,
    now redeemed and glorified,
day and night their praises offer
    to the Lamb once crucified.
No more shall they thirst and hunger,
    no more fear the scorching heat,
for the Lamb will be their shepherd,
    every need and longing meet.

3 See this vision of the future
    put to shame the world we know!
Hear the heav'nly choirs protesting
    with the victims here below!
Heal the sick and feed the hungry;
    set the broken captive free!
In the presence of the future,
    this our joyful song shall be:

        Michael Forster (b. 1946)
        based on Revelation 7: 9–17

475

All Saints   87 87 77

Melody from *Geistreiches Gesangbuch* (Darmstadt, 1698)
adpt. William Henry Monk (1823–89)

Wer sind die vor Gottes Throne

1 Who are these like stars appearing,
     these, before God's throne who stand?
Each a golden crown is wearing;
     who are all this glorious band?
         Alleluia, hark they sing,
         praising loud their heavenly King.

2 Who are these in dazzling brightness,
     clothed in God's own righteousness?
These, whose robes of purest whiteness
     shall their lustre still possess.
         Still untouched by time's rude hand,
         whence come all this glorious band?

3 These are they who have contended
     for their Saviour's honour long,
wrestling on till life was ended,
     following not the sinful throng;
         these, who well the fight sustained,
         triumph by the Lamb have gained.

4 These the_Almighty contemplating,
     kings and priests before him stand,
in his service ever waiting,
     day and night at his command:
         now in God's most holy place
         blessed they stand before his face.

T. Heinrich Schenck (1656–1727)
tr. Frances E. Cox (1812–97)
based on Revelation 7: 13–17

476

Lasst uns erfreuen (Easter Song)
88 44 88 with Alleluias

Melody from *Geistliche Kirchengesäng*
(Cologne, 1623)

1 Ye watchers and ye holy ones,
    bright seraphs, cherubim and thrones,
      raise the glad strain, alleluia!
    Cry out, dominions, princedoms, powers,
    virtues, archangels, angels' choirs,
      alleluia!

2 O higher than the cherubim,
    more glorious than the seraphim,
      lead their praises, alleluia!
    Thou bearer of the eternal Word,
    most gracious, magnify the Lord,
      alleluia!

3 Respond, ye souls in endless rest,
    ye patriarchs and prophets blessed,
      alleluia! alleluia!
    Ye holy twelve, ye martyrs strong,
    all saints triumphant, raise the song
      alleluia!

4 O friends, in gladness let us sing,
    supernal anthems echoing,
      alleluia! alleluia!
    To God the Father, God the Son,
    and God the Spirit, Three in One,
      alleluia!

Athelstan Riley (1858–1945)

477

FIRST TUNE

St Michael (Old 134th)   66 86 (SM)

Later abridged form of melody for
Psalm 101 in the *Genevan Psalter*
(1551)

For an explanation of the small notes above the stave, see the Musical Preface.

SECOND TUNE

Franconia   66 86 (SM)

From a six-line melody in J. B. König's
Harmonischer Liederschatz (1738)
adpt. William Henry Havergal (1793–1870)

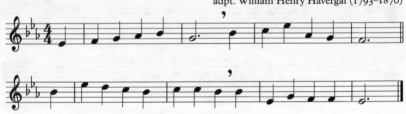

THE ANNUNCIATION OF OUR LORD TO THE BLESSED VIRGIN MARY
MARCH 25

1 We praise you, Lord, today,
    this day so long foretold,
  whose promise shone with cheering ray
    on waiting saints of old.

2 The prophet gave the sign
    for all in faith to read:
  a virgin, born of David's line,
    shall bear the promised seed.

3 Ask not how this should be,
    but worship and adore,
  like her, whom God's own majesty
    came down to shadow o'er.

4 She humbly bowed her head
    to hear the gracious word,
  Mary, the pure and lowly maid,
    the favoured of the Lord.

5 Blessèd shall be her name
    in all the Church on earth,
  through whom that wondrous
        mercy came,
    the incarnate Saviour's birth.

6 Jesus the Virgin's Son,
    we praise you and adore,
  with Father, Spirit you are One
    and blessed for evermore.

Anon. (1847) altd.
based on Luke 1: 26–38

478

Yanworth 10 10 10 10

John Barnard (b. 1948)

Alternative tune: 712 WOODLANDS

1 Go forth and tell! O Church of God, awake!
   God's saving news to all the nations take:
      proclaim Christ Jesus, Saviour, Lord and King,
      that all the world his worthy praise may sing.

2 Go forth and tell! God's love embraces all;
   he will in grace respond to all who call:
      how shall they call if they have never heard
      the gracious invitation of his word?

3 Go forth and tell where still the darkness lies;
   in wealth or want, the sinner surely dies:
      give us, O Lord, concern of heart and mind,
      a love like yours which cares for all mankind.

4 Go forth and tell! The doors are open wide:
   share God's good gifts—let no one be denied;
      live out your life as Christ your Lord shall choose,
      your ransomed powers for his sole glory use.

5 Go forth and tell! O Church of God, arise!
   Go in the strength which Christ your Lord supplies;
      go till all nations his great name adore
      and serve him, Lord and King for evermore.

James E. Seddon (1915–83)

479

Go, tell it on the mountain   North American traditional spiritual

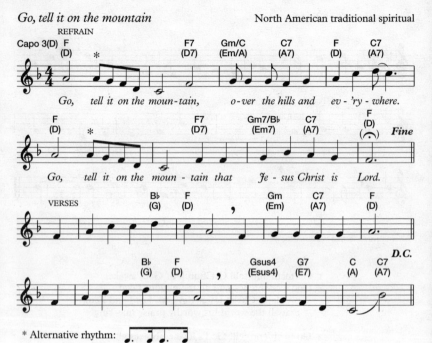

* Alternative rhythm:

> *Go, tell it on the mountain,*
> *over the hills and ev'rywhere.*
> *Go, tell it on the mountain*
> *that Jesus Christ is Lord.*

1 O when I was a seeker,
     I sought both night and day;
   I asked the Lord to guide me,
     and he showed me the way.

2 Then he made me a watchman
     upon a city wall,
   to tell of his salvation,
     that Jesus died for all.

3 Go tell it to your neighbour
     in darkness here below;
   go with the words of Jesus,
     that all the world may know.

based on a North American traditional spiritual

480

Freely, freely

Jimmy Owens

He said: 'Free - ly, free - ly you have re - ceived,
free - ly, free - ly give;_____ go in my name and be-
-cause you be - lieve, o - thers will know that I live'._____

1 God forgave my sin in Jesus' name;
I've been born again in Jesus' name,
and in Jesus' name I come to you
to share his love as he told me to.

He said:
'Freely, freely you have received,
freely, freely give;
go in my name and because you believe,
others will know that I live'.

2 All power is given in Jesus' name,
in earth and heaven in Jesus' name;
and in Jesus' name I come to you
to share his power as he told me to.

*3 God gives us life in Jesus' name,
he lives in us in Jesus' name;
and in Jesus' name I come to you,
to share his peace as he told me to.

Carol Owens

481

Benson

Melody by Millicent D. Kingham (1866–1927)
Words by A. C. Ainger (1841–1919) altd.

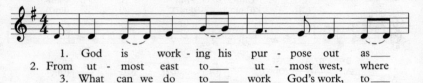

1. God is work-ing his pur-pose out as___
2. From ut - most east to___ ut - most west, where
3. What can we do to___ work God's work, to___
4. March we___ forth in the strength of God, with the
5. All we can do is___ no - thing worth un -

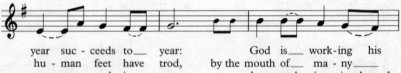

year suc - ceeds to___ year: God is___ work-ing his
hu - man feet have trod, by the mouth of__ ma - ny___
pros - per_ and in - crease_ love and_ jus - tice through-
ban - ner of Christ un - furled, that the light of the glo - rious___
-less God bless - es the deed; vain - ly we hope for the

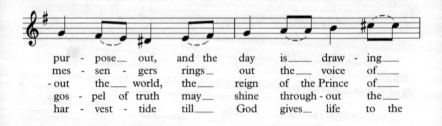

pur - pose_ out, and the day is___ draw - ing___
mes - sen - gers rings_ out the___ voice of___
-out the___ world, the___ reign of the Prince of___
gos - pel of truth may_ shine through - out the___
har - vest - tide till___ God gives_ life to the

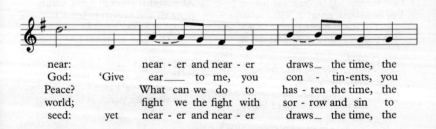

near: near - er and near - er draws_ the time, the
God: 'Give ear___ to me, you con - tin-ents, you
Peace? What can we do to has - ten the time, the
world; fight we the fight with sor - row and sin to
seed: yet near - er and near - er draws_ the time, the

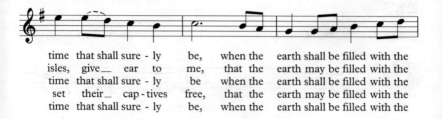

time that shall sure - ly be, when the earth shall be filled with the
isles, give_ ear to me, that the earth may be filled with the
time that shall sure - ly be when the earth shall be filled with the
set their_ cap - tives free, that the earth may be filled with the
time that shall sure - ly be, when the earth shall be filled with the

glo - ry of God, as the wa - ters co - ver the sea.
glo - ry of God, as the wa - ters co - ver the sea.'
glo - ry of God, as the wa - ters co - ver the sea?
glo - ry of God, as the wa - ters co - ver the sea.
glo - ry of God, as the wa - ters co - ver the sea.

1 God is working his purpose out as year succeeds to year:
   God is working his purpose out, and the day is drawing near:
      nearer and nearer draws the time, the time that shall surely be,
      when the earth shall be filled with the glory of God, as the waters cover the sea.

2 From utmost east to utmost west, where human feet have trod,
   by the mouth of many messengers rings out the voice of God:
      'Give ear to me, you continents, you isles, give ear to me,
      that the earth may be filled with the glory of God, as the waters cover the sea.'

3 What can we do to work God's work, to prosper and increase
   love and justice throughout the world, the reign of the Prince of Peace?
      What can we do to hasten the time, the time that shall surely be
      when the earth shall be filled with the glory of God, as the waters cover the sea?

4 March we forth in the strength of God, with the banner of Christ unfurled,
   that the light of the glorious gospel of truth may shine throughout the world;
      fight we the fight with sorrow and sin to set their captives free,
      that the earth may be filled with the glory of God, as the waters cover the sea.

5 All we can do is nothing worth unless God blesses the deed;
   vainly we hope for the harvest-tide till God gives life to the seed:
      yet nearer and nearer draws the time, the time that shall surely be,
      when the earth shall be filled with the glory of God, as the waters cover the sea.

A. C. Ainger (1841–1919)

482

Jesus bids us shine 10 11 10 10

Edwin Excell (1851–1921)

1 Jesus bids us shine with a pure clear light,
like a little candle burning in the night;
    in this world of darkness so we must shine,
    you in your small corner and I in mine.

2 Jesus bids us shine, first of all for him;
well he sees and knows it, if our light is dim;
    he looks down from heav'n to see us shine,
    you in your small corner and I in mine.

3 Jesus bids us shine, then, for all around;
many kinds of darkness in this world abound—
    sin and want and sorrow; so we must shine,
    you in your small corner and I in mine.

Susan Warner (1819–89)

483

Camber 65 65

Martin Shaw (1875–1958)

Alternative tune: 213 AU CLAIR DE LA LUNE (1) (which covers two verses at a time)

1 Jesus went to worship
   in the synagogue;
   with his friends and neighbours
   sang his praise to God.

2 We, like Jesus, worship
   in the Church today;
   still, with friends and neighbours,
   sing our songs and pray.

3 When the service ended,
   Jesus took his praise
   into streets and houses,
   spelling out God's ways.

4 People came to Jesus,
   frightened, hurt and sad;
   helping them to worship,
   Jesus made them glad.

5 Holy Spirit, help us
   when this service ends,
   still to follow Jesus,
   still to be his friends.

6 When our neighbours meet us,
   may they, with surprise,
   catch a glimpse of Jesus
   rising in our eyes.

Alan Gaunt (b. 1935)

484

Crucifer   10 10 with Refrain   Sydney H. Nicholson (1875–1947)

REFRAIN

Lift high the cross, the love of Christ pro - claim till

Fine

all the world_____ a - dore_____ his sa - cred name!

VERSES

v. 2

D.C.

Lift high the cross, the love of Christ proclaim
till all the world adore his sacred name!

1 Come, Christians, follow where our captain trod,
  our king victorious, Christ the Son of God:

2 Each new-born soldier of the crucified
  is signed with the cross, the seal of him who died:

3 This is the sign that Satan's armies fear
  and angels veil their faces to revere:

4 Saved by the cross on which their Lord was slain,
  see Adam's children their lost home regain:

5 From north and south, from east and west they raise
  in growing unison their songs of praise:

6 Let every race and every language tell
  of him who saves our souls from death and hell!

7 Lord Christ, once lifted high on Calvary's tree,
  as thou promised, draw us all to thee:

8 Set up thy throne, that earth's despair may cease
  beneath the shadow of its healing peace:

Michael Robert Newbolt (1874–1956) altd.
based on *George William Kitchin* (1827–1912)
v. 7 based on John 12: 32

485

Festal Song   66 86 (SM)

William Henry Walter (1825–93)

Alternative tune: 370, 461i CARLISLE

1 Rise up and serve the Lord!
   Have done with lesser things;
   give heart and soul and mind and strength
   to serve the King of kings.

2 Rise up and serve the Lord!
   His kingdom tarries long;
   proclaim the day of truth and love,
   and end the night of wrong.

3 Lift high the cross of Christ!
   Tread where his feet have trod;
   and, quickened by the Spirit's power,
   rise up and serve your God!

   William P. Merrill (1867–1954) altd.

486

Charles Wood (1866–1926)
written for *Hymns Ancient and Modern* (1904)

Rangoon   68 88 78 6

1 People of God, arise
   with the gospel of hope and peace,
till the noise of the warriors' cries
   and the anguish of suff'ring cease;
    when the universe shall blaze
    with the glory of perfect praise.
People of God, arise!

2 People of God, arise:
   in the name of our God protest,
when the innocent victim dies,
   or the weak are by fear oppressed.
    Let the Church's voice be heard
    with the ringing prophetic word.
People of God, arise!

3 People of God, arise!
   In the name of the Lord of life,
stand for truth in the face of lies,
   offer love in the place of strife;
    for his promise will not fail,
    his compassion will yet prevail.
People of God, arise!

Michael Forster (b. 1946)

487

FIRST TUNE

From strength to strength   66 86 D (DSM)   E. W. Naylor (1867–1934)

SECOND TUNE

St Ethelwald   66 86 (SM)   William Henry Monk (1823–89)

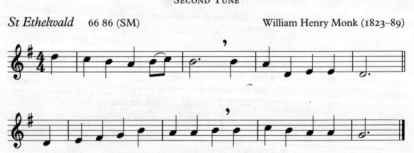

This tune is sung twice for each verse.

1 Soldiers of Christ, arise,
    and put your armour on,
strong in the strength which God supplies
    through his eternal Son;
strong in the Lord of hosts,
    and in his mighty power:
who in the strength of Jesus trusts
    is more than conqueror.

2 Stand, then, in his great might,
    with all his strength endued;
and take, to arm you for the fight,
    the panoply of God.
To keep your armour bright
    attend with constant care,
still walking in your Captain's sight
    and watching unto prayer.

3 From strength to strength go on,
    wrestle, and fight and pray;
tread all the powers of darkness down,
    and win the well-fought day;
that, having all things done,
    and all your conflicts past,
ye may o'ercome, through Christ alone,
    and stand complete at last.

Charles Wesley (1707–88) altd.
based on Ephesians 6: 10–18

488

Morning light 76 76 D

G. J. Webb (1803–87)

OPTIONAL INTERLUDE *(between verses)*

Trumpet

1 Stand up, stand up for Jesus,
    you soldiers of the cross!
  Lift high his royal banner,
    it must not suffer loss.
  From victory unto victory,
    his army he shall lead,
  till every foe is vanquished,
    and Christ is Lord indeed.

2 Stand up, stand up for Jesus!
    The trumpet call obey;
  forth to the mighty conflict
    in this his glorious day.
  Be strong in faith and serve him
    against unnumbered foes;
  let courage rise with danger,
    and strength to strength oppose.

3 Stand up, stand up for Jesus!
    Stand in his strength alone;
  the arm of flesh will fail you,
    you dare not trust your own.
  Put on the gospel armour,
    each piece put on with prayer;
  where duty calls, or danger,
    be never wanting there.

4 Stand up, stand up for Jesus!
    The strife will not be long;
  this day the noise of battle,
    the next the victor's song.
  To all who are triumphant
    a crown of life shall be;
  they with the King of glory
    shall reign eternally.

George Duffield (1808–88) altd.
based on Ephesians 6: 11
& Revelation 2: 10–11

489

Evangel   76 76 D with Refrain   William Howard Doane (1832–1915)

REFRAIN

Tell me the old, old sto - ry, tell me the old, old sto - ry,

tell me the old, old sto - ry of Je - sus and_ his love.

1 Tell me the old, old story
    of unseen things above,
  of Jesus and his glory,
    of Jesus and his love.
  Tell me the story simply,
    as to a little child;
  for I am weak and weary,
    and helpless and defiled:

      Tell me the old, old story
      of Jesus and his love.

2 Tell me the story slowly
    that I may take it in,
  that wonderful redemption,
    God's remedy for sin.
  Tell me the story often,
    for I forget so soon;
  the early dew of morning
    has passed away at noon:

3 Tell me the story softly
    with earnest tones and grave;
  remember, I'm the sinner
    whom Jesus came to save.
  Tell me the story always,
    if you would really be,
  in any time of trouble,
    a comforter to me:

4 Tell me the same old story
    when you have cause to fear
  that this world's empty glory
    is costing me too dear:
  yes, and when that world's glory
    shall dawn upon my soul,
  tell me the old, old story,
    'Christ Jesus makes you whole':

Catherine Hankey (1834–1911) altd.

490

Walk in the light

Damien Lundy (b. 1944)

1 The Spirit lives to set us free,
   walk, walk in the light;
   he binds us all in unity,
   walk, walk in the light.

   Walk in the light,
   walk in the light,
   walk in the light,
   walk in the light of the Lord.

2 Jesus promised life to all,
   the dead were wakened by his call,

3 He died in pain on Calvary,
   to save the lost like you and me,

4 We know his death was not the end,
   he gave his Spirit to be our friend,

5 By Jesus' life our wounds are healed,
   the Father's kindness is revealed,

6 The Spirit lives in you and me,
   his light will shine for all to see,

Damien Lundy (b. 1944)

491

Fulda (Walton) 88 88 (LM)

William Gardiner (1770–1853)
Sacred Melodies (vol. 2, 1815)

1 We have a gospel to proclaim,
    good news for all throughout the earth;
  the gospel of a Saviour's name:
    we sing his glory, tell his worth.

2 Tell of his birth at Bethlehem,
    not in a royal house or hall,
  but in a stable dark and dim:
    the Word made flesh, a light for all.

3 Tell of his death at Calvary,
    hated by those he came to save,
  in lonely suffering on the cross
    for all he loved his life he gave.

4 Tell of that glorious Easter morn:
    empty the tomb, for he was free;
  he broke the power of death and hell
    that we might share his victory.

5 Tell of his reign at God's right hand,
    by all creation glorified;
  he sends his Spirit on his Church
    to live for him, the Lamb who died.

6 Now we rejoice to name him King:
    Jesus is Lord of all the earth.
  This gospel-message we proclaim;
    we sing his glory, tell his worth.

Edward J. Burns (b. 1938)

THE CHURCH'S WITNESS AND MISSION

492

FIRST TUNE

German traditional melody, adpt. in

Paderborn   10 10 11 11   *Paderborn Gesangbuch* (1765)

Alternative tune: 708 LAUDATE DOMINUM

SECOND TUNE

Houghton   10 10 11 11   Henry J. Gauntlett (1805–1876)

1 Ye servants of God, your master proclaim,
and publish abroad his wonderful name:
 the name all-victorious of Jesus extol;
 his kingdom is glorious, and rules over all.

2 God ruleth on high, almighty to save;
and still he is nigh, his presence we have;
 the great congregation his triumph shall sing,
 ascribing salvation to Jesus our King.

3 Salvation to God, who sits on the throne!
Let all cry aloud, and honour the Son;
 the praises of Jesus the angels proclaim,
 fall down on their faces and worship the Lamb.

4 Then let us adore, and give him his right:
all glory and power, all wisdom and might,
 all honour and blessing, with angels above,
 and thanks never-ceasing, and infinite love.

Charles Wesley (1707–88)
based on Revelation 4: 9–11; 5: 11–14

493

Hyfrydol   87 87 D   Rowland Hugh Pritchard (1811–87)

1 Ye that know the Lord is gracious,
 ye for whom a corner-stone
stands, of God elect and precious,
 laid that ye may build thereon,
see that on that sure foundation
 ye a living temple raise,
towers that may tell forth salvation,
 walls that may re-echo praise.

2 Living stones, by God appointed
 each to his allotted place,
kings and priests, by God anointed,
 shall ye not declare his grace?
Ye, a royal generation,
 tell the tidings of your birth,
tidings of a new creation
 to an old and weary earth.

3 Tell the praise of him who called you
 out of darkness into light,
broke the fetters that enthralled you,
 gave you freedom, peace and sight:
tell the tale of sins forgiven,
 strength renewed and hope restored,
till the earth, in tune with heaven,
 praise and magnify the Lord.

Cyril A. Alington (1872–1955)
based on 1 Peter 2: 6–10

494

Beauty for brokenness   Words and music by Graham Kendrick (b. 1950)

1. Beau - ty for bro - ken - ness,
2. Shel - ter for fra - gile lives,
3. Re - fuge from cruel_ wars,
4. Rest for the ra-vaged earth,
5. Light-en our dark - ness,

hope for des - pair,   Lord, in your   suff-'ring world
cures for their ills,   work for the   crafts - men,
ha - vens from fear,   ci - ties for   sanc - tu - 'ry,
o - ceans and streams,   plun-dered and   poi - soned— our
breathe on this flame,   un - til your   jus - tice burns

this is our prayer.   Bread for the   child - ren,
trade for their skills.   Land for the   dis-pos-sessed,
free-doms to share.   Peace to the   kill-ing fields,
fu - ture, our dreams.   Lord, end our   mad - ness,
bright - ly a - gain;   un - til the   na - tions

jus - tice, joy, peace,   sun - rise to   sun - set your
rights for the weak,   voi - ces to   plead the cause of
scorched earth to green,   Christ for the   bit - ter-ness, his
care - less-ness, greed,   make us con - tent_ with the
learn of your ways,   seek your sal - va - tion and

1. BRIDGE

king-dom in - crease.
those who can't speak.
cross for the pain.
things that we need.
bring you their praise.

SOCIAL JUSTICE

God of the poor, ___ friend of the ___ weak, give us com-pas - sion, we pray: melt our cold hearts, let tears fall like ___ rain; come, change our love ___ from a spark ___ to a ___ flame. ___

The Refrain may be omitted after verses 1 and 3

1 Beauty for brokenness,
　　hope for despair,
　Lord, in your suff'ring world
　　this is our prayer.
　Bread for the children,
　　justice, joy, peace,
　sunrise to sunset
　　your kingdom increase.

　　　God of the poor,
　　　friend of the weak,
　　　give us compassion, we pray:
　　　melt our cold hearts,
　　　let tears fall like rain;
　　　come, change our love
　　　from a spark to a flame.

2 Shelter for fragile lives,
　　cures for their ills,
　work for the craftsmen,
　　trade for their skills.
　Land for the dispossessed,
　　rights for the weak,
　voices to plead the cause ⌣
　　of those who can't speak.

3 Refuge from cruel wars,
　　havens from fear,
　cities for sanctu'ry,
　　freedoms to share.
　Peace to the killing fields,
　　scorched earth to green,
　Christ for the bitterness,
　　his cross for the pain.

4 Rest for the ravaged earth,
　　oceans and streams,
　plundered and poisoned—
　　our future, our dreams.
　Lord, end our madness,
　　carelessness, greed,
　make us content with ⌣
　　the things that we need.

5 Lighten our darkness,
　　breathe on this flame,
　until your justice burns ⌣
　　brightly again;
　until the nations
　　learn of your ways,
　seek your salvation
　　and bring you their praise.

Graham Kendrick (b. 1950)

659

495

Chereponi

Ghana folk-song
collected by Tom Colvin (1925–2000)

Jesu,[1] Jesu,
fill us with your love,
show us how to serve
the neighbours we have from you.

1 Kneels at the foot of his friends,
silently washes their feet;
master who acts as a slave to them.

2 Neighbours are rich folk and poor,
neighbours are black, brown and white,
neighbours are nearby and far away.

3 These are the ones we should serve,
these are the ones we should love;
all these are neighbours to us and you.

4 Loving puts us on our knees,
serving as though we were slaves,
this is the way we should live with you.

Tom Colvin (1925–2000)
based on John 13: 3–11

[1] 'Jesu' should be pronounced 'Yay-soo' as it is in Ghana
and in other countries.

496

Alleluia, dulce carmen   87 87 87
Melody from
An Essay on the Church Plain Chant (1782)
probably by Samuel Webbe the elder (1740–1816)

1 For the healing of the nations,
    Lord, we pray with one accord,
for a just and equal sharing
    of the things that earth affords.
To a life of love in action
    help us rise and pledge our word.

2 Lead us forward into freedom;
    from despair your world release,
that, redeemed from war and hatred,
    all may come and go in peace.
Show us how through care and goodness
    fear will die and hope increase.

3 All that kills abundant living,
    let it from the earth be banned:
pride of status, race or schooling,
    dogmas that obscure your plan.
In our common quest for justice
    may we hallow life's brief span.

4 You, Creator-God, have written
    your great name on humankind;
for our growing in your likeness
    bring the life of Christ to mind;
that by our response and service
    earth its destiny may find.

Fred Kaan (b. 1929)

497

Brockham   88 88 (LM)

Melody by Jeremiah Clarke (*c.*1673–1707)
in Playford's *The Divine Companion* (1709)

Alternative tunes: 226 HERONGATE   306 ILLSLEY

1 The Church of Christ, in every age
   beset by change but Spirit-led,
  must claim and test its heritage
   and keep on rising from the dead.

2 Across the world, across the street,
   the victims of injustice cry
  for shelter and for bread to eat,
   and never live until they die.

3 Then let the servant Church arise,
   a caring Church, that longs to be
  a partner in Christ's sacrifice,
   and clothed in Christ's humanity.

4 For he alone, whose blood was shed,
   can cure the fever in our blood,
  and teach us how to share our bread
   and feed the starving multitude.

5 We have no mission but to serve,
   in full obedience to our Lord:
  to care for all, without reserve,
   and spread his liberating Word.

F. Pratt Green (b. 1903) altd.

498

Sharpthorne   66 66 336   Erik Routley (1917–82)

1 What does the Lord require for praise and offering?
   What sacrifice desire, or tribute bid you bring?
       Do justly;
       love mercy;
       walk humbly with your God.

2 Rulers of earth give ear! Should you not justice know?
   Will God your pleading hear, while crime and cruelty grow?
       Do justly;
       love mercy;
       walk humbly with your God.

3 All who gain wealth by trade, for whom the worker toils,
   think not to win God's aid, if greed your commerce soils:
       Do justly;
       love mercy;
       walk humbly with your God.

4 Still down the ages ring the prophet's stern commands:
   to merchant, worker, king he brings God's high demands:
       Do justly;
       love mercy;
       walk humbly with your God.

5 How shall our life fulfil God's law so hard and high?
   Let Christ endue our will with grace to fortify;
       then justly,
       in mercy,
       we'll humbly walk with God.

Albert F. Bayly (1901–84)
based on Micah 6: 6–8

499

Neighbour   Sydney Carter (b. 1915)

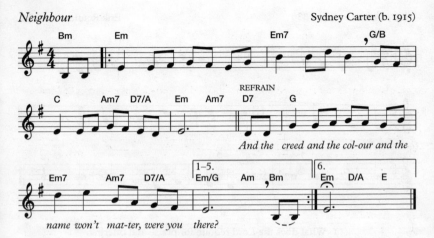

And the creed and the col-our and the name won't mat-ter, were you there?

1 When I needed a neighbour, were you there,
  were you there?
  When I needed a neighbour, were you there?

   *And the creed and the colour
   and the name won't matter,
   were you there?*

2 I was hungry and thirsty, were you there,
  were you there?
  I was hungry and thirsty, were you there?

3 I was cold, I was naked, were you there,
  were you there?
  I was cold, I was naked, were you there?

4 When I needed a shelter, were you there,
  were you there?
  When I needed a shelter, were you there?

5 When I needed a healer, were you there,
  were you there?
  When I needed a healer, were you there?

6 Wherever you travel, I'll be there,
  I'll be there.
  Wherever you travel, I'll be there.

   *And the creed and the colour
   and the name won't matter,
   I'll be there.*

Sydney Carter (b. 1915)
based on Matthew 25: 31–46

500

Cross over the road

Pamela Verrall

1. Would you walk by on the o-ther side, when some-one called for aid?___ Would you walk by on the o-ther side, and would you be a-fraid?

REFRAIN

Cross o-ver the road, my friend, ask the Lord his strength to lend, his com-pas-sion has no end, cross o-ver the road.

1 Would you walk by on the other side,
   when someone called for aid?
 Would you walk by on the other side,
   and would you be afraid?

   Cross over the road, my friend,
   ask the Lord his strength to lend,
   his compassion has no end,
   cross over the road.

2 Would you walk by on the other side,
   when you saw a loved one stray?
 Would you walk by on the other side,
   or would you watch and pray?

3 Would you walk by on the other side,
   when starving children cried?
 Would you walk by on the other side,
   and would you not provide?

Pamela Verrall
based on Luke 10: 30–37

501

Ahasuerus Fritsch (1629–1701)
adpt. J. S. Bach (1685–1750)

Darmstadt (O Gott, du frommer Gott)
67 67 66 66

Alternative tune: 361 NUN DANKET

1 Christ is the world's true light,
  its captain of salvation,
the day-star shining bright,
  to all in every nation:
new life, new hope awakes
  when we accept his way;
freedom her bondage breaks
  and night is turned to day.

2 In Christ all races meet,
  their ancient feuds forgetting,
the whole round world complete
  from sunrise to its setting:
when Christ is throned as Lord,
  all shall forsake their fear,
to ploughshare beat the sword,
  to pruning-hook the spear.

3 One Lord, in one great name
    unite us all who own you;
  cast out our pride and shame
    that hinder to enthrone you:
  the world has waited long,
    has laboured long in pain;
  to heal its ancient wrong,
    come, Prince of Peace, and reign.

George W. Briggs (1875–1959) altd.
based on John 8: 12 & Isaiah 2: 4–5

502

The supreme sacrifice   10 10 10 10   Charles Harris (1865–1936)

Holborn   10 10 10 10   Eric H. Thiman (1900–75)

Suitable for Remembrance Sunday observance

1 God! As with silent hearts we bring to mind
   how hate and war diminish humankind,
       we pause—and seek in worship to increase
       our knowledge of the things that make for peace.

2 Hallow our will as humbly we recall
   the lives of those who gave and give their all.
       We thank you, Lord, for women, children, men
       who seek to serve in love, today as then.

3 Give us deep faith to comfort those who mourn,
   high hope to share with all the newly born,
       strong love in our pursuit of human worth:
       'lest we forget' the future of this earth.

4 So, Prince of Peace, disarm our trust in power,
   teach us to coax the plant of peace to flower.
       May we, im-passioned by your living Word,
       remember forward to a world restored.

Fred Kaan (b. 1929)

503

St Francis

Sebastian Temple (1928–97)
arr. Donald Davison (b. 1937)

much to be con-soled as to con - sole;_____ to be

un - der - stood as to un - der - stand, to be

loved, as to love with all my soul!_____

1 Make me a channel of your peace:
   where there is hatred let me bring your love,
   where there is injury, your pardon, Lord,
   and where there's doubt, true faith in you:
   O Master, grant that I may never seek
   so much to be consoled as to console;
   to be understood as to understand,
   to be loved, as to love with all my soul!

2 Make me a channel of your peace:
   where there's despair in life let me bring hope,
   where there is darkness, only light,
   and where there's sadness, ever joy:
   O Master, grant that I may never seek
   so much to be consoled as to console;
   to be understood as to understand,
   to be loved, as to love with all my soul!

3 Make me a channel of your peace:
   it is in pardoning that we are pardoned,
   in giving of ourselves that we receive,
   and in dying that we're born to eternal life.

Sebastian Temple (1928–97)
based on The Prayer of Francis of Assisi

504

The pollen of peace

Words and music by Roger Courtney (b. 1954)
written for the Corrymeela Community

PEACE AND RECONCILIATION

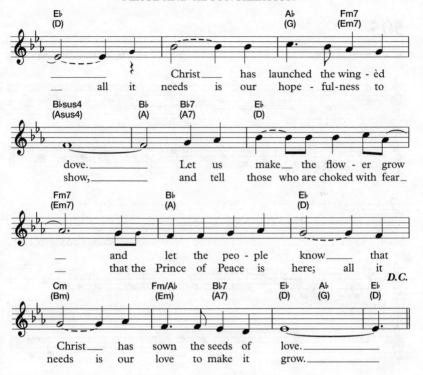

*O let us spread the pollen of peace
throughout our land,
let us spread the pollen of peace
throughout our land.
Let us spread the pollen of peace,
and make all hatred cease;
let us spread the pollen of peace
throughout our land.*

1 O Christ has sown the seeds of love;
Christ has launched the wingèd dove.
  Let us make the flower grow
  and let the people know
that Christ has sown the seeds of love.

2 All it needs is our love to make it grow;
all it needs is our hopefulness to show,
  and tell those who are choked with fear
  that the Prince of peace is here;
all it needs is our love to make it grow.

Roger Courtney (b. 1945)
written for The Corrymeela Community

505

St Andrew   87 87

E. H. Thorne (1834–1916)

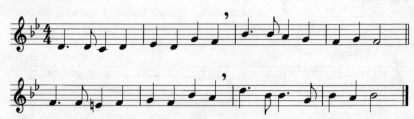

Ellen   87 87

Alison Cadden (b. 1965)

1 Peace be to this congregation:
   peace to every soul therein:
  peace the earnest of salvation,
   peace the fruit of pardoned sin:

2 peace that speaks its heavenly giver;
   peace to worldly minds unknown;
  peace divine, that lasts for ever;
   peace that comes from God alone.

3 God of peace, be present, near us;
   fix in all our hearts your home.
  With your gracious presence cheer us;
   let your blessèd kingdom come.

Charles Wesley (1707–88) altd.

506

London New 86 86 (CM)

Melody from the *Scottish Psalter* (1635)
adpt. in Playford's *Psalmes* (1671)

For an explanation of the small notes above the stave, see the Musical Preface.

York (The Stilt)   86 86 (CM)

Melody from the *Scottish Psalter* (1615)

1 Pray that Jerusalem may have ⌣
    peace and felicity:
  let them that love thee and thy peace
    have still prosperity.

2 Therefore I wish that peace may still ⌣
    within thy walls remain,
  and ever may thy palaces
    prosperity retain.

3 Now, for my friends' and neighbours' sake,
    peace be in thee, I'll say;
  and for the house of God our Lord
    I'll seek thy good alway.

From the Scottish Psalter 1650
based on Psalm 122

507

FIRST TUNE

Elmwood   87 87   Anthony F. Carver (b. 1947)

SECOND TUNE

The treasure of peace   87 87   Donald Davison (b. 1937)

1 Put peace into each other's hands
   and like a treasure hold it,
   protect it like a candle-flame,
   with tenderness enfold it.

2 Put peace into each other's hands
   with loving expectation;
   be gentle in your words and ways
   in touch with God's creation.

3 Put peace into each other's hands
   like bread we break for sharing;
   look people warmly in the eye:
   our life is meant for caring.

4 As at communion, shape your hands ⌣
   into a waiting cradle;
   the gift of Christ receive, revere,
   united round the table.

5 Put Christ into each other's hands,
   he is love's deepest measure;
   in love make peace, give peace a chance
   and share it like a treasure.

Fred Kaan (b. 1929)

508

Peace to you

Words and music by Graham Kendrick (b. 1950)

Peace to you:
we bless you now in the name of the Lord. Peace to you:
we bless you now in the name of the Prince of Peace—
peace to you, peace to you, peace to you, peace to you, peace to you.

This song is very effective, e.g. at the Peace, if sung several times by different groups: it is best begun and ended softly.

Peace to you:
we bless you now in the name of the Lord.
Peace to you:
we bless you now in the name of the Prince of Peace—
peace to you.

Graham Kendrick (b. 1950)

509

St Cecilia 66 66   Leighton George Hayne (1836–83)

1 Your kingdom come, O God;
   your rule, O Christ, begin;
   break with your iron rod
   the tyrannies of sin.

2 Where is your reign of peace
   and purity and love?
   When shall all hatred cease
   as in the realms above?

3 When comes the promised time,
   the end of strife and war;
   when lust, oppression, crime⌣
   and greed shall be no more?

4 O Lord our God, arise
   and come in your great might!
   Revive our longing eyes
   which languish for your sight.

5 On lands both near and far
   thick darkness gathers yet:
   arise, O Morning Star,
   arise and never set!

Lewis Hensley (1824–1905) altd.

510

FIRST TUNE

Ebenezer Prout (1835–1909)
adpt. Eric H. Thiman (1900–75)
and compilers of *Rejoice and Sing* (1991)

Herstmonceux   4 666 68

SECOND TUNE

Praying for peace   4 666 68   Donald Davison (b. 1937)

1. We pray for peace, but not the ea-sy peace, built on com-pla-cen-cy and not the truth of God. We pray for real_____ peace, the peace_ God's_ love a-lone can seal._____ 2. We come._____

1 We pray for peace,
but not the easy peace,
built on complacency
and not the truth of God.
We pray for real peace,
the peace God's love alone can seal.

2 We pray for peace,
but not the cruel peace,
leaving God's poor bereft
and dying in distress;
we pray for real peace,
enriching all the human race.

3 We pray for peace,
and not the evil peace,
defending unjust laws
and nursing prejudice,
but for the real peace
of justice, mercy, truth and love.

4 We pray for peace:
holy communion
with Christ our risen Lord
and every living thing;
God's will fulfilled on earth
and all his creatures reconciled.

5 We pray for peace,
and for the sake of peace,
look to the risen Christ
who gives the grace we need,
to serve the cause of peace
and make our own self-sacrifice.

6 God, give us peace:
if you withdraw your love,
there is no peace for us
nor any hope of it.
With you to lead us on,
through death or tumult, peace will come.

Alan Gaunt (b. 1935)

511

Gerard 11 11 11 5

Arthur Hutchings (1906–89)

Alternative tune: 53 CHRISTE SANCTORUM

1 Father of mercy, God of consolation,
   look on your people, gathered here to praise you,
   pity our weakness, come in power to aid us,
        source of all blessing.

2 Son of the Father, Lord of all creation,
   come as our Saviour, Jesus, friend of sinners,
   grant us forgiveness, lift our downcast spirit,
        heal us and save us.

3 Life-giving Spirit, be our light in darkness,
   come to befriend us, help us bear our burdens,
   give us true courage, breathe your peace around us,
        stay with us always.

4 God in Three Persons, Father, Son and Spirit,
   come to renew us, fill your Church with glory,
   grant us your healing, pledge of resurrection,
        foretaste of heaven.

James Quinn (b. 1919)

512

Kilmarnock   86 86 (CM)   Neil Dougall (1776–1862)

1 From you all skill and science flow,
   all pity, care, and love,
   all calm and courage, faith and hope—
   O pour them from above;

2 impart them, Lord, to each and all,
   as each and all have need,
   to rise like incense, each to you,
   in noble thought and deed.

3 And hasten, Lord, that perfect day
   when pain and death shall cease,
   and your just rule shall fill the earth
   with health and light and peace;

4 when ever blue the sky shall gleam,
   and ever green the sod,
   and our rude work deface no more
   the paradise of God.

Charles Kingsley (1819–75) altd.

513

Daniel   88 88 (LM)

Irish traditional melody

Alternative tune: 76ii, 77, 539 WAREHAM

1 O Christ, the Healer, we have come
    to pray for health, to plead for friends.
How can we fail to be restored,
    when reached by love that never ends?

2 From every ailment flesh endures
    our bodies clamour to be freed;
yet in our hearts we would confess
    that wholeness is our deepest need.

*3 How strong, O Lord, are our desires,
    how weak our knowledge of ourselves!
Release in us those healing truths
    unconscious pride resists or shelves.

4 In conflicts that destroy our health
    we recognise the world's disease;
our common life declares our ills:
    is there no cure, O Christ, for these?

5 Grant that we all, made one in faith,
    in your community may find
the wholeness that, enriching us,
    shall reach and prosper humankind.

F. Pratt Green (b. 1903)

514

Ye banks and braes   88 88 D (DLM)   Scottish traditional melody

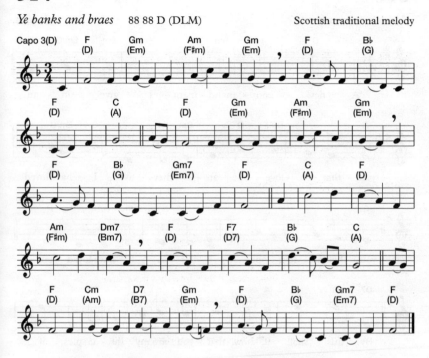

1 We cannot measure how you heal
    or answer every sufferer's prayer;
  yet we believe your grace responds
    where faith and doubt unite to care.
Your hands, though bloodied on the cross,
    survive to hold and heal and warn,
  to carry all through death to life
    and cradle children yet unborn.

2 The pain that will not go away,
    the guilt that clings from things
        long past,
  the fear of what the future holds,
    are present as if meant to last.
But present too is love which tends
    the hurt we never hoped to find,
  the private agonies inside,
    the memories that haunt the mind.

3 So some have come who need your help,
    and some have come to make amends,
  as hands which shaped and saved the world
    are present in the touch of friends.
Lord, let your Spirit meet us here
    to mend the body, mind and soul,
  to disentangle peace from pain
    and make your broken people whole.

John L. Bell (b. 1949)
and *Graham Maule* (b. 1958)

515

A new commandment   Anon.

'A new com-mand-ment I give un-to you, that you love one an-o-ther as I have loved you, that you love one an-o-ther as I have loved you.

By this shall all know that you are my dis-ci-ples, if you have love one to an-o-ther. By this shall all know that you are my dis-ci-ples, if you have love one to an-o-ther.'

John 13: 34–35

516

Frogmore   64 64

Walter Parratt (1841–1924)

1 Belovèd, let us love: love is of God;
  in God alone has love its true abode.

2 Belovèd, let us love: for they who love
  are born of God, his children from above.

3 Belovèd, let us love: for love is rest,
  and they who have no love remain unblessed.

4 Belovèd, let us love: for love is light,
  and those who have no love dwell in the night.

5 Belovèd, let us love: for only thus
  shall we behold that God who first loved us.

Horatius Bonar (1808–89) altd.
based on 1 John 4: 7–12

517

Servant song 87 87

Richard Gillard (b. 1953)

1 Brother, sister, let me serve you,
    let me be as Christ to you.
  Pray that I may have the grace to
    let you be my servant, too.

2 We are pilgrims on a journey,
    and companions on the road;
  we are here to help each other
    walk the mile and bear the load.

3 I will hold the Christ-light for you
    in the night-time of your fear;
  I will hold my hand out to you,
    speak the peace you long to hear.

4 I will weep when you are weeping;
    when you laugh I'll laugh with you.
  I will share your joy and sorrow
    till we've seen this journey through.

5 When we sing to God in heaven
    we shall find such harmony,
  born of all we've known together
    of Christ's love and agony.

6 Won't you let me be your servant,
    let me be as Christ to you?
  Pray that I may have the grace to
    let you be my servant, too.

Richard Gillard (b. 1953)

518

Bind us together

Bob Gillman

Bind us together, Lord,
bind us together
with cords that cannot be broken.
Bind us together, Lord,
bind us together,
O bind us together with love.

1 There is only one God.
   There is only one King.
   There is only one body;
   that is why we sing:

2 Made for the glory of God,
   purchased by his precious Son.
   Born with the right to be free,
   for Jesus the vict'ry has won.

3 We are the fam'ly of God.
   We are the promise divine.
   We are God's chosen desire.
   We are the glorious new wine.

Bob Gillman altd.

519

Dunedin 88 88 (LM) Vernon Griffiths (1894–1985)

Alternative tune: 457 WARRINGTON

1 Come, all who look to Christ today,
   stretch out your hands, enlarge your mind,
together share his living way
   where all who humbly seek will find.

2 Come, all who will from every race;
   find here new powers of brotherhood,
accept the Spirit's strong embrace,
   which binds us to the common good.

3 Come, young and old from every church,
   bring all your treasuries of prayer,
join the dynamic Spirit's search
   to press beyond the truths we share.

4 Bring your tradition's richest store,
   your hymns and rites and cherished creeds;
explore our visions, pray for more,
   since God delights to meet fresh needs.

5 Come, trust in Christ and live in peace,
   anticipate that final light
when strife and bigotry shall cease,
   and faith be lost in praise and sight.

Richard G. Jones (b. 1926)

520

Ubi caritas   12 12 12 12 with Refrain   A. Gregory Murray (1905–92)

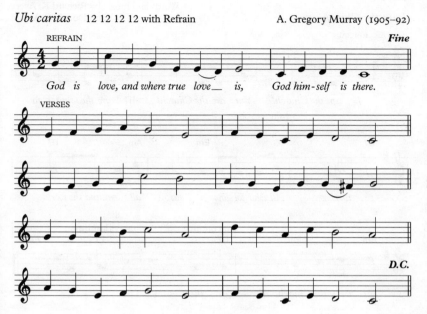

God is love, and where true love is, God himself is there.

Ubi caritas et amor

God is love, and where true love is, God himself is there.

1   Here in Christ we gather, love of Christ our calling.
    Christ, our love, is with us, gladness be his greeting.
    Let us all revere and love him, God eternal.
    Loving him, let us love Christ in one another.
    God is love, and where true love is, God himself is there.

2   When we Christians gather, members of one Body,
    let there be in us no discord, but one spirit.
    Banished now be anger, strife and every quarrel.
    Christ, our God, be present always here among us.
    God is love, and where true love is, God himself is there.

3   Grant us love's fulfilment, joy with all the blessèd,
    when we see your face, O Saviour, in its glory.
    Shine on us, O purest Light of all creation,
    be our bliss while endless ages sing your praises.
    God is love, and where true love is, God himself is there.

From the Latin Liturgy of Maundy Thursday
tr. *James Quinn* (b. 1919) altd.

For another translation, see no 531.

521

I am the Church

Words and music by Richard K. Avery
and Donald S. Marsh

REFRAIN

I am the Church! You are the Church! We are the Church to-ge-ther! All who fol-low Je-sus, all a-round the world, yes we're the Church to-ge-ther. 1. The -ge-ther

Church is not a build-ing, the Church is not a stee-ple. The Church is not a rest-ing-place, the Church is a peo-ple.

I am the Church! You are the Church!
We are the Church together!
All who follow Jesus, all around the world,
yes we're the Church together.

1 The Church is not a building, the Church is not a steeple.
The Church is not a resting-place, the Church is a people.

2 We're many kinds of people with many kinds of faces:
all colours and all ages, too, from all times and places.

3 Sometimes the Church is marching, sometimes it's bravely burning,
sometimes it's riding, sometimes hiding, always it's learning!

4 And when the people gather there's singing and there's praying,
there's laughing and there's crying sometimes, all of it saying:

5 I count if I am ninety, or nine, or just a baby;
there's one thing I am sure about and I don't mean maybe:

Richard K. Avery

522

Clonmel   86 86 D (DCM)

Irish traditional melody

This tune covers two verses at a time.

A 76 76 D version of this tune (e.g. for use at no. 593) is obtained by slurring the 8th and 9th notes of each system.

SECOND TUNE

From *A Selection of Original Sacred Music*
(Glasgow, 1833)
adpt. from a song by François H. Barthélémon
(1741–1808)

Ballerma   86 86 (CM)

Alternative tune: 206 KILMARNOCK

1 In Christ there is no east or west,
       in him no south or north,
    but one great fellowship of love
       throughout the whole wide earth.

2 In him shall true hearts everywhere
       their high communion find,
    his service is the golden cord
       close-binding humankind.

3 Join hands, then, people of the faith,
       whate'er your race may be!
    Who serves my Father as his child
       is surely kin to me.

4 In Christ now meet both east and west,
       in him meet south and north,
    all Christlike souls are one in him,
       throughout the whole wide earth.

John Oxenham [*W. A. Dunkerley*] (1852–1941) altd.
            based on 1 Corinthians 12: 12–13;
                              Galatians 3: 28

523

Dumfermline 86 86 (CM) Melody from *Scottish Psalter* (1615)

Alternative tune: 623 BELMONT

1 Help us to help each other, Lord,
     each other's cross to bear;
   let us our friendly aid afford
     and show our loving care.

2 Help us to build each other up,
     out little stock improve;
   increase our faith, confirm our hope,
     and perfect us in love.

3 Up into thee, our living Head,
     let us in all things grow,
   till thou hast made us free indeed,
     and spotless here below.

4 Touched by the loadstone[1] of thy love,
     let all our hearts agree;
   and ever toward each other move,
     and ever move toward thee.

5 To thee, inseparably joined,
     let all our spirits cleave;
   O may we all the loving mind
     that was in thee, receive.

6 This is the bond of perfectness,
     thy spotless charity;
   O let us still, we pray, possess
     the mind that was in thee.

Charles Wesley (1707–88) altd.

[1]A 'Loadstone' (or 'Lodestone') is a piece of naturally magnetic iron ore which, if free to rotate, will point to the magnetic north—hence its use as a compass from ancient times. When 'touched' by a loadstone, other pieces of suitable material acquire an induced magnetism, and will then also point north ('let all out hearts agree') and be attracted to the loadstone and to each other (lines 3 and 4). The loadstone is thus a striking metaphor for the power of Christ's love in the Christian community.

524

Rousseau's Dream   87 87 D

Adpt. from a *divertissement* Air by
Jean Jacques Rousseau (1712–78)

May the grace of Christ our Saviour,
  and the Father's boundless love,
with the Holy Spirit's favour,
  rest upon us from above.
Thus may we abide in union
  with each other and the Lord,
and possess in sweet communion
  joys which earth cannot afford.

John Newton (1725–1807)
based on 2 Corinthians 13: 13

525

Let there be love

Words and music by Dave Bilbrough

Let there be love shared among us,
let there be love in our eyes,
may now your love sweep this nation,
cause us, O Lord, to arise;
give us a fresh understanding
of brotherly love that is real,
let there be love shared among us,
let there be love.

Dave Bilbrough

526

Tredegar   87 87 87

Guthrie Foote (1897–1972)

Alternative tune: 275ii TRIUMPH

1 Risen Lord, whose name we cherish,
    all the stars are in your hand!
  Walk today among your people,
    light each candle on its stand;
  look in mercy, not in judgment,
    on your Church in every land.

2 For, divided in your service,
    we have chosen selfish ways,
  lived in bitterness of spirit,
    quickly let our anger blaze;
  often blindly followed leaders,
    sought our glory, not your praise.

3 Yet your Church has also triumphed,
    told of love's great offering,
  in its life shown forth your goodness,
    drawn from death its cruel sting;
  wakened to the needs of many,
    soothed the sorrows life can bring.

4 So, we pray, that by your Spirit
    all your scattered flock may find
  that deep unity you prayed for
    and would share with all mankind;
  by this gift our fears and envies
    shall in truth be left behind.

5 Risen Lord, your hand is knocking
    at each church's bolted door!
  Enter now, and dwell within us,
    trust and fellowship restore;
  that your Father's joys together
    all may taste for evermore.

David Mowbray (b. 1938)

Words: © David Mowbray/Jubilate Hymns

527

Everton   87 87 D   Henry Smart (1813–79)

Bethany (Smart)   87 87 D   Henry Smart (1813–79)

1 Son of God, eternal Saviour,
   source of life and truth and grace,
Son of Man, whose birth among us
   hallows all our human race,
Christ, our Head, who, throned in glory,
   for your own will ever plead,
fill us with your love and pity,
   heal our wrongs and help our need.

2 Bind us all as one together
   in your Church's sacred fold,
weak and wealthy, poor and healthy,
   sad and joyful, young and old.
Is there want, or pain, or sorrow?
   Make us all the burden share.
Are there spirits crushed and broken?
   Teach us, Lord, to soothe their care.

3 As you, Lord, have lived for others,
   so may we for others live;
freely have your gifts been granted,
   freely may your servants give.
Yours the gold and yours the silver,
   yours the wealth of sea and land,
we but stewards of your bounty,
   held in trust as from your hand.

4 Come, O Christ, and reign above us,
   King of love, and Prince of peace:
hush the storm of strife and passion,
   bid its cruel discords cease:
by your patient years of toiling,
   by your silent hours of pain,
quench our fevered thirst of pleasure,
   shame our selfish greed of gain.

5 Son of God, eternal Saviour,
   source of life and truth and grace,
Son of Man, whose birth among us
   hallows all our human race,
in your love you prayed the Father
   that your people should be one;
grant, O Christ, our hope's fruition,
   here on earth your will be done.

Somerset C. Lowry (1855–1932) altd.

528

Aurelia   76 76 D   S. S. Wesley (1810–76)

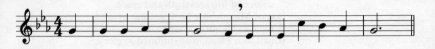

Alternative tune: 451 KING'S LYNN

1 The Church's one foundation
    is Jesus Christ her Lord;
she is his new creation
    by water and the word:
from heaven he came and sought her
    to be his holy bride;
with his own blood he bought her,
    and for her life he died.

2 Elect from every nation,
    yet one o'er all the earth,
her charter of salvation
    one Lord, one faith, one birth;
one holy name she blesses,
    partakes one holy food,
and to one hope she presses
    with every grace endued.

*3 The world with scornful wonder
    may see her sore oppressed,
by schisms rent asunder,
    by heresies distressed;
yet saints their watch are keeping,
    their cry goes up, 'How long?';
and soon the night of weeping
    shall be the morn of song.

4 'Mid toil and tribulation,
    and tumult of her war,
she waits the consummation
    of peace for evermore;
till with the vision glorious
    her longing eyes are blessed,
and the great Church victorious
    shall be the Church at rest.

5 Yet she on earth has union
    with God the Three-in-One,
and mystic sweet communion
    with those whose rest is won:
O happy ones and holy!
    Lord, give us grace that we,
like them the meek and lowly,
    on high may dwell with thee.

Samuel J. Stone (1839–1900) altd.
based on 1 Corinthians 3: 11 & Ephesians 5: 25–27

529

Thornbury 76 76 D

Basil Harwood (1859–1949)

Church, one Faith, one Lord._____

1 Thy hand, O God, has guided
   thy flock, from age to age;
the wondrous tale is written,
   full clear, on every page;
thy people owned thy goodness,
   and we their deeds record;
and both of this bear witness:
   one Church, one Faith, one Lord.

2 Thy heralds brought glad tidings
   to greatest, as to least;
they summoned all to hasten
   and share the great King's feast;
their gospel of redemption,
   sin pardoned, earth restored,
was all in this enfolded:
   one Church, one Faith, one Lord.

*3 And we, shall we be faithless?
   Shall hearts fail, hands hang down?
Shall we evade the conflict
   and cast away our crown?
Not so: in God's deep counsels
   some better thing is stored;
we will maintain, unflinching,
   one Church, one Faith, one Lord.

4 Thy mercy will not fail us,
   nor leave thy work undone;
with thy right hand to help us,
   the victory shall be won;
and then, by all creation,
   thy name shall be adored,
and this shall be our anthem:
   one Church, one Faith, one Lord.

Edward H. Plumptre (1821–91) altd.
based on Ephesians 4: 4–5

530

Ubi caritas et amor

Jaques Berthier (1923–94)
for the Taizé Community

U - bi ca - ri - tas et a - mor,

u - bi ca - ri - tas De - us i - bi est.

VERSES *(Cantor)*

1. Your love, O Je - sus Christ, has gath - ered us to - geth - er.

2. May your love, O Je - sus Christ, be fore - most in our lives.

3. Let us love one an - oth - er as God has loved us.

*Choose either part.

The refrain is sung by all in continuous repetition: it may be enhanced by use of the Choir Version.
The verses may be sung by one or more cantors during the second half of the refrain.

4. Let us be one in love to-geth-er in the one bread of Christ.

5. The love of God in Je-sus Christ bears e-ter-nal joy.

6. The love of God in Je-sus Christ will ne-ver have an end.

[1]*Ubi caritas et amor,*
ubi caritas Deus ibi est.

1 Your love, O Jesus Christ, has gathered us together.

2 May your love, O Jesus Christ, be foremost in our lives.

3 Let us love one another as God has loved us.

4 Let us be one in love together in the one bread of Christ.

5 The love of God in Jesus Christ bears eternal joy.

6 The love of God in Jesus Christ will never have an end.

Taizé Community

[1] Translation: Where charity (i.e. 'loving-kindness') and love are found, God himself is there.

531

Maisemore   86 86 (CM)   John Dykes Bower (1905–81)

Alternative tunes: 462i ST BOTOLPH, 374i CONTEMPLATION

Ubi caritas et amor

1 Where love and loving-kindness dwell,
   there God will ever be:
one Father, Son, and Spirit, bound
   in perfect charity.

2 Brought here together into one
   by Christ our shepherd-king,
now let us in his love rejoice,
   and of his goodness sing.

3 Here too let God, the living God,
   both loved and honoured be;
and let us each the other love
   with true sincerity.

4 Brought here together by Christ's love,
   let no ill-will divide,
nor quarrels break the unity
   of those for whom he died.

5 Let envy, jealousy and strife
   and all contention cease,
for in our midst serves Christ the Lord,
   our sacrament of peace.

6 Together may we with the saints
   your face in glory view,
and ever in your kingdom feast,
   O Christ our God, with you.

From the Latin Liturgy of Maundy Thursday
tr. *Geoffrey Preston* (1936–77) altd.

For another translation, see no. 520.

532

Monks Gate (2)   75 75 66 65

English traditional melody, coll. and adpt.
R. Vaughan Williams (1872–1958)

1 Who are we who stand and sing?
    We are God's people.
What this bread and wine we bring?
    Food for God's people.
As once with twelve Christ spake,
poured wine, and bread did break;
he now of us will make
    a faithful people.

2 What command does Christ impart
    to us his people?
Soul and strength and mind and heart;
    serve me, my people.
As he in love came low,
our world and work to know;
to life he bids us go
    to be his people.

3 Who are we who say one creed?
    We are God's people.
What the word we hear and read?
    Word of God's people.
Through time, in every race,
from earth to farthest space,
we'll be, with Christ's good grace,
    a faithful people.

Herbert O'Driscoll (b. 1928)

533

Rhuddlan   87 87 87

Welsh traditional melody from E. Jones'
Musical Relics of the Welsh Bards (1800)

Alternative tune: 267 REGENT SQUARE

1 God of grace and God of glory,
   on your people pour your power;
crown your ancient Church's story,
   bring her bud to glorious flower.
      Grant us wisdom,
      grant us courage
   for the facing of this hour.

2 See how hosts of evil round us
   scorn your Christ, attack his ways!
From the fears that long have bound us
   free our hearts to faith and praise.
      Grant us wisdom,
      grant us courage
   for the living of these days.

3 Save us from weak resignation
   to the evils we deplore;
let the search for your salvation
   be our glory evermore.
      Grant us wisdom,
      grant us courage,
   serving you whom we adore.

4 Cure your children's warring madness,
   bend our pride to your control;
shame our wanton, selfish gladness,
   rich in things and poor in soul.
      Grant us wisdom,
      grant us courage,
   lest we miss your kingdom's goal.

   Harry Emerson Fosdick (1878–1969) altd.

534

National Anthem   664 6664

Origin uncertain. Popularised in 1745
by the setting of Thomas Arne (1710–78)

For use in Northern Ireland

1 God save our gracious *Queen*,
long live our noble *Queen*,
  God save the *Queen*.
Send *her* victorious,
happy and glorious,
long to reign over us;
  God save the *Queen*.

2 Thy choicest gifts in store
on *her* be pleased to pour,
  long may *she* reign.
May *she* defend our laws,
and ever give us cause
to sing with heart and voice
  'God save the *Queen*'.

*3 Lord, make your mercies known
not on this land alone,
  but on each shore.
Soon may the nations be
in love and unity,
and form one family
  the whole world o'er.

vv. 1 & 2 Anon. (*c.* 1745) altd.
v. 3 *W. E. Hickson* (1803–70) altd.

535

Rhuddlan   87 87 87

Welsh traditional melody from E. Jones'
Musical Relics of the Welsh Bards (1800)

1 Judge eternal, throned in splendour,
    Lord of lords and King of kings,
with your living fire of judgment
    purge this realm of bitter things:
solace all its wide dominion
    with the healing of your wings.

2 Still the weary folk are pining
    for the hour that brings release:
and the city's crowded clangour
    cries aloud for sin to cease;
and the homesteads and the woodlands
    plead in silence for their peace.

3 Crown, O God, your own endeavour;
    cleave our darkness with your sword;
feed the faithless and the hungry
    with the riches of your word:
cleanse the body of this nation
    through the glory of the Lord.

Henry Scott Holland (1847–1918) altd.

536

St Columba (2) 86 86 (CM) Irish traditional melody

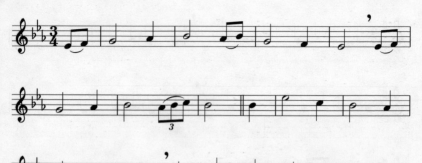

1 Lord, while for all the world we pray,
   of every clime and coast,
 O hear us for our native land,
   the land we love the most.

2 O guard our shores from every foe;
   with peace our borders bless;
 with prosperous times our cities crown,
   our fields with plenteousness.

3 In love of knowledge, truth, and God
   may we united be;
 and let our hills and valleys shout⌣
   the songs of liberty.

4 Lord of the nations, thus to you
   our country we commend;
 O be her refuge and her trust,
   her everlasting friend.

John R. Wreford (1800–81) altd.

537

St Anne 86 86 (CM)

Later form of a melody in
A Supplement to the New Version (1708)
probably by William Croft (1678–1727)

For the significance of the small notes below the bass stave, see the Musical Preface.

1 O God, our help in ages past,
   our hope for years to come,
   our shelter from the stormy blast,
   and our eternal home.

2 Beneath the shadow of thy throne
   thy saints have dwelt secure;
   sufficient is thine arm alone,
   and our defence is sure.

3 Before the hills in order stood,
   or earth received her frame,
   from everlasting thou art God,
   to endless years the same.

4 A thousand ages in thy sight
   are like an evening gone;
   short as the watch that ends the night
   before the rising sun.

5 Time, like an ever-rolling stream,
   soon bears us all away;
   we fly forgotten, as a dream
   dies at the opening day.

6 O God, our help in ages past,
   our hope for years to come,
   be thou our guard while troubles last,
   and our eternal home.

Isaac Watts (1674–1748) altd.
based on Psalm 90: 1–6

538

Gathering clouds

Words and music by Graham Kendrick (b. 1950)

1. O___ Lord,___ the clouds are ga - ther - ing, the
(2.) Lord,___ o - ver the na - tions now where
(3.) Lord,___ dark powers are poised to flood our
(4.) Lord,___ your glo - rious cross shall tower tri -

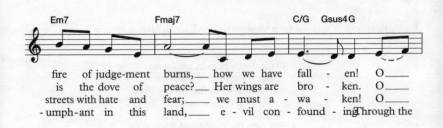

fire of judge-ment burns,___ how we have fall - en! O___
is the dove of peace?___ Her wings are bro - ken. O___
streets with hate and fear;___ we must a - wa - ken! O___
-umph-ant in this land,___ e - vil con - found - ing. Through the

Lord,___ you stand ap - palled to see your laws of love so
Lord,___ while pre-cious child - ren starve the tools of war in -
Lord,___ let love re - claim the lives that sin would sweep a -
fire___ your suff-'ring Church dis-plays the glo - ries of her

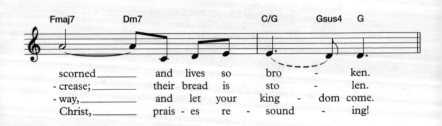

scorned___ and lives so bro - ken.
- crease;___ their bread is sto - len.
- way,___ and let your king - dom come.
Christ,___ prais - es re - sound - ing!

OUR COUNTRY

based on Isaiah 58: 6–9; Amos 5: 24

539

Wareham   88 88 (LM)   William Knapp (1698–1768)

1 Rejoice, O land, in God thy might;
   his will obey, him serve aright;
      for thee the saints uplift their voice:
      fear not, O land, in God rejoice.

2 Glad shalt thou be, with blessing crowned,
   with joy and peace thou shalt abound;
      yea, love with thee shall make his home
      until thou see God's kingdom come.

3 He shall forgive thy sins untold:
   remember thou his love of old;
      walk in his way, his word adore,
      and keep his truth for evermore.

Robert Bridges (1844–1930)
based on Joel 2: 21

540

Christchurch   66 66 88   Charles Steggall (1826–1905)

O   Lord, stretch forth thy might-y hand, and   guard and bless our na-tive land.

1 To thee our God we fly
    for mercy and for grace;
  O hear our lowly cry,
    and hide not thou thy face.

    O Lord, stretch forth thy mighty hand,
    and guard and bless our native land.

2 Arise, O Lord of hosts!
    Be jealous for thy name,
  and drive from out our coasts
    the sins that put to shame.

3 Thy best gifts from on high
    in rich abundance pour,
  that we may magnify
    and praise thee more and more.

*4 The powers ordained by thee
    with heavenly wisdom bless,
  may they thy servants be,
    and rule in righteousness.

*5 The Church of thy dear Son
    inflame with love's pure fire;
  bind her once more in one,
    and life and truth inspire.

*6 Give peace, Lord, in our time;
    O let no foe draw nigh,
  nor lawless deed of crime
    insult thy majesty.

7 Though weak and wayward, still
    thy people, Lord, are we;
  and for our God we will
    none other have but thee.

W. Walsham How (1823–97) altd.

541

Drakes Broughton   87 87   Edward Elgar (1857–1934)

Alternative tune: 225ii WYCHBOLD

1 God of Eve and God of Mary,
   God of love and mother-earth,
 thank you for the ones who with us
   shared their life and gave us birth.

2 As you came to earth in Jesus,
   so you come to us today;
 you are present in the caring
   that prepares us for life's way.

3 Thank you that the Church, our Mother,
   gives us bread and fills our cup,
 and the comfort of the Spirit
   warms our hearts and lifts us up.

4 Thank you for belonging, shelter,
   bonds of friendship, ties of blood,
 and for those who have no children,
   yet are parents under God.

5 God of Eve and God of Mary,
   Christ our brother, human Son,
 Spirit, caring like a Mother,
   take our love and make us one!

Fred Kaan (b. 1929)

542

Bunessan   55 54 D   Scots Gaelic traditional melody

For this tune with guitar chords, see nos. 44, 58.
Alternative tune: 611ii ADDINGTON

1 Lord of creation, giver of gladness,
    in celebration we come today;
   loved ones around us, hope shining strongly,
     your love completing our deepest joy.

2 Lord of our past days, life's rich surprises,
    clearing our pathways you wisely led:
   through painful learning we have moved forward,
     working and earning our daily bread.

3 Lord of tomorrow: what will it bring us?
    Blessing or sorrow, all unexplored:
   each situation calls us to trust you,
     our true salvation is Christ the Lord.

4 Lord, in your keeping, we are safe always;
    waking or sleeping you watch us still:
   save us from losing love's precious jewel,
     help us in choosing your gracious will.

David Mowbray (b. 1938)

543

Warrington   88 88 (LM)   Ralph Harrison (1748–1810)

1 Lord of the home, your only Son
    received a mother's tender love,
  and from an earthly father won
    his vision of your home above.

2 Help us, O Lord, our homes to make
    your Holy Spirit's dwelling place;
  our hands' and hearts' devotion take
    to be the servants of your grace.

3 May we with joy our homes prepare
    that, were our Lord a child once more,
  he might be glad our hearth to share,
    and find a welcome at our door.

4 Lord, may your Spirit sanctify
    each household duty we fulfil;
  may we our Master glorify
    in glad obedience to your will.

Albert F. Bayly (1901–84) altd.

544

O perfect Love   11 10 11 10   Joseph Barnby (1838–96)

Alternative tunes: 127, 157 HIGHWOOD   70 STRENGTH AND STAY (written for these words)

1 O perfect Love, all human thought transcending,
   lowly we kneel in prayer before your throne,
that theirs may be the love which knows no ending,
   who now for evermore are joined in one.

2 O perfect Life, be now their full assurance
   of tender charity and steadfast faith,
of patient hope, and quiet brave endurance,
   with childlike trust that fears not pain or death.

3 Grant them the joy which brightens earthly sorrow;
   grant them the peace which calms all earthly strife;
and to life's day the glorious unknown morrow
   that dawns upon eternal love and life.

Dorothy Frances Gurney (1858–1932) altd.

545

Pleading Saviour   87 87 D   Melody in *Christian Lyre* (1830)

Alternative tune: 710 ODE TO JOY

1 Sing of Eve and sing of Adam,
    children in the dawn of earth,
who with dust and death within them,
    yet by God were given birth.
Side by side they named creation,
    both from Eden's peace were hurled,
living in their pain and passion
    all the story of the world.

2 Sing of Abraham and Sarah
    who, in leaving home and land,
gave themselves in faithful freedom,
    reaching out for Yahweh's[1] hand.
From their love God formed a people,
    chosen until time be done,
and among their generations
    God would bring to birth a Son.

3 Sing of Mary, sing of Joseph,
    keepers of the wondrous boy,
called by God to high vocation,
    sharing sorrow, sharing joy,
sharing love, and by that loving
    in their home in Nazareth,
forming one whose grace and glory
    suffered, died and conquered death.

4 Sing of man and sing of woman,
    each the other's joy and crown,
male and female both transfigured
    in the Lord of life come down.
Called to equal co-relation,
    where their gifts, becoming one,
bring to birth a new creation,
    and the will of God is done.

Herbert O'Driscoll (b. 1928)

[1] Yahweh is the Hebrew name of God in the Old Testament.

546

An cúilfhionn rua   12 12 13 11   Irish traditional melody

The slurs refer to the English text; metrical irregularities in the Irish text are not indicated, but are easily accommodated.

REPENTANCE

1 A Aonmhic na hÓighe, a stór, is a sciath na mbocht,
 in éiric an chrainn le'r ceangladh tú gan locht,
 braon de do thrócaire doirt ar ár n-anam anocht,
 is ná lig ar seoid níos mó mé, ach cloígh mo chorp.

2 A Rí na bhfeart, go n-aclaí tú mo chroí,
 is go dtuga tú leat mé ar neamh mar a bhfuil na naoimh,
 admhaím anois mo locht duit, mo cham agus mo chlaon,
 go bhfuil mé faoi ghlasa ag peacai dubha an tsaoil.

3 A Rí na ndúl, thug cabhair is amharc don dall,
 d'fhulaing sciúrsaí an chine daonna dár gceannach ar chrann,
 agus d'fhulaing go humhal d'úirchneas á cheangal go teann,
 tabhair maithiúnas dúinne, an scúid bocht peacach, do chlann.

Cathal Buí Mac Giolla Ghunna (d. 1756) altd.

1 *O Mary's dear Son, my treasure, shield of the poor,*
 who, faultless, was tied, the cruel cross to endure,
 now pour on my soul a drop of your merciful cure.
 Let me not stray, but keep my body subdued.

2 *O King of all power, I pray you, make soft my heart,*
 and bring me to heav'n, where all your saints have a part.
 My guilt I confess, that often from truth I depart,
 for by the world's dark sins I still am enchained.

3 *Creation's great King, who gave new sight to the blind,*
 who scourging endured when you redeemed humankind,
 and humbly allowed your captors your flesh tight to bind,
 forgive us all, poor sinners, your family.

tr. *Donald A. R. Caird* (b. 1925)
and *Gary Hastings* (b. 1956)
Versified *Donald Davison* (b. 1937)

547

Stracathro   86 86 (CM)   Charles Hutcheson (1792–1860)

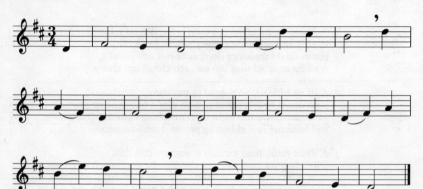

1 Approach, my soul, the mercy-seat
    where Jesus answers prayer;
  there humbly fall before his feet,
    for none can perish there.

2 Thy promise is my only plea,
    with this I venture nigh;
  thou callest burdened souls to thee,
    and such, O Lord, am I.

3 Bowed down beneath a load of sin,
    by Satan sorely pressed,
  by war without, and fears within,
    I come to thee for rest.

4 Be thou my shield and hiding-place,
    that, sheltered near thy side,
  I may my fierce accuser face,
    and tell him thou hast died.

5 O wondrous love, to bleed and die,
    to bear the cross and shame,
  that guilty sinners, such as I,
    might plead thy gracious Name!

John Newton (1725–1807)

548

Song 46　10 10　　　　　　　　　　　Orlando Gibbons (1583–1625)

1 Drop, drop, slow tears,
   and bathe those beauteous feet,
   which brought from heaven ⌣
   the news and Prince of Peace.

2 Cease not, wet eyes,
   his mercies to entreat;
   to cry for vengeance ⌣
   sin doth never cease.

3 In your deep floods
   drown all my faults and fears;
   not let his eye ⌣
   see sin, but through my tears.

Phineas Fletcher (1582–1650)

549

Repton   86 88 6 extended

C. Hubert H. Parry (1848–1918)
from a song in his oratorio *Judith* (1888)

1 Dear Lord and Father of mankind,
    forgive our foolish ways;
  re-clothe us in our rightful mind,
  in purer lives thy service find,
    in deeper reverence, praise.

2 In simple trust like theirs who heard,
    beside the Syrian sea,
  the gracious calling of the Lord,
  let us like them, without a word
    rise up and follow thee.

3 O Sabbath rest by Galilee,
    O calm of hills above,
  where Jesus knelt to share with thee
  the silence of eternity,
    interpreted by love.

4 Drop thy still dews of quietness,
    till all our strivings cease;
  take from our souls the strain and stress,
  and let our ordered lives confess
    the beauty of thy peace.

5 Breathe through the heats of our desire
    thy coolness and thy balm;
  let sense be dumb, let flesh retire;
  speak through the earthquake, wind and fire,
    O still small voice of calm.

John G. Whittier (1807–92)

550

FIRST TUNE

North American folk hymn melody
in *A Supplement to the Kentucky Harmony* (1820)

Forgive our sins   86 86 (CM)

SECOND TUNE

from W. Anchors'
A Choice Collection of Psalm Tunes (c.1721)

Walsall   86 86 (CM)

Alternative tune: 11i EPWORTH

1 'Forgive our sins as we forgive',
    you taught us, Lord, to pray;
but you alone can grant us grace
    to live the words we say.

2 How can your pardon reach and bless
    the unforgiving heart
that broods on wrongs, and will not let
    old bitterness depart?

3 In blazing light your cross reveals
    the truth we dimly knew:
what trivial debts are owed to us,
    how great our debt to you!

4 Lord, cleanse the depths within our souls
    and bid resentment cease.
Then, bound to all in bonds of love,
    our lives will spread your peace.

Rosamond E. Herklots (1905–87)
based on Matthew 6: 12

551

Billing   86 86 (CM)   Richard R. Terry (1865–1938)

1 How can we sing with joy to God,
   how can we pray to him,
   when we are far away from God
   in selfishness and sin?

2 How can we claim to do God's will
   when we have turned away ⌣
   from things of God to things of earth,
   and willed to disobey?

3 How can we praise the love of God
   which all his works make known,
   when all our works turn from his love
   to choices of our own?

4 God knows the sinful things we do,
   the godless life we live,
   yet in his love he calls to us,
   so ready to forgive.

5 So we will turn again to God—
   his ways will be our ways,
   his will our will, his love our love,
   and he himself our praise!

                                        Brian Foley (b. 1919)

552

I hear thy welcome voice   66 86 (SM) with Refrain   Lewis Hartsough (1828–72)

REFRAIN

I am com-ing, Lord! Com - ing now to thee!

Wash me, cleanse me in the blood that flowed on Cal-va - ry.

1 I hear thy welcome voice
      that calls me, Lord, to thee,
   for cleansing in thy precious blood
      that flowed on Calvary.

   I am coming, Lord!
   Coming now to thee!
   Wash me, cleanse me in the blood
   that flowed on Calvary.

2 Though coming weak and vile,
      thou didst my strength assure;
   thou dost my vileness fully cleanse
      till spotless all and pure.

3 'Tis Jesus calls me on
      to perfect faith and love,
   to perfect hope, and peace, and trust,
      for earth and heaven above.

4 'Tis Jesus who confirms
      the blessèd work within,
   by adding grace to welcomed grace,
      where reigned the power of sin.

5 All hail, atoning blood!
      All hail, redeeming grace!
   All hail, the gift of Christ our Lord,
      our strength and righteousness.

Lewis Hartsough (1828–72)

553

Hollingside　77 77 D　　　　　　　　　　John Bacchus Dykes (1823–76)

Aberystwyth　77 77 D　　　　　　　　　　Joseph Parry (1841–1903)

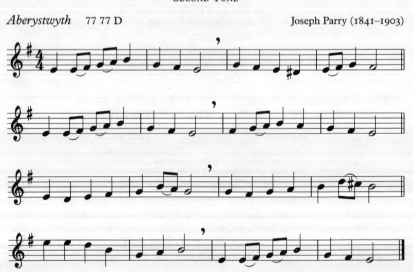

REPENTANCE

1 Jesu, lover of my soul,
   let me to thy bosom fly,
while the nearer waters roll,
   while the tempest still is high;
hide me, O my Saviour, hide,
   till the storm of life be past;
safe into the haven guide,
   O receive my soul at last.

2 Other refuge have I none,
   hangs my helpless soul on thee;
leave, ah leave me not alone,
   still support and comfort me;
all my trust on thee is stayed,
   all my help from thee I bring;
cover my defenceless head
   with the shadow of thy wing.

3 Thou, O Christ, art all I want;
   more than all in thee I find;
raise the fallen, cheer the faint,
   heal the sick, and lead the blind;
just and holy is thy name,
   I am all unrighteousness;
false and full of sin I am,
   thou art full of truth and grace.

4 Plenteous grace with thee is found,
   grace to cover all my sin;
let the healing streams abound:
   make and keep me pure within.
Thou of life the fountain art,
   freely let me take of thee,
spring thou up within my heart,
   rise to all eternity.

Charles Wesley (1707–88)

FAITH AND DISCIPLESHIP

554

FIRST TUNE

Southwell   66 86 (SM)

Adapted from Psalm 45 in
The Psalmes in English Meter (1579)
by William Damon (1540–91)

SECOND TUNE

St Bride   66 86 (SM)

Samuel Howard (1710–82)

For the significance of the small notes above the stave in both tunes, see the Musical Preface.

Μνώεο, Χριστέ

1 Lord Jesus, think on me,
    and purge away my sin;
  from earth-born passions set me free,
    and make me pure within.

2 Lord Jesus, think on me,
    with many a care oppressed;
  let me your loving servant be,
    and taste your promised rest.

3 Lord Jesus, think on me,
    nor let me go astray;
  through darkness and perplexity,
    Lord, point the heavenly way.

4 Lord Jesus, think on me,
    that, when the flood is past,
  I may the eternal brightness see,
    and share your joy at last.

Synesius (375–430)
tr. *Allen W. Chatfield (1808–96)* altd.

734

555

Harwich   10 11 11 12

Later form of a melody by
Benjamin Milgrove (1731–1810)

1. re - bel - lious _ way;

Alternative tune: 423, 618 SLANE (2)

1 Lord of creation, forgive us, we pray,
   for following Adam's rebellious way;
      subdue our ambitions and restless desires,
      and open our hearing to the Word who inspires.

2 Sad and bereft, O what beauty we lose,
   in seeking creation to own and abuse!
      O how we exploit her for profit and gain,
      not hearing her protest nor aware of her pain.

3 Keep our religion from poison and stain,
   and let us not use it for glory or gain;
      in truer perspective our vision restore
      as you and you only we exalt and adore.

4 Point us to Christ, in whose passion we see
   forgiveness and mercy both priceless and free.
      At last may we stand in the light of his face,
      in kinship created, and forgiven by grace.

Michael Forster (b. 1946)

735

556

Lord, have mercy

Graham Kendrick (b. 1950)

Lord, have mercy on us,
come and heal our land.
Cleanse with your fire,
heal with your touch:
humbly we bow
and call upon you now.
O Lord, have mercy on us.
O Lord, have mercy on us.

Graham Kendrick (b. 1950)

557

Petra (*Redhead no. 76*) 77 77 77

Richard Redhead (1820–1901)
using the shape of a Spanish *Tantum ergo*

1 Rock of ages, cleft for me,
let me hide myself in thee;
  let the water and the blood,
  from thy riven side which flowed,
be of sin the double cure,
cleanse me from its guilt and power.

2 Not the labours of my hands
can fulfil thy law's demands;
  could my zeal no respite know,
  could my tears for ever flow,
all for sin could not atone;
thou must save, and thou alone.

3 Nothing in my hand I bring,
simply to thy Cross I cling;
  naked, come to thee for dress;
  helpless, look to thee for grace;
foul, I to the fountain fly;
wash me, Saviour, or I die.

4 While I draw this fleeting breath,
when my eyelids close in death,
  when I soar through tracts unknown,
  see thee on thy judgement throne;
Rock of ages, cleft for me,
let me hide myself in thee.

Augustus M. Toplady (1740–78)
based on Exodus 33: 21–23

558

Abba Father

Words and music by Dave Bilbrough

Abba Father, let me be ⌣
yours, and yours alone.
May my will for ever be
evermore your own.

Never let my heart grow cold,
never let me go.
Abba Father, let me be ⌣
yours, and yours alone.

Dave Bilbrough

559

All to Jesus   87 87 with Refrain   W. S. Weedon (1842–1908)

REFRAIN

I sur-ren-der all,   I sur-ren-der all,

all to thee, my bless-ed Sa-viour, I sur-ren-der all.

1 All to Jesus I surrender,
   all to him I freely give;
   I will ever love and trust him,
      in his presence daily live.

I surrender all,
I surrender all,
all to thee, my blessèd Saviour,
I surrender all.

2 All to Jesus I surrender,
   humbly at his feet I bow,
  worldly pleasures all forsaken,
    take me, Jesus, take me now.

3 All to Jesus I surrender,
   make me, Saviour, wholly thine;
  let me feel the Holy Spirit,
    truly know that thou art mine.

4 All to Jesus I surrender,
   Lord, I give myself to thee;
  fill me with thy love and power,
    let thy blessing fall on me.

5 All to Jesus I surrender,
   now I feel the sacred flame;
  Oh, the joy of full salvation!
    Glory, glory to his name!

J. W. Van Deventer (1855–1939)

560

Emain Macha   86 86 88

Charles Wood (1866–1926)
written for the (*Irish*) *Church Hymnal* (1919 edition)

SECOND TUNE

Tibradden   86 86 88

adpt. from a setting of these words by
Joseph Groocock (1913–1997)

OPTIONAL BRIDGE AND CODA

The complete setting (from which this tune has been extracted) was written for St Columba's College, Rathfarnham, where for many years the composer was Director of Music.

COMMITMENT

Im aonarán dom ins an sliabh

1 Alone with none but thee, my God,
    I journey on my way;
  what need I fear when thou art near,
    O King of night and day?
  More safe am I within thy hand,
  than if a host did round me stand.

2 My destined time is fixed by thee,
    and death doth know his hour.
  Did warriors strong around me throng,
    they could not stay his power;
  no walls of stone can me defend
  when thou thy messenger dost send.

3 My life I yield to thy decree,
    and bow to thy control
  in peaceful calm, for from thine arm
    no power can wrest my soul.
  Could earthly omens e'er appal
  whoever heeds the heavenly call!

4 The child of God can fear no ill,
    his chosen dread no foe;
  we leave our fate with thee, and wait
    thy bidding when to go.
  'Tis not from chance our comfort springs,
  Thou art our trust, O King of kings.

Attrib. *Columba* (*c*.520–597)
tr. Anon.

561

Beneath the Cross of Jesus   76 86 86 86   Ira D. Sankey (1840–1908)

1 Beneath the Cross of Jesus
   I fain would take my stand,
the shadow of a mighty rock
   within a weary land;
a home within the wilderness,
   a rest upon the way,
from the burning of the noon-tide heat,
   and the burden of the day.

2 There lies beneath its shadow,
   but on the further side,
the darkness of an open grave
   that gapes both deep and wide;
and there between us stands the cross,
   two arms outstretched to save,
like a watchman set to guard the way
   from that eternal grave.

3 Upon that Cross of Jesus
   mine eye at times can see
the very dying form of one
   who suffered there for me.
And from my stricken heart,
   with tears
   two wonders I confess—
the wonders of redeeming love,
   and my own worthlessness.

4 I take, O Cross, thy shadow
   for my abiding-place;
I ask no other sunshine than
   the sunshine of his face:
content to let the world go by,
   and count its gain but loss,
my sinful self my only shame,
   my glory all—the Cross.

Elizabeth C. Clephane (1830–69)
based on Isaiah 32: 2;
Galatians 6: 4

742

562

Blessed assurance   99 99 with Refrain   Phoebe Palmer Knapp (1839–1908)

REFRAIN

This is my sto - ry, this is my song, prais-ing my Sav - iour all the day long. This is my sto - ry, this is my song, prais-ing my Sav - iour all the day long.

1 Blessèd assurance, Jesus is mine:
  O what a foretaste of glory divine!
      Heir of salvation, purchase of God;
      born of his Spirit, washed in his blood.

    *This is my story, this is my song,
    praising my Saviour all the day long. (twice)*

2 Perfect submission, perfect delight,
  visions of rapture burst on my sight;
      angels descending bring from above
      echoes of mercy, whispers of love.

3 Perfect submission, all is at rest,
  I in my Saviour am happy and blessed;
      watching and waiting, looking above,
      filled with his goodness, lost in his love.

Fanny J. Crosby [Frances J. van Alstyne] (1820–1915)

563

Ich halte treulich still   66 86 D (DSM)

Melody from Schemelli's
Musikalisches Gesangbuch (1736)
probably by J. S. Bach (1685–1750)

Alternative tune: 145ii NARENZA (sung twice fot each verse)

COMMITMENT

Befiehl du deine Wege

1 Commit your ways to God,
    your works into his hands,
and rest on his unchanging word,
    who heaven and earth commands.
He points the clouds their course,
    whom wind and seas obey,
he shall direct your wandering feet,
    he shall prepare your way.

2 Put all your trust in God;
    in duty's path go on;
walk in his strength with faith and hope,
    so shall your work be done.
No profit can you gain
    by self-consuming care;
to him commend your cause; his ear
    attends the softest prayer.

3 Give to the winds your fears;
    hope, and be undismayed;
God hears your sighs and counts your tears,
    God shall lift up your head.
With patience wait his time,
    then shall your eyes behold
the Sun of joy and happiness
    his brightest beams unfold.

4 Leave to his sovereign sway
    to choose and to command;
so you shall, wondering, own his way
    how wise, how strong his hand.
Let us, in life and death,
    his steadfast truth declare,
and publish, with our final breath,
    his love and guardian care.

Paul Gerhardt (1607–76)
tr. *John Wesley* (1703–91) and others altd.

564

Deus meus

Irish traditional hymn melody
Words by Maolíosa Ó Brolcháin (d. 1086)

Irish/Latin version

1. De - us me - us, ad - iu - va me,
2. Do - mi - ne, da____ quod pe - to a te,
3. Tu - um a - mo - rem si - cut vis,
4. Do - mi - ne, Do - mi - ne, ex - au - di me,

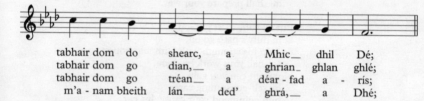

tabhair dom do shearc, a Mhic____ dhil Dé;
tabhair dom go dian,____ a ghrian____ ghlan ghlé;
tabhair dom go tréan____ a déar - fad a - rís;
m'a - nam bheith lán____ ded' ghrá,____ a Dhé;

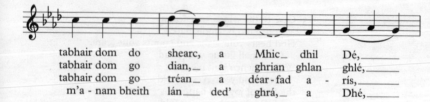

tabhair dom do shearc, a Mhic____ dhil Dé,____
tabhair dom go dian,____ a ghrian ghlan ghlé,____
tabhair dom go tréan____ a déar - fad a - rís,____
m'a - nam bheith lán____ ded' ghrá,____ a Dhé,____

De - us me - us, ad - iu - va me.
Do - mi - ne, da____ quod pe - to a te.
tu - um a - mo - rem si - cut vis.
Do - mi - ne, Do - mi - ne, ex - au - di me.

COMMITMENT

Words by Maolíosa Ó Brolcháin (d. 1086)
tr. Donald A. R. Caird (b. 1925)
and Gary Hastings (b. 1956)
Versified Donald Davison (b. 1937)

English version

1. O my God,— in help— draw near,
2. Grant me what— I seek— of you,
3. Your deep love,— just as— you will,
4. Hear my prayer, O Lord— a - bove,

give me your love,— Re - deem - er dear;
give it in plen - ty, O Sun bright and true;
give to me strong - ly, I pray— you still;
now let my soul— be filled with your love;

give me your love,— Re - deem - er dear,____
give it in plen - ty, O Sun bright and true,____
give to me strong - ly, I pray— you still,____
now let my soul— be filled with your love,____

O my God,— in help— draw near.
grant me what— I seek— of you.
your deep love,— just as— you will.
hear my prayer,— O Lord— a - bove.

565

Father, I place

Words and music by Jenny Hewer

1 Father, I place into your hands
   the things that I can't do.
   Father, I place into your hands
   the times that I've been through.
   Father, I place into your hands
   the way that I should go,
   for I know I always can trust you.

2 Father, I place into your hands
   my friends and family.
   Father, I place into your hands
   the things that trouble me.
   Father, I place into your hands
   the person I would be,
   for I know I always can trust you.

3 Father, I love to seek your face,
   I love to hear your voice.
   Father I love to sing your praise,
   and in your name rejoice.
   Father I love to walk with you
   and in your presence rest,
   for I know I always can trust you.

4 Father, I want to be with you
   and do the things you do.
   Father, I want to speak the words
   that you are speaking too.
   Father, I want to love the ones
   that you will draw to you,
   for I know that I am one with you.

Jenny Hewer

566

Duke Street   88 88 (LM)

Melody from H. Boyd's
Psalm and Hymn Tunes (Glasgow, 1793)
later attrib. John L. Hatton (d. 1793)

SECOND TUNE

St Benet   88 88 (LM)

Cedric Borgnis (b. 1909)

vv. 1 & 4

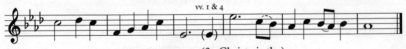

(2. Christ is the)
(3. Christ is its)

1 Fight the good fight with all thy might!
   Christ is thy strength, and Christ thy right;
      lay hold on life, and it shall be
      thy joy and crown eternally.

2 Run the straight race through God's good grace,
   lift up thine eyes, and seek his face;
      life with its path before us lies;
      Christ is the way, and Christ the prize.

3 Cast care aside, lean on thy guide;
   his boundless mercy will provide;
      trust, and thy trusting soul shall prove
      Christ is its life, and Christ its love.

4 Faint not nor fear, his arms are near;
   he changeth not, and thou art dear;
      only believe, and thou shalt see
      that Christ is all in all to thee.

John S. B. Monsell (1811–75) altd.
based on 1 Timothy 6: 11–12

567

Song 34 (Angels' Song) 88 88 (LM) Orlando Gibbons (1583–1625)

1 Forth, in thy name, O Lord, I go,
    my daily labour to pursue;
  thee, only thee, resolved to know,
    in all I think, or speak, or do.

2 The task thy wisdom hath assigned
    O let me cheerfully fulfil;
  in all my works thy presence find,
    and prove thy good and perfect will.

3 Thee may I set at my right hand,
    whose eyes my inmost substance see,
  and labour on at thy command,
    and offer all my works to thee.

4 Give me to bear thy easy yoke,
    and every moment watch and pray,
  and still to things eternal look,
    and hasten to thy glorious day;

5 for thee delightfully employ
    whate'er thy bounteous grace hath given,
  and run my course with even joy,
    and closely walk with thee to heaven.

Charles Wesley (1707–88)

568

Father, we adore you

Terrye Coelho (b. 1952)

1 Father, we adore you,
  lay our lives before you:
    how we love you!

2 Jesus, we adore you,
  lay our lives before you:
    how we love you!

3 Spirit, we adore you,
  lay our lives before you:
    how we love you!

Terrye Coelho (b. 1952)

569

St Bees   77 77

John Bacchus Dykes (1823–76)

1 Hark, my soul, it is the Lord;
    'tis thy Saviour, hear his word;
      Jesus speaks, and speaks to thee,
      'Say, poor sinner, lov'st thou me?

2 'I delivered thee when bound,
    and, when bleeding, healed thy wound;
      sought thee wandering, set thee right,
      turned thy darkness into light.

3 'Can a woman's tender care
    cease toward the child she bear?
      Yes, she may forgetful be;
      yet will I remember thee.

4 'Mine is an unchanging love,
    higher than the heights above,
      deeper than the depths beneath,
      free and faithful, strong as death.

5 'Thou shalt see my glory soon,
    when the work of grace is done;
      partner of my throne shalt be;
      say, poor sinner, lov'st thou me?'

6 Lord, it is my chief complaint,
    that my love is weak and faint:
      yet I love thee and adore;
      O for grace to love thee more!

William Cowper (1731–1800)
based on John 21: 15 & Isaiah 49: 15 (v. 3)

570

Sing hosanna   10 8 10 9 with Refrain

Traditional melody

Sing ho-san-na, sing ho-san-na, sing ho-san-na to the King of kings!

Sing ho-san-na, sing ho-san-na, sing ho-san-na to the King!

*1 Give me oil in my lamp, keep me burning,
   give me oil in my lamp, I pray;
   give me oil in my lamp, keep me burning,
   keep me burning till the break of day.

   Sing hosanna, sing hosanna,
   sing hosanna to the King of kings!
   Sing hosanna, sing hosanna,
   sing hosanna to the King!

2 Give me joy in my heart, keep me praising,
   give me joy in my heart, I pray;
   give me joy in my heart, keep me praising,
   keep me praising till the break of day.

3 Give me peace in my heart, keep me loving,
   give me peace in my heart, I pray;
   give me peace in my heart, keep me loving,
   keep me loving till the break of day.

4 Give me love in my heart, keep me serving,
   give me love in my heart, I pray;
   give me love in my heart, keep me serving,
   keep me serving till the break of day.

Traditional
v. 1 based on Matthew 25: 8

571

Gurab tú mo Bheatha

Seán Ó Riada (1931–71)

COMMITMENT

1 Gurab tú mo Bheatha, a choimhde chroí,
 ní ní neach eile ach Rí seacht nimhe,
 gurab tú mo mhachnamh de ló is d'oíche,
 gurab tú mo radharc i mo chodladh choíche.

2 Gurab tú mo labhradh, gurab tú mo thuigse,
 go mba thusa domsa, go mba mise duitse,
 gurab tusa m'athair, gurab mé do leanbh,
 go mba tusa liomsa agus mise leatsa.

3 Gurab tú mo lúireach, gurab tú mo chlaíomh,
 gurab tú mo mhórgacht, gurab tusa m'aoibhneas,
 gurab tú mo dhídean, gurab tú mo dhaingean,
 go mba tú dom' thógáil do chuallacht na n-aingeal.

4 Gurab tú gach maitheas dom' chorp's dom' anam,
 gurab tú mo fhlaitheas ar neamh is ar talamh,
 gurab tú id' aonar príomhshearc mo chroí,
 ná raibh aon neach eile, a ard-Rí nimhe.

Anon. 10th-century Irish

1 *May you live within me, O my heart's companion,*
 may I trust none other than the King of heaven,
 may you be my thinking through the day and night,
 may you be my vision when I lie asleep.

2 *May you be my speaking, may you be my wisdom,*
 you for ever for me, and I for you;
 may you be my Father, may I be your child,
 you for ever with me, and I with you.

3 *May you be my breast-plate, may you be my sword,*
 may you be my honour, may you be my joy,
 may you be my shelter, may you be my fortress,
 may you raise me heav'nward to the hosts of angels.

4 *May you be each good thing for my soul and body,*
 may you be my ruler both in heav'n and earth,
 may you be the first love of my heart for ever,
 may there be none other, High King of heaven.

tr. *Donald A. R. Caird* (b. 1925)
and *Gary Hastings* (b. 1956)
Versified *Donald Davison* (b. 1937)

FAITH AND DISCIPLESHIP

572

First Tune

Munster   88 88 (LM)

Irish traditional melody

Second Tune

Seirkeiran   88 88 (LM)

Edwin Owen (b. 1910)

Baoth an croidhe, a Mhic Dé

1 How great the tale, that there should be,
in God's Son's heart, a place for me;
   that on a sinner's lips like mine
   the Cross of Jesus Christ should shine!

2 Christ Jesus, bend me to thy will,
my feet to urge, my griefs to still;
   that e'en my flesh and blood may be
   a temple sanctified to thee.

3 No rest, no calm my soul may win,
because my body craves to sin;
   till thou, dear Lord, thyself impart,
   peace on my head, light in my heart.

4 May consecration come from far,
soft shining like the evening star.
   My toilsome path make plain to me,
   until I come to rest in thee.

From the Irish of
Murdoch O'Daly of Connaught (13th cent.)
tr. *Eleanor Hull* (1860–1935)

573

I am thine, O Lord   10 7 10 7 with Refrain   W. H. Doane (1832–1915)

REFRAIN

Draw me near - er,   bless-ed Lord, to the cross where thou hast   died;

draw me near-er,   near-er,   bless-ed Lord, to thy pre-cious, pierc-ed   side.

1 I am thine, O Lord, I have heard thy voice,
   and it told thy love to me;
 but I long to rise in the arms of faith,
   and be closer drawn to thee.

 Draw me nearer, blessèd Lord,
   to the cross where thou hast died;
 draw me nearer, nearer, blessèd Lord,
   to thy precious, piercèd side.

2 Consecrate me now to thy service, Lord,
   by the power of grace divine;
 let my soul look up with a steadfast hope,
   and my will be lost in thine.

3 O the pure delight of a single hour
   that before thy throne I spend,
 when I kneel in prayer and with thee, my God,
   I commune as friend with friend.

4 There are depths of love that I cannot know
   till I cross the narrow sea;
 there are heights of joy that I may not reach
   till I rest in peace with thee.

Fanny J. Crosby [Frances J. van Alstyne] (1820–1915)

574

I give you all the honour

Words and music by Carl Tuttle

I give you all the hon - our and
(2.) Spi - rit moves up - on me now you
(3.) bro - ken chains that bound me, you've

praise that's due your name, for you are the King of
meet my deep-est need, and I lift my hands up
set this cap-tive free, I will lift my voice to

glo - ry, the cre - a - tor of all things.
to your throne, your mer - cy I've re - ceived.
praise your name for all e - ter-ni - ty.

REFRAIN

And I wor - ship you, I give my

life to you, I fall down on my

knees. Yes, I wor - ship you,

COMMITMENT

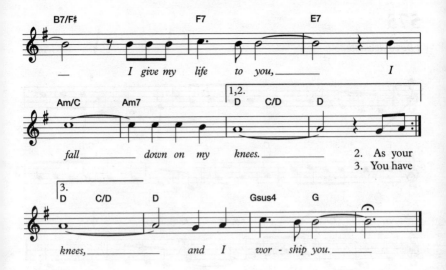

I give my life to you, _____ I fall _____ down on my knees. _____

2. As your
3. You have

and I wor - ship you. _____

1 I give you all the honour
   and praise that's due your name,
   for you are the King of glory,
   the creator of all things.

   And I worship you,
   I give my life to you,
   I fall down on my knees.
   Yes, I worship you,
   I give my life to you,
   I fall down on my knees.

2 As your Spirit moves upon me now
   you meet my deepest need,
   and I lift my hands up to your throne,
   your mercy I've received.

3 You have broken chains that bound me,
   you've set this captive free,
   I will lift my voice to praise your name
   for all eternity.

Carl Tuttle

575

I have decided

Anon.

1 I have decided to follow Jesus,
   I have decided to follow Jesus,
   I have decided to follow Jesus,
      no turning back, no turning back.

2 The world behind me, the cross before me,
   The world behind me, the cross before me,
   The world behind me, the cross before me,
      no turning back, no turning back.

3 Though none go with me, I still will follow,
   Though none go with me, I still will follow,
   Though none go with me, I still will follow,
      no turning back, no turning back.

4 Will you decide now to follow Jesus?
   Will you decide now to follow Jesus?
   Will you decide now to follow Jesus?
      No turning back, no turning back?

Cliff Barrows and *Don Hustad* (b. 1918)

576

Kingsfold   86 86 D (DCM)

Adapted from an English folk song
by R. Vaughan Williams (1872–1958)

Alternative tune: 245 THIRD MODE MELODY

1 I heard the voice of Jesus say,
    'Come unto me and rest;
 lay down, O weary one, lay down
    your head upon my breast'.
 I came to Jesus as I was,
    so weary, worn and sad;
 I found in him a resting-place,
    and he has made me glad.

2 I heard the voice of Jesus say,
    'Behold, I freely give
 the living water, thirsty one,
    stoop down and drink and live'.
 I came to Jesus, and I drank
    from that life-giving stream;
 my thirst was quenched, my soul revived,
    and now I live in him.

3 I heard the voice of Jesus say,
    'I am this dark world's light:
 look unto me, your morn shall rise,
    and all your day be bright'.
 I looked to Jesus, and I found
    in him my Star, my Sun;
 and in that Light of life I'll walk
    till travelling days are done.

Horatius Bonar (1808–89) altd.
based on Matthew 11: 28

577

I know whom I have believed
86 86 (CM) with Refrain

James McGranahan (1840–1907)

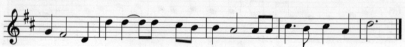

REFRAIN

But 'I know whom I have be-liev-ed___ and am per-suad-ed___ that he is

a-ble to keep that which I've com-mit-ted un-to him a-gainst that day.'

1 I know not why God's wondrous grace
    to me has been made known;
nor why, unworthy as I am,
    he claimed me for his own.

> *But 'I know whom I have believèd*
> *and am persuaded that he is able*
> *to keep that which I've committed*
> *unto him against that day.'*

2 I know not how this saving faith
    to me he did impart;
or how believing in his word
    brought peace within my heart.

3 I know not how the Spirit moves,
    convincing us of sin;
revealing Jesus through the word,
    creating faith in him.

4 I know not what of good or ill
    may be reserved for me—
of weary ways or golden days
    before his face I see.

D. W. Whittle (1840–1901)
based on 2 Timothy 1: 12

578

I need thee   64 64 with Refrain

Robert Lowry (1826–99)

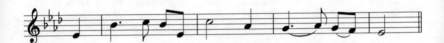

REFRAIN

I need thee, O I need thee, ev - ery hour I need thee;

O bless me now, my Sav-iour! I come__ to thee.

1 I need thee every hour,
   most gracious Lord;
no tender voice like thine ⌣
   can peace afford.

> *I need thee, O I need thee,*
> *every hour I need thee;*
> *O bless me now, my Saviour!*
> *I come to thee.*

2 I need thee every hour,
   stay thou near by;
temptations lose their power
   when thou art nigh.

3 I need thee every hour,
   in joy or pain;
come quickly and abide,
   or life is vain.

4 I need thee every hour,
   teach me thy will;
and thy rich promises ⌣
   in me fulfil.

5 I need thee every hour,
   most holy one;
O make me thine indeed,
   thou blessèd Son!

Annie S. Hawks (1835–1918)

579

Houston

Words and music by
Kathleen Thomerson (b. 1934)

1. I want to walk as a child of the light.
2. I want to see the bright-ness of God.
3. I'm look-ing for the com-ing of Christ.

I want to fol - low Je - sus.
I want to look at Je - sus.
I want to be with Je - sus.

God set the stars to give light to the world. The
Clear Sun of right-eous-ness, shine on my path, and
When we have run with pa-tience the race, we

star of my life is Je - sus.
show me the way to the Fa - ther.
shall know the joy of Je - sus.

REFRAIN

In him there is no dark-ness at all; the

---

* The Capo 1 chords are provided for performance (with guitar) in the original key (D flat).

COMMITMENT

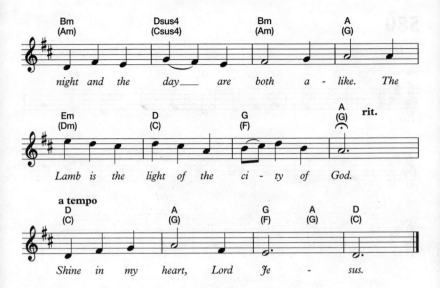

night and the day___ are both a - like. The

Lamb is the light of the ci - ty of God.

a tempo

Shine in my heart, Lord Je - sus.

1 I want to walk as a child of the light.
I want to follow Jesus.
God set the stars to give light to the world.
The star of my life is Jesus.

> *In him there is no darkness at all;*
> *the night and the day are both alike.*
> *The Lamb is the light of the city of God.*
> *Shine in my heart, Lord Jesus.*

2 I want to see the brightness of God.
I want to look at Jesus.
Clear Sun of righteousness, shine on my path,
and show me the way to the Father.

3 I'm looking for the coming of Christ.
I want to be with Jesus.
When we have run with patience the race,
we shall know the joy of Jesus.

Kathleen Thomerson (b. 1934)
Refrain based on Psalm 139: 12
v. 2 based on John 14: 8

765

580

Es Buurebuebli

Swiss traditional melody

Fol - low him, fol - low him, yield your life to him, he has con - quered death, he is King of kings. Ac - cept the joy which he gives to those who yield their lives___ to him._____

COMMITMENT

1 I want to walk with Jesus Christ,
   all the days I live of this life on earth,
   to give to him complete control
   of body and of soul:

   Follow him, follow him, yield your life to him,
   he has conquered death, he is King of kings.
   Accept the joy which he gives to those
   who yield their lives to him.

2 I want to learn to speak to him,
   to pray to him, confess my sin,
   to open my life and let him in,
   for joy will then be mine:

3 I want to learn to speak of him,
   my life must show that he lives in me;
   my deeds, my thoughts, my words must speak
   all of his love for me:

4 I want to learn to read his Word,
   for this is how I know the way
   to live my life as pleases him,
   in holiness and joy:

5 O Holy Spirit of the Lord,
   enter now into this heart of mine;
   take full control of my selfish will
   and make me wholly thine:

C. Simmonds

581

Here I am, Lord

Words and music by Daniel Schutte

COMMITTMENT

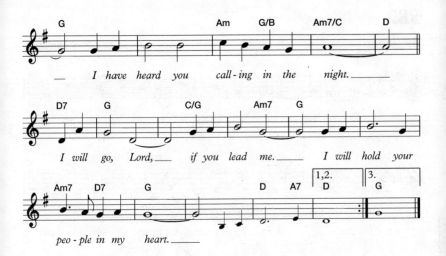

I have heard you call-ing in the night.

I will go, Lord, if you lead me. I will hold your

peo-ple in my heart.

1 I, the Lord of sea and sky,
   I have heard my people cry.
      All who dwell in dark and sin
      my hand will save.
   I, who made the stars of night,
   I will make their darkness bright.
      Who will bear my light to them?
      Whom shall I send?

   Here I am, Lord.
   Is it I, Lord?
   I have heard you calling in the night.
   I will go, Lord,
   if you lead me.
   I will hold your people in my heart.

2 I, the Lord of snow and rain,
   I have borne my people's pain.
      I have wept for love of them.
      They turn away.
   I will break their hearts of stone,
   give them hearts for love alone.
      I will speak my word to them.
      Whom shall I send?

3 I, the Lord of wind and flame,
   I will tend the poor and lame.
      I will set a feast for them,
      my hand will save.
   Finest bread I will provide
   till their hearts be satisfied.
      I will give my life to them.
      Whom shall I send?

Daniel Schutte
based on Isaiah 6: 8
and 1 Samuel 3

582

All for Jesus

Robin Mark

Je - sus,____ all for Je - sus,____ all I am or have____ and ev-er hope to be.____

Je - sus,____ all for Je - sus,____ all I am or have____ and ev-er hope to be.____

All__ my____ am-bi-tions, hopes and plans,__ I sur--ren-der these____ in-to__ your hands.____

COMMITMENT

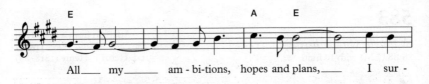

All__ my__ am-bi-tions, hopes and plans,__ I sur-

-ren-der these__ in-to__ your hands.__ For it's

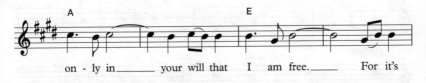

on-ly in__ your will that I am free.__ For it's

D.C. al Fine

on-ly in__ your will_ that I am free.

Jesus, all for Jesus,
all I am or have and ever hope to be.
Jesus, all for Jesus,
all I am or have and ever hope to be.

All my ambitions, hopes and plans,
I surrender these into your hands.
All my ambitions, hopes and plans,
I surrender these into your hands.
For it's only in your will that I am free.
For it's only in your will that I am free.

Jesus, all for Jesus,
all I am or have and ever hope to be.
Jesus, all for Jesus,
all I am or have and ever hope to be.

Robin Mark

771

583

St Finbar (St Catherine)
88 88 (LM) with Refrain

Adapted from a melody in
The Cross of Jesus Music (1864)
ed. Henri F. Hémy (1818–88)

REFRAIN

Je - su, my Lord, I thee a - dore,

O make me love thee more and more!

1 Jesu, my Lord, my God, my all,
    hear me, blessed Saviour, when I call;
        hear me, and from thy dwelling-place
        pour down the riches of thy grace.

Jesu, my Lord, I thee adore,
O make me love thee more and more!

2 Jesu, too late I thee have sought;
    how can I love thee as I ought?
        And how extol thy matchless fame,
        the glorious beauty of thy Name?

3 Jesu, what didst thou find in me,
    that thou hast dealt so lovingly?
        How great the joy that thou
            hast brought,
        so far exceeding hope or thought.

4 Jesu, of thee shall be my song,
    to thee my heart and soul belong;
        all that I am or have is thine,
        and thou, blessed Saviour, thou art mine.

Henry Collins (1827–1919)

COMMITMENT

584

St Andrew   87 87

E. H. Thorne (1834–1916)

SECOND TUNE

St Nicholas (Redhead no. 143)   87 87

Richard Redhead (1820–1901)

1 Jesus calls us! O'er the tumult ‿
    of our life's wild restless sea
  day by day his voice is sounding,
    saying, 'Christian, follow me':

2 as of old apostles heard it
    by the Galilean lake,
  turned from home and toil and kindred,
    leaving all for his dear sake.

3 Jesus calls us from the worship ‿
    of the vain world's golden store,
  from each idol that would keep us,
    saying, 'Christian, love me more!'

4 In our joys and in our sorrows,
    days of toil and hours of ease,
  still he calls, in cares and pleasures,
    'Christian, love me more than
      these!'

5 Jesus calls us! By your mercies,
    Saviour, may we hear your call,
  give to you our heart's obedience,
    serve and love you best of all.

Cecil Frances (Fanny) Alexander (1818–95) altd.
based on Matthew 4: 18–22;
Mark 1: 16–20; John 21: 15

773

585

Quem pastores   88 87   14th-century German carol melody

Alternative tune: 414 CHARING

1 Jesus, good above all other,
  gentle child of gentle mother,
  in a stable born our brother,
      give us grace to persevere.

2 Jesus, cradled in a manger,
  for us facing every danger,
  living as a homeless stranger,
      make we thee our King most dear.

3 Jesus, for thy people dying,
  risen Master, death defying,
  Lord in heaven, thy grace supplying,
      keep us to thy presence near.

4 Jesus, who our sorrows bearest,
  all our thoughts and hopes thou sharest,
  thou to us the truth declarest;
      help us all thy truth to hear.

5 Lord, in all our doings guide us;
  pride and hate shall ne'er divide us;
  we'll go on with thee beside us,
      and with joy we'll persevere.

Percy Dearmer (1867–1936)

586

Saffron Walden   88 86   Arthur Henry Brown (1830–1926)

Alternative tune: 587 MISERICORDIA

1 Just as I am, thine own to be,
   friend of the young, who lovest me,
   to consecrate myself to thee,
      O Jesus Christ, I come.

2 In the glad morning of my day,
   my life to give, my vows to pay,
   with no reserve and no delay,
      with all my heart I come.

3 I would live ever in the light,
   I would work ever for the right,
   I would serve thee with all my might;
      therefore to thee I come.

4 Just as I am, young, strong, and free
   to be the best that I can be
   for truth, and righteousness, and thee,
      Lord of my life, I come.

Marianne Farningham (1834–1909)

587

Misericordia   88 86   Henry Smart (1813–79)

Alternative tune: 586 SAFFRON WALDEN

1 Just as I am, without one plea,
   but that thy Blood was shed for me,
   and that thou bidd'st me come to thee,
      O Lamb of God, I come.

*2 Just as I am, and waiting not
   to rid my soul of one dark blot,
   to thee, whose Blood can cleanse each
      spot,
      O Lamb of God, I come.

3 Just as I am, though tossed about
   with many a conflict, many a doubt,
   fightings and fears, within, without,
      O Lamb of God, I come.

4 Just as I am, poor, wretched, blind;
   sight, riches, healing of the mind,
   yea, all I need, in thee to find,
      O Lamb of God, I come.

5 Just as I am, thou wilt receive,
   wilt welcome, pardon, cleanse,
      relieve;
   because thy promise I believe,
      O Lamb of God, I come.

6 Just as I am (thy love unknown
   has broken every barrier down),
   now to be thine, yea, thine alone,
      O Lamb of God, I come.

7 Just as I am, of that free love,
   the breadth, length, depth, and height to prove,
   here for a season, then above,
      O Lamb of God, I come.

Charlotte Elliott (1789–1871)

588

Moville   76 76 D

Irish traditional melody

The hymn was written for this tune.

1 Light of the minds that know him,
    may Christ be light to mine!
My sun in risen splendour,
    my light of truth divine;
my guide in doubt and darkness,
    my true and living way,
my clear light ever shining,
    my dawn of heaven's day.

2 Life of the souls that love him,
    may Christ be ours indeed!
The living bread from heaven
    on whom our spirits feed;
who died for love of sinners
    to bear our guilty load,
and make of life's brief journey
    a new Emmaus road.

3 Strength of the wills that serve him,
    may Christ be strength to me,
who stilled the storm and tempest,
    who calmed the tossing sea;
his Spirit's power to move me,
    his will to master mine,
his cross to carry daily
    and conquer in his sign.

4 May it be ours to know him
    that we may truly love,
and loving, fully serve him
    as serve the saints above;
till in that home of glory
    with fadeless splendour bright,
we serve in perfect freedom,
    our Strength, our Life, our Light.

Timothy Dudley-Smith (b. 1926)
based on a prayer of *Augustine* (354–430)

589

Galilee   88 88 (LM)

Philip Armes (1836–1908)

Winscott   88 88 (LM)

S. S. Wesley (1810–76)

1 Lord, speak to me that I may speak
   in living echoes of your tone;
 as you have sought, so let me seek
   your wandering children, lost, alone.

2 O lead me, Lord, that I may lead
   the stumbling and the straying feet;
 and feed me, Lord, that I may feed
   your hungry ones with manna sweet.

3 O teach me, Lord, that I may teach
   the precious truths which you impart;
 and wing my words, that they may reach
   the hidden depths of many a heart.

4 O fill me with your fullness, Lord,
   until my heart shall overflow
 in kindling thought and glowing word,
   your love to tell, your praise to show.

5 O use me, Lord, use even me,
   just as you will, and when, and where;
 until at last your face I see,
   your rest, your joy, your glory share.

Frances Ridley Havergal (1836–79) altd.

590

Olivet   664 6664

Later form of a melody by
Lowell Mason (1792–1872)

1 My faith looks up to thee,
  thou Lamb of Calvary,
    Saviour divine:
  now hear me while I pray;
  take all my guilt away;
  O let me from this day
    be wholly thine!

2 While life's dark maze I tread,
  and griefs around me spread,
    be thou my guide;
  bid darkness turn to day,
  wipe sorrow's tears away,
  nor let me ever stray
    from thee aside.

3 May thy rich grace impart
  strength to my fainting heart,
    my zeal inspire;
  as thou hast died for me,
  O may my love to thee
  pure, warm, and changeless be,
    a living fire.

Ray Palmer (1808–87)

591

O happy day   88 88 (LM) with Refrain

Ron Jones (b. 1915)

REFRAIN

O hap-py day,____ O hap-py day,____ when Je-sus

washed my sins a - way;____ he taught me how____ to watch and

pray,____ and live re - joi - cing ev - ery day;____ O hap-py

day,____ O hap-py day,____ when Je-sus washed my sins a - way.____

COMMITMENT

1 O happy day that fixed my choice
   on thee, my Saviour and my God!
Well may this glowing heart rejoice,
   and tell its raptures all abroad.

     O happy day, O happy day,
     when Jesus washed my sins away;
     he taught me how to watch and pray,
     and live rejoicing every day;
     O happy day, O happy day,
     when Jesus washed my sins away.

2 'Tis done, the great transaction's done!
   I am my Lord's, and he is mine!
He drew me, and I followed on,
   charmed to confess the voice divine.

3 Now rest, my long-divided heart,
   fixed on this blissful centre, rest;
nor ever from thy Lord depart,
   with him of ev'ry good possessed.

4 High heav'n, that heard the solemn vow,
   that vow renewed shall daily hear;
till in life's latest hour I bow,
   and bless in death a bond so dear.

Philip Doddridge (1702–51)

591

Festus   88 88 (LM)

Adapted from a melody in
Freylinghausen's *Geistreiches Gesangbuch*
(Halle, 1704)

When this tune is used, the Refrain is omitted.
Alternative tunes (also omitting the Refrain): 351i SAMSON   543, 671 WARRINGTON

1 O happy day that fixed my choice
   on thee, my Saviour and my God!
   Well may this glowing heart rejoice,
   and tell its raptures all abroad.

2 'Tis done, the great transaction's done!
   I am my Lord's, and he is mine!
   He drew me, and I followed on,
   charmed to confess the voice divine.

3 Now rest, my long-divided heart,
   fixed on this blissful centre, rest;
   nor ever from thy Lord depart,
   with him of ev'ry good possessed.

4 High heav'n, that heard the solemn vow,
   that vow renewed shall daily hear;
   till in life's latest hour I bow,
   and bless in death a bond so dear.

Philip Doddridge (1702–51)

592

St Margaret   88 886

A. L. Peace (1844–1912)

1 O Love that wilt not let me go,
     I rest my weary soul in thee:
  I give thee back the life I owe,
  that in thine ocean depths its flow ⌣
     may richer, fuller be.

2 O Light that followest all my way,
     I yield my flickering torch to thee:
  my heart restores its borrowed ray,
  that in thy sunshine's blaze its day ⌣
     may brighter, fairer be.

3 O Joy that seekest me through pain,
     I cannot close my heart to thee:
  I trace the rainbow through the rain,
  and feel the promise is not vain,
     that morn shall tearless be.

4 O Cross that liftest up my head,
     I dare not ask to fly from thee:
  I lay in dust life's glory dead,
  and from the ground there blossoms red
     life that shall endless be.

George Matheson (1842–1906)

593

Wolvercote   76 76 D   W. H. Ferguson (1874–1950)

Missionary   76 76 D   Lowell Mason (1792–1872)

Alternative tunes: 313 DAY OF REST   522i CLONMEL   529 THORNBURY

COMMITMENT

1 O Jesus, I have promised
   to serve thee to the end;
be thou for ever near me,
   my Master and my Friend.
I shall not fear the battle
   if thou art by my side,
nor wander from the pathway,
   if thou wilt be my guide.

2 O let me feel thee near me:
   the world is ever near;
I see the sights that dazzle,
   the tempting sounds I hear;
my foes are ever near me,
   around me and within;
but, Jesus, draw thou nearer,
   and shield my soul from sin.

3 O let me hear thee speaking
   in accents clear and still,
above the storms of passion,
   the murmurs of self-will.
O speak to reassure me,
   to hasten or control:
O speak and make me listen,
   thou guardian of my soul.

4 O Jesus, thou hast promised
   to all who follow thee,
that where thou art in glory,
   there shall thy servant be;
and, Jesus, I have promised
   to serve thee to the end;
O give me grace to follow,
   my Master and my Friend.

5 O let me see thy foot-marks,
   and in them plant mine own;
my hope to follow duly
   is in thy strength alone.
O guide me, call me, draw me,
   uphold me to the end;
and then in heaven receive me,
   my Saviour and my Friend.

John E. Bode (1816–74)

594

Petrie's Crown 11 11 11 11

Irish traditional melody
(from the Petrie collection)

1 O Lord of creation, to you be all praise!
Most mighty your working, most wondrous your ways!
 Your glory and might are beyond us to tell,
 and yet in the heart of the humble you dwell.

2 O Lord of all power, I give you my will,
in joyful obedience your tasks to fulfil.
 Your bondage is freedom; your service is song;
 and, held in your keeping, my weakness is strong.

3 O Lord of all wisdom, I give you my mind,
rich truth that surpasses our knowledge to find;
 what eye has not seen and what ear has not heard
 is taught by your Spirit and shines from your Word.

4 O Lord of all bounty, I give you my heart;
I praise and adore you for all you impart,
 your love to inspire me, your counsel to guide,
 your presence to shield me, whatever betide.

5 O Lord of all being, I give you my all;
if I ever disown you, I stumble and fall;
 but, led in your service your word to obey,
 I'll walk in your freedom to the end of the way.

Jack C. Winslow (1882–1974) altd.

This hymn text was written without the 'O' at the start of each verse. The 'O' should only be included when it is sung to the tune PETRIE'S CROWN. The words may be sung in their original form (without an 'O' at the start of each verse) to SLANE (2) (no. 423 or no. 618).

595

Creator God   86 86 (CM)   Norman Warren (b. 1934)

1 Safe in the shadow of the Lord
  beneath his hand and power,
    I trust in him,
    I trust in him,
  my fortress and my tower.

2 My hope is set on God alone
  though Satan spreads his snare;
    I trust in him,
    I trust in him,
  to keep me in his care.

3 From fears and phantoms of the night,
  from foes about my way,
    I trust in him,
    I trust in him,
  by darkness as by day.

4 His holy angels keep my feet
  secure from every stone;
    I trust in him,
    I trust in him,
  and unafraid go on.

5 Strong in the everlasting Name,
  and in my Father's care,
    I trust in him,
    I trust in him,
  who hears and answers prayer.

6 Safe in the shadow of the Lord,
  possessed by love divine,
    I trust in him,
    I trust in him,
  and meet his love with mine.

Timothy Dudley-Smith (b. 1926)
based on Psalm 91

596

Seek ye first

Karen Lafferty (b. 1948)

REFRAIN

Al - le - lu - ia,

1. Seek ye first the king - dom of God,
2. Ask, and it shall be giv - en un - to you;
3. We shall not live by bread a - lone,

al - le - lu - ia, al - le -

and his right - eous - ness, and all these things shall be
seek, and ye shall find; knock, and the door shall be
but by ev - ery word that pro - ceeds from the

- lu - ia, al - le - lu, al - le - lu - ia!

add - ed un - to you;
o - pened un - to you; al - le - lu, al - le - lu - ia!
mouth of the Lord;

The *Alleluia* refrain is sung by soprano voices while the others repeat the verse.

v. 1 *Karen Lafferty* (b. 1948), vv. 2 & 3 anon.
based on Matthew 6: 33 & 7: 7 and Deuteronomy 8: 3

597

Lübeck (Gott sei Dank)   77 77

Adapted from a chorale in J. A. Freylinghausen's
Geistreiches Gesangbuch (Halle, 1704)

SECOND TUNE

Nottingham   77 77

attrib. W. A. Mozart (1756–91)

1 Take my life, and let it be
    consecrated, Lord, to thee;
        take my moments and my days,
        let them flow in ceaseless praise.

2 Take my hands, and let them move
    at the impulse of thy love;
        take my feet, and let them be
        swift and beautiful for thee.

3 Take my voice, and let me sing
    always, only, for my king;
        take my intellect and use
        every power as thou shalt choose.

4 Take my will, and make it thine;
    it shall be no longer mine;
        take my heart, it is thine own;
        it shall be thy royal throne.

5 Take my love; my Lord, I pour
    at thy feet its treasure store:
        take myself, and I will be
        ever, only, all, for thee.

Frances Ridley Havergal (1836–79)

598

Take this moment 75 75

John L. Bell (b. 1949)
and Graham Maule (b. 1958)

1. Take this mo-ment, sign_ and_ space; take my

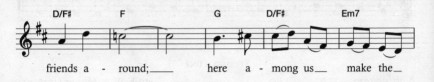

friends a - round;____ here a - mong us__ make the_

place where your love is found.____

1 Take this moment, sign and space;
   take my friends around;
here among us make the place
   where your love is found.

2 Take the time to call my name,
   take the time to mend
who I am and what I've been,
   all I've failed to tend.

3 Take the tiredness of my days,
   take my past regret;
letting your forgiveness touch
   all I can't forget.

4 Take the little child in me,
   scared of growing old;
help me here to find my worth
   made in Christ's own mould.

5 Take my talents, take my skills,
   take what's yet to be;
let my life be yours, and yet
   let it still be me.

John L. Bell (b. 1949)
and *Graham Maule* (b. 1958)

599

Breslau   88 88 (LM)   Melody in *As Hymnodus Sacer* (Leipzig, 1625)

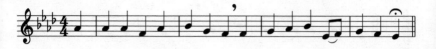

1 'Take up thy cross', the Saviour said,
   'if thou wouldst my disciple be;
deny thyself, the world forsake,
   and humbly follow after me.'

2 Take up thy cross; let not its weight
   fill thy weak spirit with alarm:
his strength shall bear thy spirit up,
   and brace thy heart, and nerve thine arm.

3 Take up thy cross, nor heed the shame,
   nor let thy foolish pride rebel:
thy Lord for thee the cross endured,
   to save thy soul from death and hell.

4 Take up thy cross then in his strength,
   and calmly every danger brave;
'twill guide thee to a better home,
   and lead to victory o'er the grave.

5 Take up thy cross, and follow Christ,
   nor think till death to lay it down;
for only they who bear the cross
   may hope to wear the glorious crown.

Charles W. Everest (1814–77) altd.
based on Luke 9: 23

600

Christmas morn   76 76 D   Edward John Hopkins (1818–1901)

Alternative tune: 36 TYROL

1 The wise may bring their learning,
   the rich may bring their wealth,
and some may bring their greatness,
   and some bring strength and health;
we, too, would bring our treasures
   to offer to the King;
we have no wealth or learning:
   what shall we children bring?

2 We'll bring the many duties
   we have to do each day;
we'll try our best to please him,
   at home, at school, at play;
and better are these treasures
   to offer to the King
than richest gifts without them;
   yet these we all may bring.

3 We'll bring him hearts that love him;
   we'll bring him thankful praise,
and souls for ever striving
   to follow in his ways:
and these shall be the treasures
   we offer to the King;
and these are gifts that ever
   our grateful hearts may bring.

Anon (1881)

601

Sandys   66 86 (SM)

English traditional carol melody
from William Sandys'
Christmas Carols Ancient and Modern (1833)

1 Teach me, my God and King,
     in all things thee to see;
  and what I do in any thing
     to do it as for thee.

2 A man that looks on glass,
     on it may stay his eye;
  or if he pleaseth, through it pass,
     and then the heaven espy.

3 All may of thee partake;
     nothing can be so mean
  which with this tincture, 'For thy sake',
     will not grow bright and clean.

4 A servant with this clause
     makes drudgery divine;
  who sweeps a room, as for thy laws,
     makes that and the action fine.

5 This is the famous stone
     that turneth all to gold;
  for that which God doth touch and own
     cannot for less be told.

6 Teach me, my God and King,
     in all things thee to see;
  and what I do in any thing
     to do it as for thee.

George Herbert (1593–1633)
based on 1 Corinthians 10: 31

602

Two little eyes

C. C. Kerr (d. 1964)

Two little eyes to look to God,
two little ears to hear his word,
  two little feet to walk in his ways,
  two little lips to sing his praise,
two little hands to do his will,
and one little heart to love him still.

C. C. Kerr (d. 1964)

603

Trust and obey　　669 D with Refrain　　　　　Daniel Brink Towner (1850–1919)

REFRAIN

Trust and o - bey, for there's no o - ther way to be hap - py in Je - sus, but to trust and o - bey.

1 When we walk with the Lord
in the light of his word,
　　what a glory he sheds on our way!
While we do his good will,
he abides with us still,
　　and with all who will trust and obey.

Trust and obey,
for there's no other way
to be happy in Jesus,
but to trust and obey.

2 Not a shadow can rise,
not a cloud in the skies,
　　but his smile quickly drives it away;
not a doubt nor a fear,
not a sigh nor a tear
　　can abide while we trust
　　　and obey.

3 But we never can prove
the delights of his love
　　until all on the altar we lay;
for the favour he shows
and the joy he bestows
　　are for those who will trust
　　　and obey.

4 Then in fellowship sweet
we will sit at his feet,
　　or we'll walk by his side in the way;
what he says we will do,
where he sends we will go—
　　never fear, only trust and obey.

John Henry Sammis (1846–1919)

604

Leoni   66 84 D

Hebrew melody noted by Thomas Olivers (1725–99)
from the singing of Meyer Lyon of
the London Great Synagogue, adpt. *c.*1770

1 We turn to Christ anew
      who hear his call today,
   his way to walk, his will pursue,
      his word obey.
   To serve him as our king
      and of his kingdom learn,
   from sin and every evil thing
      to him we turn.

2 We trust in Christ to save;
      in him new life begins:
   who by his cross a ransom gave
      from all our sins.
   Our spirits' strength and stay
      who when all flesh is dust
   will keep us in that final day,
      in him we trust.

3 We would be true to him
      till earthly journeys end,
   whose love no passing years can dim,
      our changeless friend.
   May we who bear his Name
      our faith and love renew,
   to follow Christ our single aim,
      and find him true.

Timothy Dudley-Smith (b. 1926)

605

Kelvingrove   76 76 77 76

Scottish traditional melody

1 Will you come and follow me
    if I but call your name?
  Will you go where you don't know
    and never be the same?
  Will you let my love be shown,
  will you let my name be known,
  will you let my life be grown ⌣
    in you and you in me?

2 Will you leave your self behind
    if I but call your name?
  Will you care for cruel and kind
    and never be the same?
  Will you risk the hostile stare
  should your life attract or scare?
  Will you let me answer prayer ⌣
    in you and you in me?

3 Will you let the blinded see
    if I but call your name?
  Will you set the prisoners free
    and never be the same?
  Will you kiss the leper clean,
  and do such as this unseen,
  and admit to what I mean ⌣
    in you and you in me.

4 Will you love the 'you' you hide
    if I but call your name?
  Will you quell the fear inside
    and never be the same?
  Will you use the faith you've found
  to reshape the world around,
  through my sight and touch and
    sound ⌣
    in you and you in me?

5 Lord, your summons echoes true
    when you but call my name.
  Let me turn and follow you
    and never be the same.
  In your company I'll go
  where your love and footsteps show.
  Thus I'll move and live and grow ⌣
    in you and you in me.

John L. Bell (b. 1949)
and *Graham Maule* (b. 1958)

606

As the deer

Martin Nystrom (b. 1956)

You a - lone are my strength, my shield, to

you a - lone may my spi - ri - t yield. You a - lone are my

heart's de - sire __ and I long to wor - ship you.

1 As the deer pants for the water,
    so my soul longs after you.
You alone are my heart's desire
    and I long to worship you.

> *You alone are my strength, my shield,*
> *to you alone may my spirit yield.*
>   *You alone are my heart's desire*
>   *and I long to worship you.*

2 I want you more than gold or silver,
    only you can satisfy.
You alone are the real joy-giver
    and the apple of my eye.

3 You're my friend and you are my brother,
    even though you are a king.
I love you more than any other,
    so much more than anything.

Martin Nystrom (b. 1956)
based on Psalm 42

607

Martydom   86 86 (CM)   Hugh Wilson (1766–1824)

1 As pants the hart for cooling streams
    when heated in the chase,
  so longs my soul, O God, for thee,
    and thy refreshing grace.

2 For thee, my God, the living God,
    my thirsty soul doth pine:
  O when shall I behold thy face,
    thou majesty divine?

3 Why restless, why cast down, my soul?
    Hope still, and thou shalt sing
  the praise of him who is thy God,
    thy health's eternal spring.

4 To Father, Son, and Holy Ghost,
    the God whom we adore,
  be glory, as it was, is now,
    and shall be evermore.

Nahum Tate (1652–1715)
and *Nicholas Brady* (1659–1726)
based on Psalm 42
New Version 1696

608

Be still and know

Anon.

1. Be still and know that I am God,
be still and know that I am God,
be still and know that I am God.

1 Be still and know that I am God,
   be still and know that I am God,
   be still and know that I am God.

2 I am the Lord that healeth thee. *etc.*

3 In thee, O Lord, do I put my trust. *etc.*

Anon.
v. 1 based on Psalm 46: 10
v. 2 based on Matthew 8: 7
v. 3 based on Psalm 31: 1

609

Bí, a Íosa

Irish traditional melody

1. Bí, a Ío - sa, im___ chroí - se i___ gcuimh-ne gach___
2. 'Sé, a Ío - sa mo___ rí - se, mo___ cha - ra is___ mo
3. Bí, a Ío - sa, go sior - aí im___ chroí is im___

uair, bí, a Ío - sa, im___ chroí - se le___
ghrá; 'sé, a Ío - sa mo___ dhíd - ean ar___
bhéal, bí, a Ío - sa, go___ síor - aí im___

haith - rí___ go___ luath, bí, a Ío - sa,___ im___
pheac - aí___ is ar bhás; 'sé, a Ío - sa___ mo
thuig - se___ mar an gcéann', bí, a Ío - sa,___ go

chroí - se le___ cum - ann___ go___ buan, ó, a
aoibh - neas, mo___ scá - thán___ de___ ghnáth; is a
síor - aí im___ mheabh - air___ mar___ léann, 's ó, a

Ío - sa, 'Dhé dhí - lis, ná___ scar thu - sa uaim.
Ío - sa, 'Dhé dhí - lis, ná___ scar uaim go brách.
Ío - sa, 'Dhé dhí - lis, ná___ fág mé liom féin.

Anon.
(found by Douglas Hyde in an Ulster manuscript)

1. O— Je- sus, ev-'ry mo- ment be— in my heart and
2. O— Je- sus is my king,— my— friend, and my—
3. O— Je- sus, be for ev- er in my heart and my—

mind; O— Je- sus, stir my— heart with—
love; O— Je- sus is my shel- ter from—
mouth; O— Je- sus, be for ev- er in my

sor- row— for my sins; O Je- sus,— fill—
sin- ning— and from death; O Je- sus,— my—
thought and— my— prayer; O Je- sus,— be for

my— heart with— ne- ver- fail- ing love; O—
glad- ness, my— mir- ror— all my days; O—
ev- er in— my qui- et— mind; O—

Je- sus, sweet Mas- ter, ne- ver part— from me.
Je- sus, my— dear-est Lord, ne- ver part— from me.
Je- sus, my— sweet Lord, do— not leave me a- lone.

tr. *George Otto Simms* (1910–1991)

803

610

The Call   77 77

from *Five Mystical Songs* (1911), no. 4
by R. Vaughan Williams (1872–1958)

1 Come, my Way, my Truth, my Life:
    such a way as gives us breath,
 such a truth as ends all strife,
    such a life as killeth death.

2 Come, my Light, my Feast, my Strength:
    such a light as shows a feast,
 such a feast as mends in length,
    such a strength as makes his guest.

3 Come, my Joy, my Love, my Heart:
    such a joy as none can move,
 such a love as none can part,
    such a heart as joys in love.

George Herbert (1593–1632)

611

FIRST TUNE

Addington   55 54 D

Cyril V. Taylor (1907–91)

SECOND TUNE

Bunessan (1)   55 54 D

Scots Gaelic traditional melody

For an arrangement of this tune, with guitar chords, see nos. 44, 58.

1 Christ be beside me,
  Christ be before me,
  Christ be behind me,
    King of my heart.
  Christ be within me,
  Christ be below me,
  Christ be above me,
    never to part.

2 Christ on my right hand,
  Christ on my left hand,
  Christ all around me,
    shield in the strife.
  Christ in my sleeping,
  Christ in my sitting,
  Christ in my rising,
    light of my life.

3 Christ be in all hearts ⌣
    thinking about me,
  Christ be on all tongues ⌣
    telling of me.
  Christ be the vision
    in eyes that see me,
  in ears that hear me,
    Christ ever be.

James Quinn (b. 1919)
adapted from The Breastplate of St. Patrick

612

Melita   88 88 88   John Bacchus Dykes (1823–76)

1 Eternal Father, strong to save,
  whose arm doth bind the restless wave,
    who bidd'st the mighty ocean deep
    its own appointed limits keep:
  O hear us when we cry to thee
  for those in peril on the sea.

2 O Saviour, whose almighty word
  the winds and waves submissive heard,
    who walkedst on the foaming deep
    and calm amid its rage didst sleep:
  O hear us when we cry to thee
  for those in peril on the sea.

3 O Holy Spirit, who didst sweep
  across the dark and formless deep
    to bid its angry tumult cease,
    and give, for wild confusion, peace:
  O hear us when we cry to thee
  for those in peril on the sea.

4 O Trinity of love and power,
  sustain us all in danger's hour;
    through wreck and tempest, grief and loss,
    renew the triumph of the Cross:
  and ever let there rise to thee
  glad hymns of praise from land and sea.

William Whiting (1825–78) altd.

613

Templemore   88 88 (LM)   George H. P. Hewson (1881–1972)

Alstone   88 88 (LM)   Christopher E. C. Willing (1830–1904)

Alternative tune: 436i NIAGARA

1 Eternal light, shine in my heart,
    eternal hope, lift up my eyes;
  eternal power, be my support,
    eternal wisdom, make me wise.

2 Eternal life, raise me from death,
    eternal brightness, make me see;
  eternal Spirit, give me breath,
    eternal Saviour, come to me.

3 Until by your most costly grace,
    invited by your holy word,
  at last I come before your face
    to know you, my eternal God.

Christopher Idle (b. 1938)
after *Alcuin* (c.735–804)

Words: © Christopher Idle/Jubilate Hymns

614

St Columba (2)   86 86 (CM)   Irish traditional hymn melody

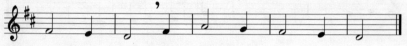

1 Great Shepherd of your people, hear;
   your presence now display;
   as you have given a place for prayer,
   so give us hearts to pray.

2 Within these walls let holy peace
   and love and concord dwell;
   here give the troubled conscience ease,
   the wounded spirit heal.

3 May we in faith receive your word,
   in faith present our prayers;
   and in the presence of the Lord
   unburden all our cares.

4 The hearing ear, the seeing eye,
   the contrite heart bestow;
   and shine upon us from on high,
   that we in grace may grow.

John Newton (1725–1807) altd.

615

Childhood 88 86

H. Walford Davies (1869–1941)
in *A Students' Hymnal* (1923)

1 I love to think that Jesus saw
    the same bright sun that shines today;
  it gave him light to do his work,
    and smiled upon his play.

2 The same white moon, with silver face,
    that sails across the sky at night,
  he used to see in Galilee,
    and watch it with delight.

3 The same great God that hears my prayers
    heard his, when Jesus knelt to pray;
  he is my Father, who will keep
    his child through every day.

Ada Skemp (1857–1927)

616

In my life

Words and music by Bob Kilpatrick

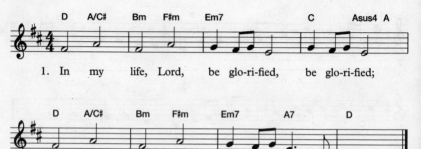

1. In my life, Lord, be glo-ri-fied, be glo-ri-fied;
in my life, Lord, be glo-ri-fied to - day.

1 In my life, Lord,
   be glorified, be glorified;
   in my life, Lord,
   be glorified today.

2 In your Church, Lord,
   be glorified, be glorified;
   in your Church, Lord,
   be glorified today.

3 In your world, Lord,
   be glorified, be glorified;
   in your world, Lord,
   be glorified today.

Bob Kilpatrick, altd.

617

Jesus, remember me

Jacques Berthier (1923–94)
for the Taizé Community

Je-sus, re - mem-ber me when you come in-to your king-dom.

Je-sus, re - mem-ber me when you come in-to your king-dom.

Jesus, remember me
when you come into your kingdom.
Jesus, remember me
when you come into your kingdom.

Taizé Community
based on Luke 23: 42

618

Slane (2)   10 11 11 12   Irish traditional melody

1 Lord of all hopefulness, Lord of all joy,
   whose trust, ever childlike, no cares could destroy,
      be there at our waking, and give us, we pray,
      your bliss in our hearts, Lord, at the break of the day.

2 Lord of all eagerness, Lord of all faith,
   whose strong hands were skilled at the plane and the lathe,
      be there at our labours, and give us, we pray,
      your strength in our hearts, Lord, at the noon of the day.

3 Lord of all kindliness, Lord of all grace,
   your hands swift to welcome, your arms to embrace,
      be there at our homing, and give us, we pray,
      your love in our hearts, Lord, at the eve of the day.

4 Lord of all gentleness, Lord of all calm,
   whose voice is contentment, whose presence is balm,
      be there at our sleeping, and give us, we pray,
      your peace in our hearts, Lord, at the end of the day.

Jan Struther [Joyce Placzek, née Torrens] (1901–53)

619

FIRST TUNE

Bangor   86 86 (CM)

Melody from William Tans'ur's
Harmony of Zion (1735)

SECOND TUNE

Windsor   86 86 (CM)

Melody from William Damon's
Psalmes (1591)

For the significance of the small notes above the stave, see the Musical Preface.

1 Lord, teach us how to pray aright
    with reverence and with fear:
  though dust and ashes in your sight,
    we may, we must draw near.

2 We perish if we cease from prayer:
    O grant us power to pray;
  and when to meet you we prepare,
    Lord, meet us by the way.

3 God of all grace, we bring to you
    a broken contrite heart;
  give what your eye delights to view—
    truth in the inward part;

4 faith in the only sacrifice
    that can for sin atone;
  to place our hopes, to fix our eyes,
    on Christ, and Christ alone;

5 patience to watch and weep and wait,
    whatever you may send;
  courage that will not hesitate
    to trust you to the end.

6 Give these, and then your will be done;
    thus, strengthened with all might,
  we, through your Spirit and your Son,
    shall pray, and pray aright.

James Montgomery (1771–1854) altd.
based on Luke 11: 1

620

O Lord, hear my prayer

Jacques Berthier (1923–94)
for the Taizé Community

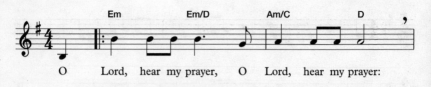

O Lord, hear my prayer, O Lord, hear my prayer:

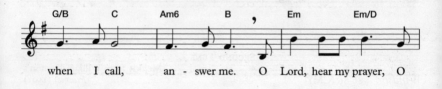

when I call, an - swer me. O Lord, hear my prayer, O

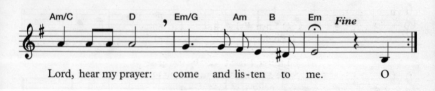

Lord, hear my prayer: come and lis-ten to me. O

O Lord, hear my prayer,
O Lord, hear my prayer:
when I call, answer me.
O Lord, hear my prayer,
O Lord, hear my prayer:
come and listen to me.

Jacques Berthier (1923–94)
based on Psalm 102: 1

621

Cornwall 886 D

S. S. Wesley (1810–76)

1 O Love divine, how sweet thou art!
  When shall I find my longing heart
    all taken up by thee?
  I thirst, I faint and die to prove
  the greatness of redeeming love,
    the love of Christ to me.

2 Stronger his love than death or hell;
  its riches are unsearchable:
    the angels born of light
  desire in vain its depths to see;
  they cannot reach the mystery,
    the length and breadth and height.

*3 God only knows the love of God;
  O that it now were shed abroad
    in this poor stony heart!
  For love I sigh, for love I pine;
  this only portion, Lord, be mine,
    be mine this better part.

4 For ever would I take my seat
  with Mary at the Master's feet:
    be this my happy choice;
  my only care, delight, and bliss,
  my joy, my heaven on earth, be this,
    to hear the Bridegroom's voice.

Charles Wesley (1707–88)

622

The love of my Lord

Estelle White (b. 1925)

1 O the love of my Lord is the essence
   of all that I love here on earth.
      All the beauty I see
      he has given to me,
   and his giving is gentle as silence.

2 Every day, every hour, every moment
   has been blessed by the strength of his love.
      At the turn of each tide
      he is there at my side,
   and his touch is as gentle as silence.

3 There've been times when I've turned from his presence,
   and I've walked other paths, other ways.
      But I've called on his name
      in the dark of my shame,
   and his mercy was gentle as silence.

Estelle White (b. 1925)

623

Belmont   86 86 (CM)

Melody probably by William Gardiner (1770–1853)
in his *Sacred Melodies* (vol. 1, 1812)

1 Our heavenly Father, through your Son,
    all hallowed be your name;
  your kingdom come, your will be done
    in heaven and earth the same.

2 You are the great provider, Lord,
    of bread by which we live.
  We are the great forgetters, Lord,
    of thanks for all you give.

3 You are the great forgiver, Lord,
    of all our constant sin.
  We are the unforgivers, Lord,
    of all our kith and kin.

4 You are the great deliverer, Lord,
    from Satan's evil snares.
  Give us the faith that trusts you, Lord,
    to banish all our cares.

5 You are the great example, where
    you give and you forgive;
  so teach us, Lord, to live your prayer,
    that we may truly live.

Patrick Stephens (1914–2000)
based on the Lord's Prayer (Matthew 6: 9–13)

624

Quietude   65 65

Harold Green (1871–1930)

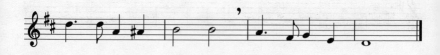

1 Speak, Lord, in the stillness,
   speak your word to me;
help me now to listen
   in expectancy.

2 Speak, O gracious Master,
   in this quiet hour;
let me see your face, Lord,
   feel your touch of power.

3 For the words you give me,
   they are life indeed;
living bread from heaven,
   now my spirit feed.

4 Speak, your servant listens—
   I await your word;
let me know your presence,
   let your voice be heard!

5 Fill me with the knowledge
   of your glorious will;
all your own good pleasure
   in my life fulfil.

E. M. (Grimes) Crawford (1868–1927)
based on 1 Samuel 3: 9

625

FIRST TUNE

Song 67   86 86 (CM)

Orlando Gibbons (1583–1625)
from E. Prys's *Llyfr y Psalmau* (1621)

SECOND TUNE

Martyrs   86 86 (CM)

Melody from the *Scottish Psalter* (1615)
1635 rhythm

Alternative tunes: 233ii AYRSHIRE   654 GRAFENBERG

1 Prayer is the soul's sincere desire,
       unuttered or expressed,
   the motion of a hidden fire
       that trembles in the breast.

2 Prayer is the burden of a sigh,
       the falling of a tear,
   the upward glancing of an eye
       when none but God is near.

3 Prayer is the simplest form of speech
       that infant lips can try;
   prayer the sublimest strains that reach
       the Majesty on high.

4 Prayer is the Christian's vital breath,
       the Christian's native air,
   our watchword at the gates of death,
       we enter heaven with prayer.

5 Nor prayer is made on earth alone:
       the Holy Spirit pleads,
   and Jesus, on the eternal throne,
       for sinners intercedes.

6 O Christ, by whom we come to God,
       the Life, the Truth, the Way,
   the humble path of prayer you trod,
       Lord, teach us how to pray.

James Montgomery (1771–1854) altd.

626

FIRST TUNE

Irish cradle song
from J. P. Lynch's *Melodies of Ireland* (c.1845)

Lynch's Lullaby   77 77 D

This tune covers two verses at a time.

SECOND TUNE

Original form of melody
by Orlando Gibbons (1583–1625)

Song 13 (1)   77 77

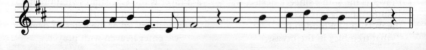

* This decorative figure is in the original, but may be omitted if desired.

For a later, simpler form of this tune, see no. 212 or no. 249.

1 'Set your troubled hearts at rest':
    hear again the word divine;
all our Father does is best;
    let his peace be yours and mine.

2 Trusting still in God above,
    set your troubled hearts at rest;
find within a Father's love
    comfort for a soul distressed.

3 When you come to make request
    know that God will answer prayer;
set your troubled hearts at rest,
    safe within a Father's care.

4 Be at peace, then, and rejoice,
    loved and comforted and blessed;
hear again the Saviour's voice:
    'Set your troubled hearts at rest'.

Timothy Dudley-Smith (b. 1926)
based on John 14: 1

FAITH AND DISCIPLESHIP

627

FIRST TUNE

Converse   87 87 D

C. C. Converse (1832–1918)

SECOND TUNE

Manor House   87 87 D

Frederick G. Carter (1913–1998)

822

1 What a friend we have in Jesus,
    all our sins and griefs to bear!
What a privilege to carry ‿
    everything to God in prayer!
O what peace we often forfeit,
    O what needless pain we bear,
all because we do not carry
    everything to God in prayer!

2 Have we trials and temptations,
    is there trouble anywhere?
We should never be discouraged:
    take it to the Lord in prayer.
Can we find a friend so faithful
    who will all our sorrows share?
Jesus knows our every weakness:
    take it to the Lord in prayer.

3 Are we weak and heavy-laden,
    cumbered with a load of care?
Jesus is our only refuge:
    take it to the Lord in prayer.
Do your friends despise, forsake you?
    Take it to the Lord in prayer:
in his arms he'll take and shield you,
    you will find a solace there.

Joseph Scriven (1819–86)

628

A Rí an Domhnaigh   Melody by Seán Ó Riada (1931–71)

The slurs shown above apply to the Irish text.

1 A Rí an Domhnaigh, tar le cabhair chugam,
  is fóir in am ón bpian mé.
  A Rí an Luain ghil, bíse buan liom,
  is ná lig uaitse féin mé.
  A Rí na Márta, a chroí na páirte,
  déan díonadh Lá an tSléibh' dom.
  A Rí Céadaoine, saor ó ghéibheann mé,
  Cé fad' óm' chaoimhghin féin mé.

2 A Rí Déardaoine, maith ár bpeacaí–ne
  a rinne do dhlí a réabadh.
  A Rí na hAoine, ná coinnigh cuimhne
  ar mo dhroch-ghníomhartha baotha.
  A Rí an tSathairn, go síoraí achainím
  mé' thabhairt thar Acheron caor-thin,
  faoi dhíon do thearmainn, trí ríocht an Aifrinn,
  suas go Parthas naofa.

Tomás Rua Ó Súilleabháin
English version tr. *Donald A. R. Caird* (b. 1925)
and *Gary Hastings* (b. 1956)
Versified *Donald Davison* (b. 1937)

HOLINESS

Unison

1. O King of Sun-day, come and help me, in time of trou-ble
2. O King of Thurs-day, grant for-give-ness for sins which tore a-

save me. O King of Mon-day, be near me al-ways, and
-part your laws. O King of Fri-day, keep not in me-mo-ry

ne-ver let me de-part from you. O King of Tues-day, O
all my fool-ish and bad acts. O King of Sat-ur-day,

heart of friend-ship sweet, pro-tect me on the
I for-ev-er pray that you will car-ry

judg-ment day. O King of Wednes-day, I
me through death, and through your sac-ri-fice

pray you, free me from bond-age, for I have strayed far.
bring me safe-ly at last to ho-ly Pa-ra-dise.

825

629

Dundee (French)   86 86 (CM)

Melody from *The CL Psalmes of David*
(Edinburgh, 1615)

For the significance of the small notes, see the Musical Preface. See also no. 199.

Ach bleib mit deiner Gnade

1 Abide among us with thy grace,
   Lord Jesus, evermore,
   nor let us e'er to sin give place,
   nor grieve him we adore.

2 Abide among us with thy word,
   Redeemer whom we love;
   thy help and mercy here afford,
   and life with thee above.

3 Abide among us with thy ray,
   O Light that light'nest all;
   and let thy truth preserve our way,
   nor suffer us to fall.

4 Abide with us to bless us still,
   O bounteous Lord of peace;
   with grace and power our spirits fill,
   our faith and love increase.

5 Abide among us as our shield,
   O Captain of thy host;
   that to the world we may not yield,
   nor e'er forsake our post.

6 Abide with us in faithful love,
   our God and Saviour be,
   thy help at need O let us prove,
   and keep us true to thee.

Joshua Stegman (1663–1713)
tr. *Catherine Winkworth (1829–78)*

630

Franconia   66 86 (SM)

From a six-line melody in J. B. König's
Harmonischer Liederschatz (1738)
adpt. William Henry Havergal (1793–1870)

1 Blessed are the pure in heart,
   for they shall see our God;
   the secret of the Lord is theirs,
   their soul is Christ's abode.

2 The Lord who left the heavens
   our life and peace to bring,
   to dwell in lowliness with us,
   our pattern and our king;

3 still to the lowly soul
   he doth himself impart,
   and for his dwelling and his throne
   chooseth the pure in heart.

4 Lord, we thy presence seek;
   may ours this blessing be:
   give us a pure and lowly heart,
   a temple meet for thee.

vv. 1 & 3 *John Keble* (1792–1866)
vv. 2 & 4 *W. J. Hall* (1703–1861) altd.
based on Matthew 5: 8

631

FIRST TUNE

Music by H. Walford Davies (1869–1941)
Words from a Book of Hours (Sarum, 1514)

God be in my head

God be in my head,

and in my un - der - stand - ing; God be in mine

eyes, and in my look-ing; God be in my mouth, and in my

speak - ing; God be in my heart, and in my think - ing;

God be at my_ end, and at my de - part - ing.

God be in my head,
and in my understanding;
God be in mine eyes,
and in my looking;
God be in my mouth,
and in my speaking;
God be in my heart,
and in my thinking;
God be at mine end,
and at my departing.

From a Book of Hours (Sarum, 1514)

HOLINESS

SECOND TUNE

Music by Martin Dalby (b. 1942)
Words from a Book of Hours (Sarum, 1514)

Pettronsen

God be in my head, and in my un-der-stand-ing;

God be in mine eyes, and in my look-ing;

God be in my mouth, and in my speak-ing;

God be in my heart, and in my think-ing;

God be at my end, and at my de-part-ing.

632

Angels' story   76 76 D

A. H. Mann (1850–1929)

1 I love to hear the story
    which angel voices tell,
how once the King of glory
    came down on earth to dwell.
I am both weak and sinful,
    but this I surely know,
the Lord came down to save me,
    because he loved me so.

2 I'm glad my blessèd Saviour
    was once a child like me,
to show how pure and holy
    his little ones might be;
and if I try to follow
    his footsteps here below,
he'll make me strong and help me,
    because he loves me so.

3 To tell his love and mercy,
    my sweetest songs I'll raise,
and though I cannot see him,
    I know he hears my praise;
for he himself has promised
    that even I may go
to sing among his angels,
    because he loves me so.

Emily H. Miller (1833–1913) altd.

633

Charles Wood (1866–1926)
written for the *Church Hymnal* (1919)

Armagh   66 66 D

Do budh mhiar dair anman-se

1 It were my soul's desire
   to see the face of God;
   it were my soul's desire
   to rest in his abode.
   It were my soul's desire
   a spirit free from gloom,
   it were my soul's desire
   new life beyond the doom.

2 It were my soul's desire
   to study zealously;
   this, too, my soul's desire,
   a clear rule set for me.
   Grant, Lord, my soul's desire,
   deep waves of cleansing sighs,
   grant, Lord, my soul's desire,
   from earthly cares to rise.

3 It were my soul's desire
   to shun the doom of hell;
   yet more my soul's desire
   within his house to dwell.
   It were my soul's desire
   to imitate my king;
   it were my soul's desire
   his endless praise to sing.

4 It were my soul's desire
   when heaven's gate is won,
   to find my soul's desire,
   clear shining like the sun.
   This still my soul's desire
   whatever life afford,
   to gain my soul's desire
   and see thy face, O Lord.

Old Irish
Versified *Eleanor Hull* (1860–1935)

634

Blaenwern   87 87 D

William P. Rowlands (1860–1937)

Love divine   87 87

John Stainer (1840–1901)

For each verse the tune is sung twice.

1 Love divine, all loves excelling,
      joy of heaven, to earth come down,
  fix in us thy humble dwelling,
      all thy faithful mercies crown;
  Jesu, thou art all compassion,
      pure unbounded love thou art,
  visit us with thy salvation,
      enter every trembling heart.

2 Come, almighty to deliver,
      let us all thy life receive;
  suddenly return, and never,
      never more thy temples leave.
  Thee we would be always blessing,
      serve thee as thy hosts above,
  pray, and praise thee without ceasing,
      glory in thy perfect love.

3 Finish then thy new creation,
      pure and spotless let us be;
  let us see thy great salvation,
      perfectly restored in thee;
  changed from glory into glory,
      till in heaven we take our place,
  till we cast our crowns before thee,
      lost in wonder, love, and praise.

Charles Wesley (1707–88)
based on Malachi 3: 1–2;
2 Corinthians 3: 18; 5: 17

635

Abridge   86 86 (CM)

Melody by Isaac Smith (1734–1805)

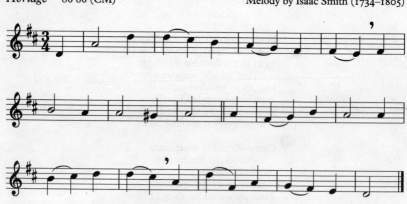

1 Lord, be my guardian and my guide,
   be near me when I call;
   uphold me when my footsteps slide,
   and hold me lest I fall.

2 The world, the flesh and Satan dwell
   around the path I tread;
   O save me from the snares of hell,
   Deliverer from the dead!

3 And if I tempted am to sin,
   and evil powers are strong;
   be present, Lord, keep watch within
   and save my soul from wrong.

4 Still let me always watch and pray,
   and know that I am frail;
   that if the tempter cross my way,
   yet he shall not prevail.

Isaac Williams (1802–1865) altd.
based on Psalm 17

636

St Leonard's   87 85   A. C. Barham Gould (1891–1953)

1 May the mind of Christ my Saviour
    live in me from day to day,
  by his love and power controlling
    all I do and say.

2 May the word of God enrich me
    with his truth from hour to hour,
  so that all may see I triumph
    only through his power.

3 May the peace of God my Father
    in my life for ever reign,
  that I may be calm to comfort
    those in grief and pain.

4 May the love of Jesus fill me
    as the waters fill the sea,
  him exalting, self abasing—
    this is victory!

5 May his beauty rest upon me
    as I seek to make him known;
  so that all may look to Jesus,
    seeing him alone.

6 May I run the race before me
    strong and brave to face the foe,
  looking only unto Jesus
    as I onward go.

Katie B. Wilkinson (1859–1928) altd.
based on Philippians 2: 5
& Hebrews 12: 1–2

637

Caithness   86 86 (CM)   Melody from *Scottish Psalter* (1635)

For the significance of the small notes above the stave, see the Musical Preface.
Alternative tune: 547 STRACATHRO

1 O for a closer walk with God,
      a calm and heavenly frame,
   a light to shine upon the road
      that leads me to the Lamb.

2 Where is the blessedness I knew
      when first I saw the Lord?
   Where is the soul-refreshing view
      of Jesus and his word?

3 What peaceful hours I once enjoyed,
      how sweet their memory still!
   But they have left an aching void
      the world can never fill.

4 Return, O holy Dove, return,
      sweet messenger of rest!
   I hate the sins that made thee mourn,
      and drove thee from my breast.

5 The dearest idol I have known,
      whate'er that idol be,
   help me to tear it from thy throne
      and worship only thee.

6 So shall my walk be close with God,
      calm and serene my frame;
   so purer light shall mark the road
      that leads me to the Lamb.

William Cowper (1731–1800)

638

Stockton   86 86 (CM)   Thomas Wright (1763–1829)

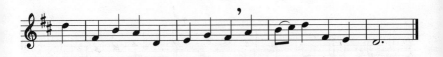

1 O for a heart to praise my God,
      a heart from sin set free;
   a heart that's cleansèd by the blood
      so freely shed for me.

2 A heart resigned, submissive, meek,
      my dear Redeemer's throne;
   where only Christ is heard to speak,
      where Jesus reigns alone;

3 a humble, lowly, contrite heart,
      believing, true and clean,
   which neither life nor death can part
      from him that dwells within;

4 a heart in every thought renewed,
      and full of love divine,
   perfect and right, and pure and good,
      a copy, Lord, of thine.

5 Thy nature, gracious Lord, impart;
      come quickly from above:
   write thy new name upon my heart,
      thy new, best name of love.

Charles Wesley (1707–88)
based on Psalm 51: 10; Ezekiel 36: 26

639

Hereford   88 88 (LM)

S. S. Wesley (1810–76)

1 O thou who camest from above,
    the pure celestial fire to impart,
kindle a flame of sacred love
    on the mean altar of my heart.

2 There let it for thy glory burn
    with inextinguishable blaze,
and trembling to its source return
    in humble prayer and fervent praise.

3 Jesus, confirm my heart's desire
    to work, and think, and speak for thee;
still let me guard the holy fire,
    and still stir up thy gift in me.

4 Still let me prove thy perfect will,
    my acts of faith and love repeat;
till death thy endless mercies seal,
    and make the sacrifice complete.

Charles Wesley (1707–88)

640

Purify my heart

Brian Doerkson

1. Pu - ri - fy___ my heart,___ let me be as gold and_ pre-cious sil - ver; pu - ri - fy___ my heart, ___ let me be as gold, pure___ gold.

2. Pu - ri - fy___ my heart,___ cleanse me from with - in and_ make me ho - ly; pu - ri - fy___ my heart, ___ cleanse me from my sin, deep with-in.

REFRAIN
Re - fin - er's fire,___ my heart's one de - sire_ ___ is to be ho - ly,

HOLINESS

set_ a - part_ for_ you,_ Lord; I choose to be

ho - ly, set_ a - part_ for_ you,_ my_ mas - ter,

rea-dy to do_ your will. _

1 Purify my heart, let me be as gold and precious silver;
  purify my heart, let me be as gold, pure gold.

  *Refiner's fire, my heart's one desire
  is to be holy, set apart for you, Lord;
  I choose to be holy, set apart for you,
  my master, ready to do your will.*

2 Purify my heart, cleanse me from within and make me holy;
  purify my heart, cleanse me from my sin, deep within.

  Brian Doerksen

641

Fortitude   11 11 11 12 with Refrain   Horatio R. Palmer (1834–1907)

Ask the Sav-iour to help you,   com-fort, strength-en, and keep you;

he is will-ing to aid you;   he will car-ry you through.

1 Yield not to temptation, for yielding is sin;
   each victory will help you some other to win;
       fight steadfastly onward; dark passions subdue;
       look ever to Jesus, he will carry you through.

> *Ask the Saviour to help you,*
> *comfort, strengthen, and keep you;*
> *he is willing to aid you;*
> *he will carry you through.*

2 Shun evil companions; bad language disdain;
   God's name hold in reverence, nor take it in vain;
       be thoughtful and earnest, kind-hearted and true;
       look ever to Jesus, he will carry you through.

3 To all overcoming God offers a crown;
   through faith we shall conquer, though often cast down;
       he who is our Saviour our strength will renew;
       look ever to Jesus, he will carry you through.

Horatio R. Palmer (1834–1907) altd.

842

642

Amazing grace   86 86 (CM)

Popular variant of early North American folk melody
(possibly of Scottish origin)

1 Amazing grace (how sweet the sound!)
   that saved a wretch like me!
I once was lost, but now am found;
   was blind, but now I see.

2 'Twas grace that taught my heart to fear,
   and grace my fears relieved:
how precious did that grace appear
   the hour I first believed!

3 Through many dangers, toils and snares
   I have already come;
'tis grace has brought me safe thus far,
   and grace will lead me home.

4 The Lord has promised good to me,
   his word my hope secures;
he will my shield and portion be
   as long as life endures.

5 Yes, when this flesh and heart shall fail,
   and mortal life shall cease,
I shall possess within the veil
   a life of joy and peace.

John Newton (1725–1807)
based on Ephesians 2: 4–8

643

Slane (1)   10 10 10 10

Irish traditional melody

PILGRIMAGE

Rop tú mo baile, a Choimdiu cride

1 Be thou my vision, O Lord of my heart,
   naught be all else to me, save that thou art;
      thou my best thought in the day and the night,
      waking or sleeping, thy presence my light.

2 Be thou my wisdom, be thou my true word,
   I ever with thee, and thou with me, Lord;
      thou my great Father, and I thy true heir;
      thou in me dwelling, and I in thy care.

3 Be thou my breast-plate, my sword for the fight;
   be thou my armour, and be thou my might;
      thou my soul's shelter, and thou my high tower,
      raise thou me heavenward, O Power of my power.

4 Riches I heed not, nor vain empty praise,
   thou mine inheritance through all my days;
      thou, and thou only, the first in my heart,
      High King of heaven, my treasure thou art!

5 High King of heaven, when the battle is done,
   grant heaven's joy to me, O bright heaven's sun,
      Christ of my own heart, whatever befall,
      still be my vision, O Ruler of all.

Early Irish
tr. *Mary Byrne* (1880–1931)
Versified *Eleanor Hull* (1860–1935) altd.

644

Pastor pastorum (Silcher) 65 65 Friedrich Silcher (1789–1860)

1 Faithful Shepherd, feed me
   in the pastures green;
   faithful Shepherd, lead me
   where your steps are seen.

2 Hold me fast, and guide me
   in the narrow way;
   so, with you beside me,
   I need never stray.

3 Daily bring me nearer
   to the heavenly shore;
   make my faith grow clearer,
   help me love you more.

4 Hallow every pleasure,
   every gift and pain,
   be my only treasure,
   all I hope to gain.

5 Day by day prepare me,
   as you see is best,
   then let angels bear me
   to your promised rest.

Thomas B. Pollock (1836–96) altd.

645

Sussex 87 87

English traditional melody
coll. & adpt. R. Vaughan Williams (1872–1958)

Alternative tunes: 225i GOTT WILL'S MACHEN   661 MARCHING

1 Father, hear the prayer we offer:
   not for ease that prayer shall be,
   but for strength that we may ever
   live our lives courageously.

2 Not for ever in green pastures
   do we ask our way to be;
   but the steep and rugged pathway
   may we tread rejoicingly.

3 Not for ever by still waters
   would we idly rest and stay;
   but would smite the living fountains
   from the rocks along our way.

4 Be our strength in hours of weakness,
   in our wanderings be our guide;
   through endeavour, failure, danger,
   Father, be thou at our side.

Maria Willis (1824–1908)

646

Austria 87 87 D

Franz Joseph Haydn (1732–1809)

Alternative tune: 3, 38, 318 ABBOT'S LEIGH (written for these words).

1 Glorious things of thee are spoken,
      Zion, city of our God;
  he whose word can ne'er be broken
  formed thee for his own abode.
  On the rock of ages founded,
      what can shake thy sure repose?
  With salvation's walls surrounded,
      thou may'st smile at all thy foes.

2 See, the streams of living waters,
      springing from eternal love,
  well supply thy sons and daughters,
      and all fear of want remove.
  Who can faint while such a river
      ever flows their thirst to assuage:
  grace which, like the Lord the giver,
      never fails from age to age?

*3 Blessed inhabitants of Zion,
      washed in the Redeemer's blood;
  Jesus, whom their souls rely on,
      makes them kings and priests to God.
  'Tis his love his people raises
      over self to reign as kings;
  and, as priests, his solemn praises
      each for a thank-offering brings.

4 Saviour, since of Zion's city
      I through grace a member am,
  let the world deride or pity,
      I will glory in thy name.
  Fading is the worldling's pleasure,
      all his boasted pomp and show;
  solid joys and lasting treasure
      none but Zion's children know.

John Newton (1725–1807)
based on Psalm 87: 2 & 46: 4

848

647

Cwm Rhondda   87 87 47 extended   John Hughes (1873–1932)

Arglwydd, arwain trwy'r anialwch

1 Guide me, O thou great Jehovah,
    pilgrim through this barren land;
I am weak, but thou art mighty;
    hold me with thy powerful hand:
      bread of heaven,
feed me now and evermore.

2 Open now the crystal fountain,
    whence the healing stream doth flow;
let the fiery, cloudy pillar
    lead me all my journey through:
      strong deliverer,
be thou still my strength and shield.

3 When I tread the verge of Jordan,
    bid my anxious fears subside;
death of death, and hell's destruction,
    land me safe on Canaan's side:
      songs of praises
I will ever give to thee.

William Williams (1717–91)
tr. *Peter Williams (1722–96)* and *William Williams*
based on Exodus 13: 21–22; 14: 26–31;
16: 4–18; 17: 4–6

648

Randolph 98 89

R. Vaughan Williams (1872–1958)

1 God be with you till we meet again;
   may he through the days direct you;
   may he in life's storms protect you;
God be with you till we meet again.

2 God be with you till we meet again;
   and when doubts and fears oppress you,
   may his holy peace possess you;
God be with you till we meet again.

3 God be with you till we meet again;
   in distress his grace sustain you;
   in success from pride restrain you;
God be with you till we meet again.

4 God be with you till we meet again;
   may he go through life beside you,
   and through death in safety guide you;
God be with you till we meet again.

Donald Hughes (1911–67)
based on *J. E. Rankin* (1828–1904)

649

Binchester   86 86 (CM)   William Croft (1678–1727)

The words were written for this tune.

O quam juvat

1 Happy are they, they that love God,
   whose hearts have Christ confessed,
 who by his cross have found their life,
   and 'neath his yoke their rest.

2 Glad is the praise, sweet are the songs,
   when they together sing;
 and strong the prayers that bow the ear
   of heaven's eternal King.

3 Christ to their homes giveth his peace,
   and makes their loves his own:
 but ah, what tares the evil one
   hath in his garden sown!

4 Sad were our lot, evil this earth,
   did not its sorrows prove
 the path whereby the sheep may find
   the fold of Jesus' love.

5 Then shall they know, they that love him,
   how hope is wrought through pain;
 their fellowship, through death itself,
   unbroken will remain.

based on O Quam Juvat by *Charles Coffin* (1676–1749)
tr. *Robert Bridges* (1844–1930) altd.

650

Sandys   66 86 (SM)

English traditional carol melody
from William Sandys'
Christmas Carols Ancient and Modern (1833)

1 In Christ, our humble head,
    we meet, and long to be
a loving people, wisely led,
    forgiving, strong and free.

2 Our walls of soaring stone,
    and tales of old renown,
can send us out and spur us on,
    or drag and weigh us down.

3 Yet saints of former years
    did not live in the past,
but shared their present joy and tears
    with Christ, the First and Last.

4 Then let us look ahead,
    expecting God will do
through Christ, arisen from the dead,
    things greater, good and new.

Brian Wren (b. 1936)

651

Westridge   85 83

Martin Shaw (1875–1958)

1 Jesus, friend of little children,
    be a friend to me;
take my hand, and ever keep me
    close to thee.

2 Teach me how to grow in goodness,
    daily as I grow;
thou hast been a child, and surely
    thou dost know.

3 Step by step, O lead me onward,
    upward into youth;
wiser, stronger, still increasing
    in thy truth.

4 Never leave me nor forsake me,
    ever be my friend;
for I need thee, from life's dawning
    to its end.

Walter J. Mathams (1853–1931)

652

Melody adapted from a chorale
by Friedrich Filitz (1804–76)
in his *Choralbuch* (1847)

1 Lead us, heavenly Father, lead us
   o'er the world's tempestuous sea;
guard us, guide us, keep us, feed us,
   for we have no help but thee;
yet possessing every blessing,
   if our God our Father be.

2 Saviour, breathe forgiveness o'er us,
   all our weakness thou dost know;
thou didst tread this earth before us,
   thou didst feel its keenest woe;
self denying, death defying,
   thou to Calvary didst go.

3 Spirit of our God, descending,
   fill our hearts with heavenly joy,
love with every passion blending,
   pleasure that can never cloy;[1]
thus provided, pardoned, guided,
   nothing can our peace destroy.

James Edmeston (1791–1867) altd.

[1] cloy = to become distasteful from excess

653

FIRST TUNE

Lux benigna   10 4 10 4 10 10

John Bacchus Dykes (1823–76)

SECOND TUNE

Sandon   10 4 10 4 10 10

C. H. Purday (1799–1885)

PILGRIMAGE

1 Lead, kindly Light, amid the encircling gloom,
   lead thou me on;
   the night is dark, and I am far from home,
   lead thou me on.
   Keep thou my feet, I do not ask to see
   the distant scene, one step enough for me.

2 I was not ever thus, nor prayed that thou
   shouldst lead me on;
   I loved to choose and see my path, but now
   lead thou me on.
   I loved the garish day, and, spite of fears,
   pride ruled my will; remember not past years.

3 So long thy power hath blessed me, sure it still
   will lead me on
   o'er moor and fen, o'er crag and torrent, till
   the night is gone,
   and with the morn those angel faces smile,
   which I have loved long since, and lost awhile.

John Henry Newman (1801–90)

654

Gräfenberg (Nun danket all)   86 86 (CM)

Melody from Johann Crüger's
Praxis Pietatis Melica
(Berlin, 1647 edn.)

Alternative tune: 531 MAISEMORE (written for these words)

1 Light of the lonely pilgrim's heart,
   Star of the coming day,
   arise, and with thy morning beams
   chase all our griefs away.

2 Come, blessèd Lord, let every shore
   and answering island sing
   the praises of thy royal name,
   and own thee as their king.

3 Bid the whole earth, responsive now
   to the bright world above,
   break forth in rapturous strains of joy
   in memory of thy love.

4 O Lord, thy fair creation groans—
   the air, the earth, the sea—
   in unison with all our hearts,
   and calls aloud for thee.

5 Thine was the cross, with all its fruits
   of grace and peace divine:
   be thine the crown of glory now,
   the palm of victory thine!

Edward Denny (1796–1880)
v. 4 based on Romans 8: 22

655

Buckland 77 77

L. G. Hayne (1836–1883)

1 Loving Shepherd of your sheep,
   keep your lamb, in safety keep;
       nothing can your power withstand,
       none can pluck me from your hand.

2 Loving Lord, you chose to give
   your own life that we might live;
       and your hands outstretched to bless
       bear the cruel nails' impress.

3 Help me praise you every day,
   gladly serve you and obey;
       like your glorious ones above,
       happy in your precious love.

4 Loving Shepherd ever near,
   teach your lamb your voice to hear;
       let my footsteps never stray
       from the straight and narrow way.

5 Where you lead me I will go,
   walking in your steps below;
       till, before my Father's throne,
       I shall know as I am known.

Jane E. Leeson (1809–81) altd.

656

Horbury 64 64 664

John Bacchus Dykes (1823–76)

Excelsior (Bethany) 64 64 6664

Lowell Mason (1792–1872)
(rhythm altered)

PILGRIMAGE

When sung to the tune EXCELSIOR (BETHANY),
the penultimate line of each verse is repeated.

1 Nearer, my God, to thee,
    nearer to thee;
  e'en though it be a cross ⌣
    that raiseth me;
  still all my song would be,
  'Nearer, my God, to thee,
    nearer to thee'.

2 Though, like the wanderer,
    the sun gone down,
  darkness comes over me,
    my rest a stone;
  yet in my dreams I'd be ⌣
  nearer, my God, to thee,
    nearer to thee.

3 There let my way appear
    steps unto heaven;
  all that thou sendest me
    in mercy given,
  angels to beckon me ⌣
  nearer, my God to thee,
    nearer to thee.

4 Then, with my waking thoughts
    bright with thy praise,
  out of my stony griefs
    Bethel I'll raise;
  so by my woes to be ⌣
  nearer, my God, to thee,
    nearer to thee.

*5 Or if on joyful wing
    cleaving the sky,
  sun, moon and stars forgot,
    upwards I fly,
  still all my song shall be,
  'Nearer my God to thee,
    nearer to thee'.

Sarah Adams (1805–1848)
based on Genesis 28: 10–22

859

657

Abridge   86 86 (CM)

Isaac Smith (1734–1805)

Salzburg   86 86 (CM)

Melody adapted from
Johann Michael Haydn (1737–1806)

PILGRIMAGE

1 O God of Bethel, by whose hand
   thy children still are fed;
who through this earthly pilgrimage
   hast all thy people led;

2 our vows, our prayers, we now present
   before thy throne of grace;
God of our fathers, be the God
   of their succeeding race.

3 Through each perplexing path of life
   our wandering footsteps guide;
give us each day our daily bread,
   and raiment fit provide.

4 O spread thy covering wings around
   till all our wanderings cease,
and at our Father's loved abode
   our souls arrive in peace.

*5 Such blessings from thy gracious hand
   our humble prayers implore;
be thou to us, O Lord our God,
   our portion evermore.

Philip Doddridge (1702–51) altd.
based on Genesis 28: 10–22

658

Southcote   99 79 with Refrain   Sydney Carter (b. 1915)

And it's   from   the old   I

tra-vel   to the new;   keep   me tra-vel-ling   a-long   with   you.

1 One more step along the world I go,
   one more step along the world I go;
      from the old things to the new
      keep me travelling along with you:

   And it's from the old I travel to the new;
   keep me travelling along with you.

2 Round the corner of the world I turn,
   more and more about the world I learn;
      all the new things that I see
      you'll be looking at along with me:

3 As I travel through the bad and good,
   keep me travelling the way I should;
      where I see no way to go
      you'll be telling me the way, I know:

4 Give me courage when the world is rough,
   keep me loving though the world is tough;
      leap and sing in all I do,
      keep me travelling along with you:

5 You are older than the world can be,
   you are younger than the life in me;
      ever old and ever new,
      keep me travelling along with you:

                                        Sydney Carter (b. 1915)

659

St Gertrude   65 65 D with Refrain   Arthur S. Sullivan (1842–1900)

REFRAIN

On-ward, Christ-ian sol - diers,— march-ing as to— war, with the cross of Je - sus go - ing on be - fore.

1 Onward, Christian soldiers,
    marching as to war,
  with the cross of Jesus
    going on before.
  Christ, the royal master,
    leads against the foe,
  forward into battle,
    see, his banners go:

    *Onward, Christian soldiers,
      marching as to war,
    with the cross of Jesus
      going on before.*

2 At the name of Jesus
    Satan's host doth flee;
  on, then, Christian soldiers,
    on to victory!
  Hell's foundations quiver
    at the shout of praise;
  lift your hearts and voices,
    loud your anthems raise:

3 Crowns and thrones may perish,
    kingdoms rise and wane,
  but the Church of Jesus
    constant will remain;
  gates of hell can never
    'gainst that Church prevail;
  we have Christ's own promise,
    and that cannot fail:

4 Onward, then, ye people,
    join our happy throng;
  blend with ours your voices
    in the triumph-song:
  glory, laud, and honour
    unto Christ the King;
  this through countless ages
    we with angels sing:

Sabine Baring-Gould (1834–1924) altd.

863

660

Newington 77 77

William D. Maclagan (1826–1910)

1 Thine for ever! God of love,
   hear us from thy throne above;
       thine for ever may we be,
       here and in eternity.

2 Thine for ever! Lord of life,
   shield us through our earthly strife;
       thou the Life, the Truth, the Way,
       guide us to the realms of day.

3 Thine for ever! O how blessed
   they who find in thee their rest!
       Saviour, Guardian, heavenly Friend,
       O defend us to the end.

4 Thine for ever! Thou our guide,
   all our wants by thee supplied,
       all our sins by thee forgiven,
       lead us, Lord, from earth to heaven.

Mary F. Maude (1819–1913)

661

Marching   87 87

Martin Shaw (1875–1958)

Igjennem Nat og Trænsgel

1 Through the night of doubt and sorrow
   onward goes the pilgrim band,
   singing songs of expectation,
   marching to the promised land.

2 Clear before us through the darkness
   gleams and burns the guiding light;
   pilgrim clasps the hand of pilgrim,
   stepping fearless through the night.

3 One the light of God's own presence,
   o'er his ransomed people shed,
   chasing far the gloom and terror,
   brightening all the path we tread:

4 one the object of our journey,
   one the faith which never tires,
   one the earnest looking forward,
   one the hope our God inspires.

*5 one the strain that lips of thousands
   lift as from the heart of one:
   one the conflict, one the peril,
   one the march in God begun:

*6 one the gladness of rejoicing
   on the far eternal shore,
   where the one almighty Father
   reigns in love for evermore.

7 Onward, therefore, Christian pilgrims,
   onward, with the cross our aid;
   bear its shame, and fight its battle,
   till we rest beneath its shade.

8 Soon shall come the great awaking,
   soon the rending of the tomb;
   then the scattering of all shadows,
   and the end of toil and gloom.

Bernhardt S. Ingeman (1789–1862)
tr. Sabine Baring-Gould (1834–1924) altd.

662

Monks Gate (1)   65 65 66 65

English traditional melody, coll. and adpt.
R. Vaughan Williams (1872–1958)

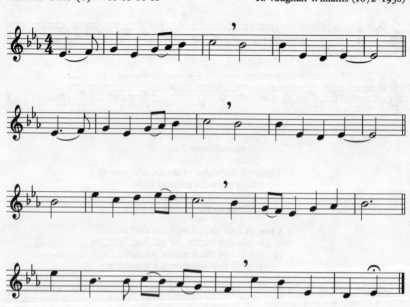

VERSION 1

1 Those who would valour see,
   let them come hither;
one here will constant be,
   come wind, come weather;
there's no discouragement
shall make me once relent
my first avowed intent
   to be a pilgrim.

2 Those who beset me round
   with dismal stories
do but themselves confound;
   my strength the more is.
No lion can affright;
I'll with a giant fight;
but I will have a right
   to be a pilgrim.

3 No evil ghost or fiend
   can daunt my spirit;
I know that at the end
   I'll life inherit.
Then fancies fly away;
whatever others say,
I'll labour night and day
   to be a pilgrim.

John Bunyan (1628–88) altd.
from 'The Pilgrim's Progress'

VERSION 2

1 He who would valiant be
   'gainst all disaster,
let him in constancy
   follow the Master.
There's no discouragement
shall make him once relent
his first avowed intent
   to be a pilgrim.

2 Who so beset him round
   with dismal stories,
do but themselves confound—
   his strength the more is.
No foes shall stay his might,
though he with giants fight:
he will make good his right
   to be a pilgrim.

3 Since, Lord, thou dost defend
   us with thy Spirit,
we know we at the end
   shall life inherit.
Then fancies flee away!
I'll fear not what men say,
I'll labour night and day
   to be a pilgrim.

Percy Dearmer (1867–1936)
after *John Bunyan* (1628–88)

663

Siyahamba

South African traditional melody
arr. Anders Nyberg and the compilers of
Rejoice and Sing (1991)

1. We are march - ing in the light of God,_ we are
march-ing in the light of God.__ We are march - ing in the
light of God, we are march-ing in the light of God.__ We are
march-ing,____ oh,__ we are march-ing in the light of God.__ We are
march-ing,____ oh,__ we are march-ing in the light of God.__

Siyahamb' ekekhanyen' kwenkos

1 We are marching in the light of God,
  we are marching in the light of God.
  We are marching in the light of God,
  we are marching in the light of God.
  We are marching, oh,
  we are marching in the light of God.
  We are marching, oh,
  we are marching in the light of God.

2 We are living in the love of God. *(etc.)*

3 We are moving in the power of God. *(etc.)*

v. 1 South African traditional Spiritual
tr. *Anders Nyberg* (1984)
English vv. 2 & 3 *Andrew Maries* (b. 1949)

664

Evan   86 86 (CM)   William Henry Havergal (1793–1870)

1 To Zion's hill I lift my eyes,
    from thence expecting aid;
  from Zion's hill, and Zion's God,
    who heaven and earth has made.

2 Then thou, my soul, in safety rest,
    thy guardian will not sleep;
  his watchful care, that Israel guards,
    will Israel's monarch keep.

3 Sheltered beneath the Almighty's wings,
    thou shalt securely rest,
  where neither sun nor moon shall thee
    by day or night molest.

4 At home, abroad, in peace, in war,
    thy God shall thee defend;
  conduct thee through life's pilgrimage
    safe to thy journey's end.

Nahum Tate (1652–1715)
and *Nicholas Brady* (1659–1726)
based on Psalm 121
New Version 1696

665

Ag Críost an síol

Seán Ó Riada (1931–71)

1. Ag__ Críost an síol; ag__ Críost an fómhar. In
1. The__ seed is Christ's, and__ his the__ sheaf; with -

ioth-(a)-lainn Dé go__ dtug-tar__ sinn. 2. Ag__
- in__ God's barn may__ we__ be__ stored. 2. The__

Críost an mhuir; ag__ Críost an__ t-iasc. I__
sea is Christ's; and__ his the__ fish; in the

líon-ta Dé go__ gcas-tar__ sinn. 3. Ó__
nets__ of God may__ we__ be__ caught. 3. From__

fhás go__ haois, is ó aois go__ bás, do__
birth to__ youth, and from youth till__ death, your__

THE CHRISTIAN HOPE

dhá láimh, a Chríost, a - nall thar - ainn. 4. Ó___
*two hands, O Christ, stretch o - ver___ us. 4. From_*

bhás go críoch, ní___ críoch ach ath-fhás, i___
death – the end? No___ end, but new life; in___

bPar - thas na nGrást go___ rabh - ai - mid.
sweet Pa - ra - dise may___ we be found.

1. Ag Críost an síol;
   ag Críost an fómhar.
   In iothlainn Dé
   go dtugtar sinn.

2. Ag Críost an mhuir;
   ag Críost an t-iasc.
   I líonta Dé
   go gcastar sinn.

3. Ó fhás go haois,
   is ó aois go bás,
   do dhá láimh, a Chríost,
   anall tharainn.

4. Ó bhás go críoch,
   ní críoch ach athfhás,
   i bParthas na nGrást
   go rabhaimid.

1. *The seed is Christ's,*
   and his the sheaf;
   within God's barn
   may we be stored.

2. *The sea is Christ's;*
   and his the fish;
   in the nets of God
   may we be caught.

3. *From birth to youth,*
   and from youth till death,
   your two hands, O Christ,
   stretch over us.

4. *From death—the end?*
   No end, but new life;
   in sweet Paradise
   may we be found.

Michael Sheehan

tr. *George Otto Simms* (1910–1991)

This hymn was written in 1916 as an expression of sympathy
for a friend whose twelve-year-old daughter had just died.

666

Finlandia   10 10 10 10 10 10

From the symphonic poem *Finlandia*
by Jean Sibelius (1865–1957)

Stille, mein Wille; dein Jesus hilft siegen

1 Be still, my soul: the Lord is on thy side;
    bear patiently the cross of grief and pain;
leave to thy God to order and provide;
    in every change he faithful will remain.
Be still, my soul: thy best, thy heavenly friend
through thorny ways leads to a joyful end.

2 Be still, my soul: thy God doth undertake
    to guide the future as he has the past.
Thy hope, thy confidence let nothing shake;
    all now mysterious shall be bright at last.
Be still, my soul: the waves and winds still know
his voice who ruled them while he dwelt below.

3 Be still, my soul: when dearest friends depart,
    and all is darkened in the vale of tears,
then shalt thou better know his love, his heart,
    who comes to soothe thy sorrow and thy fears.
Be still, my soul: thy Jesus can repay,
from his own fullness, all he takes away.

4 Be still, my soul: the hour is hastening on
    when we shall be forever with the Lord,
when disappointment, grief, and fear are gone,
    sorrow forgot, love's purest joys restored.
Be still, my soul: when change and tears are past,
all safe and blessèd we shall meet at last.

Katharina von Schlegel (1752)
tr. *Jane Laurie Borthwick* (1813–97)
based on Psalm 37: 7
and 1 Timothy 4: 10

667

Bishopthorpe 86 86 (CM)

Melody from Gardner's
Select Portions of the Psalms (*c*.1786)
ascribed to Jeremiah Clarke (*c*.1673–1707)

In the 1960 edition, this tune begins:

1 Blessed be the everlasting God,
　　the Father of our Lord!
Be his abounding mercy praised,
　　his majesty adored!

2 When from the dead he raised his Son,
　　and called him to the sky,
he gave our souls a lively hope
　　that they should never die.

3 There's an inheritance divine
　　reserved against that day;
'tis uncorrupted, undefiled,
　　and cannot fade away.

4 Saints by the power of God are kept,
　　till their salvation come:
we walk by faith as strangers here,
　　but Christ shall call us home.

Isaac Watts (1674–1748) altd.
based on 1 Peter 1: 3–5

668

Ein' feste Burg   87 87 66 667

Melody compiled or composed in 1529
by Martin Luther (1483–1546)

Ein' feste Burg

1 God is our fortress and our rock,
    our mighty help in danger;
who shields us from the battle's shock
    and thwarts the devil's anger:
        for still the prince of night
        prolongs his evil fight;
            he uses every skill
            to work his wicked will—
no earthly force is like him.

2 Our hope is fixed on Christ alone,
    the Man, of God's own choosing;
without him nothing can be won,
    and fighting must be losing:
        so let the powers accursed
        come on and do their worst,
            the Son of God shall ride
            to battle at our side,
and he shall have the victory.

3 The word of God will not be slow
    while demon hordes surround us,
though evil strike its cruellest blow
    and death and hell confound us:
        for even if distress
        should take all we possess,
            and those who mean us ill
            should ravage, wreck, or kill,
God's kingdom is immortal.

Michael Perry (1942–96)
after *Martin Luther* (1483–1546)
based on Psalm 46

669

God sent his Son

Words and music by
Gloria and William J. Gaither

1. God sent his Son, they called him Jesus;
he came to love, heal and forgive;
he lived and died to buy my pardon,
an empty grave is there to prove my Saviour lives.

2. How sweet to hold a new-born baby,
and feel the pride and joy he gives;
but greater still the calm assurance,
this child can face uncertain days because he lives.

3. And then one day I'll cross the river;
I'll fight life's final war with pain;
and then as death gives way to vict'ry,
I'll see the lights of glory and I'll know he lives.

REFRAIN

Because he lives, I can face tomorrow;

THE CHRISTIAN HOPE

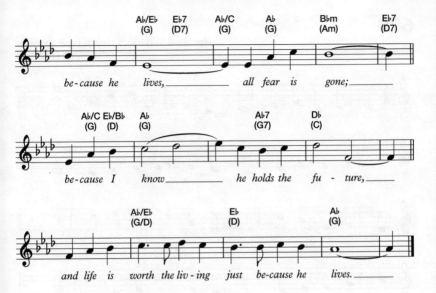

be-cause he lives, _____ all fear is gone; _____

be-cause I know _____ he holds the fu - ture, _____

and life is worth the liv-ing just be-cause he lives. _____

1 God sent his Son, they called him Jesus;
  he came to love, heal and forgive;
  he lived and died to buy my pardon,
  an empty grave is there to prove my Saviour lives.

  Because he lives, I can face tomorrow;
  because he lives, all fear is gone;
  because I know he holds the future,
  and life is worth the living just because he lives.

2 How sweet to hold a new-born baby,
  and feel the pride and joy it gives;
  but greater still the calm assurance,
  this child can face uncertain days because he lives.

3 And then one day I'll cross the river;
  I'll fight life's final war with pain;
  and then as death gives way to vict'ry,
  I'll see the lights of glory and I'll know he lives.

Gloria and William J. Gaither

670

Ewing 76 76 D

adpt. from *St Bede's*, a tune in triple metre by
Alexander Ewing (1830–95)

Alternative tune: 528 AURELIA (written for these words)

Urbs Sion aurea

1 Jerusalem the golden,
　　with milk and honey blessed;
beneath thy contemplation
　　sink heart and voice oppressed.
I know not, O I know not
　　what joys await us there,
what radiancy of glory,
　　what bliss beyond compare.

2 They stand, those halls of Zion,
　　all jubilant with song,
and bright with many an angel,
　　and all the martyr throng;
the Prince is ever in them,
　　the daylight is serene,
the pastures of the blessèd
　　are decked in glorious sheen.

3 There is the throne of David,
　　and there, from care released,
the shout of them that triumph,
　　the song of them that feast;
and they who, with their Leader,
　　have conquered in the fight,
for ever and for ever
　　are clad in robes of white.

4 O sweet and blessèd country,
　　the home of God's elect!
O sweet and blessèd country,
　　that eager hearts expect!
Jesus, in mercy bring us
　　to that dear land of rest;
who art, with God the Father,
　　and Spirit, ever blessed.

Bernard of Cluny (12th cent.)
based on Revelation 7: 14; 21: 1–7
tr. *John Mason Neale* (1818–66) altd.

671

Warrington   88 88 (LM)

Ralph Harrison (1748–1810)

Christi Blut und Gerechtigkeit

1 Jesus, thy blood and righteousness
   my beauty are, my glorious dress;
      'midst flaming worlds, in these arrayed,
      with joy shall I lift up my head.

2 When from the dust of earth I rise,
   to claim my mansion in the skies,
      e'en then shall this be all my plea,
      'Jesus hath lived, hath died for me'.

3 Bold shall I stand in thy great day,
   for who aught to my charge can lay?
      Fully through thee absolved I am
      from sin and fear, from guilt and shame.

4 This spotless robe the same appears,
   when ruined nature sinks in years;
      no age can change its glorious hue,
      the robe of Christ is ever new.

5 O let the dead now hear thy voice,
   now bid thy banished ones rejoice,
      their beauty this, their glorious dress,
      'Jesus, the Lord, our righteousness'.

Nikolaus Ludwig von Zinzendorf (1700–60)
tr. John Wesley (1703–91)

672

Regent Square   87 87 87   Henry Smart (1813–79)

Alternative tune: 326ii URBS BEATA (Plainsong)

Jerusalem luminosa

1 Light's abode, celestial Salem,
    vision whence true peace doth spring,
brighter than the heart can fancy,
    mansion of the highest King;
O how glorious are the praises
    which of thee the prophets sing!

2 There for ever and for ever
    alleluia is outpoured;
for unending, for unbroken
    is the feast-day of the Lord;
all is pure and all is holy
    that within thy walls is stored.

3 There no cloud nor passing vapour
    dims the brightness of the air;
endless noon-day, glorious noon-day
    from the Sun of suns is there;
there no night brings rest from labour,
    for unknown are toil and care.

4 O how glorious and resplendent,
    fragile body, shalt thou be,
when endued with so much beauty,
    full of health, and strong, and free,
full of vigour, full of pleasure
    that shall last eternally!

5 Now with gladness, now with courage,
    bear the burden on thee laid,
that hereafter these thy labours
    may with endless gifts be paid,
and in everlasting glory
    thou with brightness be arrayed.

6 Laud and honour to the Father,
    laud and honour to the Son,
laud and honour to the Spirit,
    ever Three and ever One,
consubstantial,[1] co-eternal,
    while unending ages run.

attrib. *Thomas à Kempis* (1380–1471)
tr. *John Mason Neale* (1818–66)

[1] Father, Son, and Holy Spirit are united in one common substance or nature.

673

Metzler's Redhead   86 86 (CM)
(St Mary Magdalene)

Contributed by Richard Redhead (1820–1901)
to *Ancient Hymn Melodies* (1859),
pub. G. Metzler (no ancient source known)

SECOND TUNE

Frisch auf, mein liebes Töchterlein
86 86 (CM)

German melody (1611)

THE CHRISTIAN HOPE

Jesu nostra redemptio

1 O Christ, our hope, our hearts' desire,
   redemption's only spring;
   creator of the world art thou,
   its Saviour and its King.

2 How vast the mercy and the love
   which laid our sins on thee,
   and led thee to a cruel death
   to set thy people free.

3 But now the bonds of death are burst,
   the ransom has been paid;
   and thou art on thy Father's throne
   in glorious robes arrayed.

4 O may thy mighty love prevail
   our sinful souls to spare;
   O may we come before thy throne,
   and find acceptance there!

5 O Christ, be thou our present joy,
   our future great reward;
   our only glory may it be
   to glory in the Lord.

6 All praise to thee, ascended Lord;
   all glory ever be
   to Father, Son, and Holy Ghost,
   through all eternity.

Latin *c.*8th century
tr. *John Chandler* (1806–76)

674

Monmohenock 76 76

John Purser Shortt (1894–1966)

Álúinn dún Mhic Mhuire

1 O fair is our Lord's own city,
   with clearest light abloom,
and full of joy and music,
   where woe can never come.

2 No guilt or condemnation
   its citizens may know,
none weary is, none anxious,
   no head by grief bent low.

3 The holy gracious Spirit
   shines there with brightest beams,
and sheds God's royal bounty
   in shining showers and streams.

4 The saints and martyrs countless,
   who in this world found woe,
find there a peace and pleasure
   the world cannot bestow.

5 From earth our faces turning
   towards the King of grace;
in prayer let us beseech him
   to bring us to that place.

Donough O'Daly – 'The Great' (d. 1244)
tr. Coslett Quin (1907–1995)

THE CHRISTIAN HOPE

675

FIRST TUNE

First strain of *Song 46*
by Orlando Gibbons (1583–1625)

Song 46   10 10

SECOND TUNE

Pax tecum   10 10

G. T. Caldbeck (1852–1918)

1 Peace, perfect peace, in this dark world of sin?
  The blood of Jesus whispers peace within.

2 Peace, perfect peace, by thronging duties pressed?
  To do the will of Jesus, this is rest.

3 Peace, perfect peace, with sorrows surging round?
  In Jesus' presence naught but calm is found.

4 Peace, perfect peace, with loved ones far away?
  In Jesus' keeping we are safe and they.

5 Peace, perfect peace, our future all unknown?
  Jesus we know, and he is on the throne.

6 Peace, perfect peace, death shadowing us and ours?
  Jesus has conquered death and all its powers.

7 It is enough: earth's struggles soon shall cease,
  and Jesus call us to heaven's perfect peace.

Edward H. Bickersteth (1825–1906) altd.

885

676

Safe in the arms 76 76 D with Refrain

William Howard Doane
(1832–1915)

1 Safe in the arms of Jesus,
  safe on his gentle breast,
 there by his love o'ershaded,
  sweetly my soul shall rest.
 Hark! 'tis the voice of angels
  borne in a song to me
 over the fields of glory,
  over the jasper sea.

  Safe in the arms of Jesus,
   safe on his gentle breast,
  there by his love o'ershaded,
   sweetly my soul shall rest.

2 Safe in the arms of Jesus,
  safe from corroding care,
 safe from the world's temptations,
  sin cannot harm me there.
 Free from the blight of sorrow,
  free from my doubts and fears;
 only a few more trials,
  only a few more tears,

3 Jesus, my heart's dear refuge,
  Jesus has died for me;
 firm on the Rock of ages
  ever my trust shall be.
 Here let me wait with patience,
  wait till the night is o'er,
 wait till I see the morning
  break on the golden shore.

Fanny J. Crosby [Frances Jane van Alstyne]
(1820–1915)

677

Boston   87 87 with Refrain   Robert Lowry (1826–99)

Yes, we'll ga-ther at the ri - ver, the beau-ti-ful, the beau-ti-ful___ ri - ver— ga-ther with the saints at the ri - ver that flows by the throne of___ God.

1 Shall we gather at the river,
    where bright angel-feet have trod,
with its crystal tide for ever
    flowing by the throne of God?

   Yes, we'll gather at the river,
   the beautiful, the beautiful river—
   gather with the saints at the river
   that flows by the throne of God.

2 On the margin of the river
    dashing up its silver spray,
we will walk and worship ever,
    all the happy golden day:

3 Ere we reach the shining river,
    lay we every burden down,
grace our spirits will deliver
    and provide a robe and crown:

4 At the smiling of the river,
    mirror of the Saviour's face,
saints, whom death will never sever,
    raise their songs of saving grace:

5 Soon we'll reach the silver river,
    soon our pilgrimage will cease;
then our happy hearts shall ever
    sing the joyful song of peace.

Robert Lowry (1826–99)
based on Revelation 22: 1–5

678

Alford   76 86 D

John Bacchus Dykes (1823–76)

1 Ten thousand times ten thousand
  give glory to the Lamb;
the angel hosts around the throne
  praise God, the great I AM.
The armies of the ransomed
  have fought with death and sin;
fling open wide the mighty gates
  and let the victors in.

2 Triumphant alleluias
  fill earth and sea and sky,
as countless voices join the song,
  and worship God on high.
O day for which creation
  and all its tribes were made!
O joy, for all its former grief
  a thousandfold repaid.

3 Bring near your great salvation,
  O Lamb for sinners slain,
to gather all your chosen ones—
  then take your power and reign!
Appear, Desire of Nations,
  your exiles long for home:
show in the heavens your promised sign,
  come, Prince and Saviour, come!

Henry Alford (1810–71) altd.
based on Daniel 7: 9–14

679

When Israel was in Egypt's land　　　　　　North American traditional spiritual

This is most effective when sung in responsorial fashion, with e.g. a soloist or a few voices singing the first and third lines of each verse, all voices answering 'Let my people go'. The Refrain should always be sung strongly.

1 When Israel was in Egypt's land,
　　Let my people go!
oppressed so hard they could not stand,
　　Let my people go!

　　Go down, Moses,
　　way down in Egypt's land;
　　tell old Pharaoh
　　to let my people go.

2 The Lord told Moses what to do,
　　Let my people go!
To lead the children of Israel through:
　　let my people go!

3 "Your foes shall not before you stand,"
　　Let my people go!
"And you'll possess fair Canaan's land."
　　Let my people go!

4 O let us from all bondage flee,
　　Let my people go!
and let us all in Christ be free,
　　Let my people go!

5 I do believe without a doubt,
　　Let my people go!
that a Christian has a right to shout,
　　Let my people go!

North American traditional spiritual
adpt. *Peter D. Smith* (b. 1938)

680

Will your anchor hold   10 9 10 9 with Refrain   W. J. Kirkpatrick (1838–1921)

We have an an-chor that keeps the soul

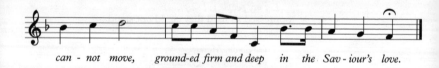

stead-fast and sure while the bil - lows roll,   fast-ened to the rock which

can - not move,   ground-ed firm and deep in the Sav - iour's love.

* A common variant of the first phrase of the refrain is:

We have an an-chor that keeps the soul

† Melody note often sung as B flat.

THE CHRISTIAN HOPE

1 Will your anchor hold in the storms of life,
   when the clouds unfold their wings of strife?
      When the strong tides lift, and the cables strain,
      will your anchor drift or firm remain?

> *We have an anchor that keeps the soul*
> *steadfast and sure while the billows roll,*
>   *fastened to the rock which cannot move,*
>   *grounded firm and deep in the Saviour's love.*

2 It will firmly hold in the straits of fear,
   when the breakers have told the reef is near,
      though the tempest rage and the wild winds blow,
      not an angry wave shall our bark o'erflow.

3 It will surely hold in the floods of death,
   when the waters cold chill our latest breath;
      on the rising tide it can never fail,
      when our hopes abide within the veil.

4 When our eyes behold through the morning light,
   the city of gold, our harbour bright,
      we shall anchor fast by the heav'nly shore,
      with the storms all past for evermore.

Priscilla J. Owens (1829–99)

681

Beulah 86 86 (CM) George M. Garrett (1834–97)

1 There is a land of pure delight,
   where saints immortal reign,
where endless day excludes the night,
   and pleasures banish pain.

2 There everlasting spring abides,
   and never-withering flowers;
death, like a narrow sea, divides
   that heavenly land from ours.

3 Sweet fields beyond the swelling flood
   stand dressed in living green;
so to the Jews old Canaan stood,
   while Jordan rolled between.

4 But timorous mortals stand and shrink
   to cross the narrow sea,
and linger shivering on the brink,
   and fear to launch away.

5 O could we make our doubts remove,
   those gloomy doubts that rise,
and see the Canaan that we love,
   with unbeclouded eyes!

6 Could we but climb where Moses stood,
   and view the landscape o'er,
not Jordan's stream, nor death's cold flood,
   should fright us from the shore.

Isaac Watts (1674–1748)
based on Deuteronomy 34

LITURGICAL MATERIAL

682

Kum ba yah   77 77   West Indian traditional melody

1 All created things, bless the Lord;
  all you heavens, bless the Lord;
  all you angels, bless the Lord;
    sing to God and praise his name.

2 Sun and moon and stars of heaven,
  rain and dew and winds that blow,
  fire and heat and ice and snow,
    sing to God and praise his name.

3 Bless the Lord, you nights and days;
  light and darkness, praise him too;
  clouds and lightnings in the sky,
    sing to God and praise his name.

4 Hills and mountains, bless the Lord;
  flowing rivers with the seas,
  flying birds and earthly beasts,
    sing to God and praise his name.

5 All who dwell upon the earth,
  priests and servants of the Lord,
  humble people, holy ones,
    sing to God and praise his name.

6 Bless the Father, bless the Son,
  bless the Spirit, Three in One;
    sound his glory all your days;
    give to God exalted praise.

Edward F. Darling (b. 1933)
based on the Canticle 'Benedicite'
(Song of the Three: 35–65)

683

Old Hundredth 88 88 (LM)

Melody from *Genevan Psalter* (1551)
(English form of rhythm in final line)

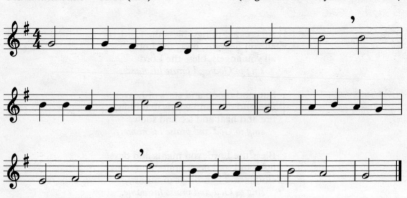

1 All people that on earth do dwell,
    sing to the Lord with cheerful voice;
  him serve with joy, his praise forth tell,
    come ye before him and rejoice.

2 The Lord, ye know, is God indeed;
    without our aid he did us make;
  we are his folk, he doth us feed,
    and for his sheep he doth us take.

3 O enter then his gates with praise,
    approach with joy his courts unto;
  praise, laud, and bless his name always,
    for it is seemly so to do.

4 For why? the Lord our God is good,
    his mercy is for ever sure;
  his truth at all times firmly stood,
    and shall from age to age endure.

5 To Father, Son, and Holy Ghost,
    the God whom heaven and earth adore,
  from us and from the angel host
    be praise and glory evermore.

William Kethe (d. 1594) altd.
based on the Canticle 'Jubilate Deo' (Psalm 100)

684

Engelberg   10 10 10 with Alleluia   Charles Villiers Stanford (1852–1924)

Al - le - lu - ia!_____

1 All praise to thee, for thou, O King divine,
  didst yield the glory that of right was thine,
  that in our darkened hearts thy grace might shine:
    Alleluia!

2 Thou cam'st to us in lowliness of thought;
  by thee the outcast and the poor were sought,
  and by thy death was God's salvation wrought:
    Alleluia!

3 Let this mind be in us which was in thee,
  who wast a servant that we might be free,
  obedient unto death on Calvary:
    Alleluia!

4 Wherefore, by God's eternal purpose, thou
  art high exalted o'er all creatures now,
  and given the Name to which all knees shall bow:
    Alleluia!

5 Let every tongue confess with one accord,
  in heaven and earth, that Jesus Christ is Lord,
  and God the Father be by all adored:
    Alleluia!

Francis Bland Tucker (1895–1984)
based on the Canticle 'The Song of Christ's Glory'
(Philippians 2: 5–11)

685

St Asaph   86 86 D (DCM)

FIRST TUNE
From Smith's *Sacred Music* (Edinburgh, 1825)
possibly by Giovanni Marie Giornovichi
(1745–1804)

SECOND TUNE

Claudius   86 86 D (DCM)

Adapted from a song by G. W. Fink (1783–1846)

1 Blessed be the God of Israël,
   the everlasting Lord.
   You come in power to save your own,
   your people Israël.
   For Israël you now raise up ⌣
   salvation's tower on high
   in David's house who reigned as king
   and servant of the Lord.

2 Through holy prophets did you speak ⌣
   your word in days of old,
   that you would save us from our foes
   and all who bear us ill.
   On Sinaï you gave to us
   your covenant of love;
   so with us now you keep your word
   in love that knows no end.

3 Of old you gave your solemn oath
   to Father Abraham;
   whose seed a mighty race should be
   and blessed for evermore.
   You vowed to set your people free
   from fear of every foe,
   that we might serve you all our days
   in goodness, love, and peace.

4 O tiny child, your name shall be
   the prophet of the Lord;
   the way of God you will prepare
   to make God's coming known.
   You shall proclaim to Israël
   salvation's dawning day,
   when God shall wipe away all sins
   with mercy and with love.

5 The rising sun shall shine on us
   to bring the light of day
   to all who sit in darkest night
   and shadow of the grave.
   Our footsteps God shall safely guide
   to walk the ways of peace,
   whose name for evermore be blessed,
   who lives and loves and saves.

James Quinn (b. 1919) altd. 1985
based on the Canticle 'Benedictus'
(Luke 1: 68–79)

686

Bless the Lord

Donald Davison (b. 1937)

INTRODUCTION

1. Bless the Lord, the God of our fore - bears:
2. Bless his ho - ly and glo - rious name:

sing his praise and ex - alt him for ev - er.

3. Bless him in his ho - ly and glo - rious tem - ple:
4. Bless him who be - holds the depths:

sing his praise and ex - alt him for ev - er.

5. Bless him seat - ed be - tween the che - ru - bim:
6. Bless him on the throne of his king - dom:
7. Bless him in the heights of heaven:

Verses may be sung by a solo voice or semi-chorus, with everyone joining in the refrain.

sing his praise and ex - alt___ him for ev - er.

(a little slower)

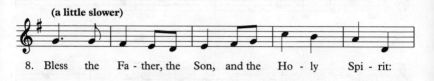

8. Bless the Fa - ther, the Son, and the Ho - ly Spi - rit:

sing his praise and ex - alt___ him for ev - er.

1 Bless the Lord, the God of our forebears:
   sing his praise and exalt him for ever.

2 Bless his holy and glorious name:

3 Bless him in his holy and glorious temple:

4 Bless him who beholds the depths:

5 Bless him seated between the cherubim:

6 Bless him on the throne of his kingdom:

7 Bless him in the heights of heaven:

8 Bless the Father, the Son, and the Holy Spirit:

The Canticle Bless the Lord
from Alternative Prayer Book (1984)
(Song of the Three: 29–34)

687

Darwall's 148th   66 66 44 44

John Darwall (1731–89)

Alternative tune: 49 ST JOHN (ADORATION)

1 Come, let us praise the Lord,
    with joy our God acclaim,
his greatness tell abroad
    and bless his saving name.
        Lift high your songs
            before his throne
            to whom alone
        all praise belongs.

2 Our God of matchless worth,
    our King beyond compare,
the deepest bounds of earth,
    the hills, are in his care.
        He all decrees,
            who by his hand
            prepared the land
        and formed the seas.

3 In worship bow the knee,
    our glorious God confess;
the great creator, he,
    the Lord our righteousness.
        He reigns unseen:
            his flock he feeds
            and gently leads
        in pastures green.

4 Come, hear his voice today,
    receive what love imparts;
his holy will obey
    and harden not your hearts.
        His ways are best;
            and lead at last,
            all troubles past,
        to perfect rest.

Timothy Dudley-Smith (b. 1926)
based on the Canticle 'Venite' (Psalm 95)

688

Earth and all stars   9 10 9 10 with Refrain   David N. Johnston (1922–87)

wor - thy of   hon - our and   glo - ry and   praise.

wor - thy of   hon - our and   glo - ry and   praise.

REFRAIN

1–3. Sing   to   the   Lord___ with   joy - ful   voice;
4. In   all   cre - a - tion   let___   it   be

sing   out   with   glad - ness, al - le - lu - ia!
now   and   for   ev - er, al - le - lu - ia!

1 Come, bless the Lord, God of our forebears,
    worthy of honour and glory and praise.
God's holy name, raise and extol it,
    worthy of honour and glory and praise.

    Sing to the Lord with joyful voice;
    sing out with gladness, alleluia!

2 Come, bless the Lord, God in his temple,
    worthy of honour and glory and praise;
and in the depths, God who sees all things,
    worthy of honour and glory and praise.

3 Come, bless the Lord, seated with angels,
    worthy of honour and glory and praise.
Worship the Lord, throned in all splendour,
    worthy of honour and glory and praise.

4 Come, bless the Lord, high King of heaven,
    worthy of honour and glory and praise;
Father and Son, Spirit most holy,
    worthy of honour and glory and praise.

    In all creation let it be
    now and for ever, alleluia!

Edward F. Darling (b. 1933)
based on the Canticle 'Bless the Lord'
(Song of the Three: 29–34)

689

Come, sing praises   99 97 with Refrain   Michael Perry (1942–96)

REFRAIN

God is king__ a - bove the moun - tains high,__ the

o - cean deep, the land and sky;__ might - y con - tin-ents and

is - lands lie__ with - in the hol - low of God's hand.

1 Come, sing praises to the Lord above,
rock of our salvation, Lord of love;
with delight into God's presence move,
for the Lord our God is King!

God is king above the mountains high,
the ocean deep, the land and sky;
mighty continents and islands lie
within the hollow of God's hand.

2 Come to worship him and bow the knee,
praise our shepherd with humility;
humble creatures in his hand are we—
sing the praise of God the king!

*3 Hear the story of God's people now,
you with stubborn hearts who will not bow;
learn what happened long ago and how ⌣
God can show you who is king!

*4 Forty years God kept the prize away,
made them wander till they would obey,
exiled all of them until the day
they would honour God as king.

Michael Perry (1942–1996)
based on the Canticle 'Venite' (Psalm 95)

690

Venite   11 10 11 10

Donald Davison (b. 1937)

INTRODUCTION

1. Come, wor-ship God who is

wor-thy of hon-our,   en - ter his pre-sence with thanks and a song!

4th time **to Coda** ⊕

He   is   the rock   of his   peo - ple's sal - va - tion,

v. 1

INTERLUDE *(optional)*

to whom our ju - bi-lant   prais-es be-long.

⊕ *CODA*   **rall.**

trust   in   his pro - mis - es,   walk in   his ways!

Alternative tune: 466 O QUANTA QUALIA

1 Come, worship God who is worthy of honour,
    enter his presence with thanks and a song!
He is the rock of his people's salvation,
    to whom our jubilant praises belong.

2 Ruled by his might are the heights of the mountains,
    held in his hands are the depths of the earth;
his is the sea, his the land, for he made them,
    king above all gods, who gave us our birth.

3 We are his people, the sheep of his pasture,
    he is our maker and to him we pray;
gladly we kneel in obedience before him—
    great is the God whom we worship this day!

4 Now let us listen, for God speaks among us,
    open our hearts and receive what he says:
peace be to all who remember his goodness,
    trust in his word and rejoice in his ways!

Michael Perry (1942–96)
based on the Canticle 'Venite' (Psalm 95)

691

Pastor pastorum (Silcher)   65 65   Friedrich Silcher (1789–1860)

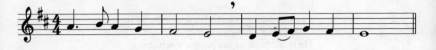

Alternative tune: 68 or 391 GLENFINLAS

1 Faithful vigil ended,
   watching, waiting cease:
   Master, grant your servant
   his discharge in peace.

2 All your Spirit promised,
   all the Father willed,
   now these eyes behold it
   perfectly fulfilled.

3 This your great deliverance
   sets your people free;
   Christ, their light, uplifted
   all the nations see.

4 Christ, your people's glory!
   Watching, doubting cease:
   grant to us your servants
   our discharge in peace.

Timothy Dudley-Smith (b. 1926)
based on the Canticle 'Nunc Dimittis'
(Luke 2: 29–32)

692

Wansford   88 88 (LM)   Stanley Vann (b. 1910)

1 Glory to God in highest heav'n;
   let all creation sing his praise:
peace to his people on the earth;
   justice and truth are all his ways.

2 Almighty Father, and our God,
   Lord God of hosts, our heav'nly King,
we worship you, we give you thanks,
   and to your glory here we sing.

3 Jesus, the Father's only Son,
   O Lamb that takes our sin away,
seated beside the Father's throne,
   hear us and save us, as we pray.

4 For you alone are Lord most high;
   you, Jesus Christ, the Holy One;
now and for ever glorified,
   thrice holy Father, Spirit, Son.

Michael Forster (b. 1946)
based on 'Gloria in Excelsis'

693

Cuddesdon   65 65 D

W. H. Ferguson (1874–1950)

Alternative tunes: 94i EVELYNS   94ii CAMBERWELL

1 Glory in the highest to the God of heaven!
   Peace to all your people through the earth be given!
      Mighty God and Father, thanks and praise we bring,
      singing Alleluia to our heavenly King.

2 Jesus Christ is risen, God the Father's Son!
   With the Holy Spirit, you are Lord alone!
      Lamb once killed for sinners, all our guilt to bear,
      show us now your mercy, now receive our prayer.

3 Christ the world's true Saviour, high and holy one,
   seated now and reigning from your Father's throne:
      Lord and God, we praise you! Highest heaven adores:
      in the Father's glory, all the praise be yours!

Christopher Idle (b. 1938)
based on 'Gloria in Excelsis'

694

Sicilian mariners   87 87

18th-century Italian or Sicilian melody
printed in W. D. Tattersall's
Improved Psalmody (1794)

1 Glory, honour, endless praises
      here we offer, King of kings.
   You are source of all our being,
      Lord of all created things.

2 Glory, honour, endless praises
      to the Lamb who has been slain:
   by your blood you ransomed sinners,
      set your people free again.

3 Called to serve from every nation,
      kings and priests, we praise you, Lord,
   and to Father and to Spirit
      lift our hearts with one accord.

Edwin Le Grice (1911–92)
based on the Canticle 'Glory and Honour and Power'
(Revelation 4: 4 & 5: 9, 10, 13b)

695

Heathlands   77 77 77   Henry Smart (1813–79)

1 God of mercy, God of grace,
  show the brightness of your face;
      shine upon us, Saviour, shine,
      fill your Church with light divine;
  and your saving health extend ⌣
  to the earth's remotest end.

2 Let the peoples praise you, Lord!
  Be by all that live adored;
      let the nations shout and sing ⌣
      glory to their Saviour King;
  at your feet their tribute pay
  and your holy will obey.

3 Let the peoples praise you, Lord!
  Earth shall then her fruits afford;
      God to us his blessing give,
      we to God devoted live:
  all below, and all above,
  one in joy and light and love.

Henry Francis Lyte (1793–1847) altd.
based on the Canticle 'Deus Misereatur' (Psalm 67)

696

Rustington   87 87 D

C. Hubert H. Parry (1848–1918)

1 God, we praise you! God, we bless you!
    God, we name you sovereign Lord!
Mighty King whom angels worship,
    Father, by your Church adored:
all creation shows your glory,
    heaven and earth draw near your throne,
singing, 'Holy, holy, holy,
    Lord of hosts, and God alone!'

2 True apostles, faithful prophets,
    saints who set their world ablaze,
martyrs, once unknown, unheeded,
    join one growing song of praise,
while your Church on earth confesses
    one majestic Trinity:
Father, Son and Holy Spirit,
    God, our hope eternally.

3 Jesus Christ, the King of glory,
    everlasting Son of God,
humble was your virgin mother,
    hard the lonely path you trod:
by your cross is sin defeated,
    hell confronted face to face,
heaven opened to believers,
    sinners justified by grace.

4 Christ, at God's right hand victorious,
    you will judge the world you made:
Lord, in mercy help your servants
    for whose freedom you have paid:
raise us up from dust to glory,
    guard us from all sin today;
King enthroned above all praises,
    save your people, God, we pray.

Christopher Idle (b. 1938)
based on the Canticle 'Te Deum'

697

Nassau (Würtemburg) (2)   77 77 6

Later form of a melody in *Hundert
geistlicher Arien* (Dresden, 1694)
adpt. by William Henry Monk (1823–89)

1 Great and wonderful your deeds,
  God, from whom all power proceeds:
    true and right are all your ways—
    who shall not give thanks and praise?
    To your name be glory!

2 King of nations, take your crown!
  Every race shall soon bow down:
    holy God and Lord alone,
    justice in your deeds is shown;
    all have seen your glory.

3 To the one almighty God,
  to the Lamb who shed his blood,
    to the Spirit now be given,
    by the hosts of earth and heaven,
    love and praise and glory!

Christopher Idle (b. 1938)
based on the Canticle 'Great and Wonderful'
(Revelation 15: 3–4)

916

698

Salvator mundi 76 76

Edward F. Darling (b. 1933)

Hear us as we pray to you, help and heal us, Jesus.

1 Jesus, Saviour of the world,
  come to us in mercy.

  Hear us as we pray to you,
  help and heal us, Jesus.

2 By your cross and life laid down
  you have freed your people.

3 In the greatness of your love
  heal us in our weakness.

4 Saviour and Deliverer,
  help us all to praise you.

5 Jesus, come and dwell with us;
  hear us now and always;

6 and when you in glory come,
  may we share your kingdom.

Edward F. Darling (b. 1933)
based on the Canticle 'Jesus, Saviour of the World'

699

Sebaste

John Stainer (1840–1901)

1. Hail, gladdening Light, of his pure glo - ry poured,

who is the immortal Fa - ther, heaven - ly, blessed,

Ho - li - est of Ho - lies, Je - su Christ our Lord.

2. Now we are come to the sun's hour of rest,

the lights of eve - ning round us shine:

we hymn the Fa - ther, Son, and Ho - ly Spi - rit di - vine.

3. Worthiest art thou at all times to be sung

with un-de-fi-led tongue, Son of our

God, giv-er of life, a - lone;

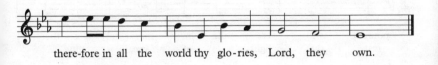

there-fore in all the world thy glo-ries, Lord, they own.

Φῶς ἱλαρὸν ἁγίας δόξης

1 Hail, gladdening Light, of his pure glory poured,
who is the immortal Father, heavenly, blessed,
Holiest of Holies, Jesu Christ our Lord.

2 Now we are come to the sun's hour of rest,
the lights of evening round us shine:
we hymn the Father, Son, and Holy Spirit divine.

3 Worthiest art thou at all times to be sung
with undefilèd tongue,
Son of our God, giver of life, alone;
therefore in all the world thy glories, Lord, they own.

Greek Canticle Phos Hilaron (3rd cent. or earlier)
tr. *John Keble* (1792–1866)

699

Hail, gladdening Light

SECOND TUNE

From a setting by Geoffrey Shaw (1879–1943)
adpt. David Drinkell (b. 1955)

1. Hail, gladd-ening Light, of his pure glo - ry poured, who is the im - mor - tal Fa - ther, heaven - ly, blessed, Ho - li - est of Ho - lies, Je - su Christ our Lord.

2. Now we are come to the sun's hour of rest, the lights of eve - ning round us shine: we hymn the Fa - ther, Son, and Ho - ly Spi - rit di - vine.

3. Worth - i - est art thou at all times to be sung with un - de - fi - led tongue,

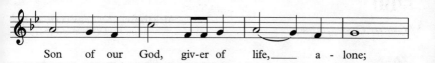

Son of our God, giv-er of life,___ a - lone;

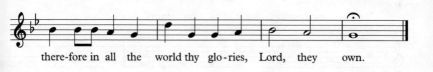

there-fore in all the world thy glo-ries, Lord, they own.

Φῶς ἱλαρὸν ἁγίας δόξης

1 Hail, gladdening Light, of his pure glory poured,
who is the immortal Father, heavenly, blessed,
Holiest of Holies, Jesu Christ our Lord.

2 Now we are come to the sun's hour of rest,
the lights of evening round us shine:
we hymn the Father, Son, and Holy Spirit divine.

3 Worthiest art thou at all times to be sung
with undefilèd tongue,
Son of our God, giver of life, alone;
therefore in all the world thy glories, Lord, they own.

Greek Canticle 'Phos hilaron' (3rd cent. or earlier)
tr. *John Keble* (1792–1866)

700

Grosser Gott   78 78 77

Melody from *Katholisches Gesangbuch*
(Vienna, *c.*1774) adpt.

1 Holy God, we praise thy name,
    Lord of all, we bow before thee;
  all on earth thy power proclaim,
    all in heaven above adore thee,
  boundless is thy vast domain,
  everlasting is thy reign.

2 Hear the loud celestial hymn
    angel choirs above are raising;
  cherubim and seraphim,
    in unceasing chorus praising,
  fill the heavens with sweet accord:
  Holy, holy, holy Lord.

3 Holy Father, Holy Son,
    Holy Spirit, three we name thee,
  while in essence only one,
    undivided God we claim thee,
  and adoring bend the knee,
  while we own the mystery.

4 Spare thy people, Lord, we pray,
    by a thousand snares surrounded;
  keep us free from sin today,
    never let us be confounded:
  all my trust I place in thee,
  never, Lord, abandon me.

Clarence Alphonsus Walworth (1820–1900)
adapted by *Anthony G. Petti* (1932–85)
based on the Canticle 'Te Deum'

701

Jubilate Deo

Fred Dunn (1907–79)

If desired, bars 9 & 10 may be repeated in place of bars 13 & 14.

Jubilate, ev'rybody,
serve the Lord in all your ways,
and come before his presence singing:
enter now his courts with praise.
For the Lord our God is gracious,
and his mercy everlasting.
Jubilate, jubilate, jubilate Deo![1]

Fred Dunn (1907–1979)
based on the Canticle 'Jubilate' (Psalm 100)

[1] Be joyful in God

702

Sunset   98 98

George Gilbert Stocks (1877–1960)

The tune is sung twice.
Alternative tune: 705 RENDEZ À DIEU

Φῶς ἱλαρὸν ἁγίας δόξης

Light of the world, in grace and beauty,
　　mirror of God's eternal face,
transparent flame of love's free duty,
　　you bring salvation to our race.
Now, as we see the lights of evening,
　　we raise our voice in hymns of praise;
worthy are you of endless blessing,
　　sun of our night, lamp of our days.

Greek Canticle 'Phos hilaron'
(3rd century or earlier)
tr. *Paul Gibson* (b. 1932)

703

Melody contributed by
William Croft (1678–1727)
to Playford's *The Divine Companion* (1709)

Croft's 136th   66 66 88

For the significance of the small notes above the stave, see the Musical Preface.
Alternative tune: 392, 540 CHRISTCHURCH

1 Now lives the Lamb of God,
   our Passover, the Christ,
who once with nails and wood
   for us was sacrificed:

*Come, keep the feast, the anthem sing
that Christ indeed is Lord and King!*

2 Now risen from the dead
   Christ never dies again;
in us, with Christ as head,
   sin nevermore shall reign:

3 In Adam all must die,
   forlorn and unforgiven;
in Christ all come alive,
   the second Man from heaven:

4 Give praise to God alone
   who life from death can bring;
whose mighty power can turn
   the winter into spring:

David Mowbray (b. 1939)
based on the Canticle Easter Anthems
1 Corinthians 5: 7–8; 15: 20–22;
Romans 6: 9–11

925

704

FIRST TUNE

Mary sang a song 99 99

Michael Perry (1942–96)

INTRODUCTION AND BRIDGE

1. Ma - ry sang a song, a song of love, mag - ni-fied the might - y Lord a - bove; me - lo-dies of praise his name ex-tol from the ve - ry depths of Ma - ry's soul:

SECOND TUNE

Mary's song 99 99

Donald Davison (b. 1937)

OPTIONAL BRIDGE BETWEEN VERSES

1 Mary sang a song, a song of love,
  magnified the mighty Lord above;
    melodies of praise his name extol
    from the very depths of Mary's soul:

2 'God the Lord has done great things for me,
  looked upon my life's humility;
    happy, they shall call me from this day,
    merciful is he whom we obey.

3 'To the humble soul our God is kind,
  to the proud he brings unease of mind.
    Who uplifts the poor, pulls down the strong?
    God alone has power to right the wrong.

4 'He, who has been Israel's strength and stay,
  fills the hungry, sends the rich away;
    he has shown his promise firm and sure,
    faithful to his people evermore.'

5 This was Mary's song as we recall,
  mother to the Saviour of us all:
    magnify his name and sing his praise;
    worship and adore him all your days.

Michael Perry (1942–96)
based on the Canticle 'Magnificat' (Luke 1: 46–55)

705

Rendez à Dieu   98 98 D

Melody from
La Forme des Prières (Strasbourg, 1545)
adpt. or composed by Louis Bourgeois (*c.*1510–61)
(second line as in Genevan Psalter of 1551)

THE CANTICLES

1 New songs of celebration render
   to him who has great wonders done.
Love sits enthroned in ageless splendour:
   come and adore the mighty one.
He has made known his great salvation
   which all his friends with joy confess:
he has revealed to every nation
   his everlasting righteousness.

2 Joyfully, heartily resounding,
   let every instrument and voice
peal out the praise of grace abounding,
   calling the whole world to rejoice.
Trumpets and organs, set in motion ‿
   such sounds as make the heavens ring;
all things that live in earth and ocean,
   make music for your mighty king.

3 Rivers and seas and torrents roaring,
   honour the Lord with wild acclaim;
mountains and stones look up adoring
   and find a voice to praise his name.
Righteous, commanding, ever glorious,
   praises be his that never cease:
just is our God, whose truth victorious
   establishes the world in peace.

Erik Routley (1917–1982)
based on the Canticle 'Cantate Domino' (Psalm 98)

706

Alternative tune: 125, 204 CRÜGER

1 O bless the God of Israel
    who comes to set us free;
who visits and redeems us,
    and grants us liberty.
The prophets spoke of mercy,
    of rescue and release;
God shall fulfil the promise
    to bring our people peace.

2 He comes! the Son of David,
    the one whom God has given;
he comes to live among us
    and raise us up to heaven:
before him goes the herald,
    forerunner in the way,
the prophet of salvation,
    the messenger of Day.

3 Where once were fear and darkness
    the sun begins to rise—
the dawning of forgiveness
    upon the sinner's eyes,
to guide the feet of pilgrims
    along the paths of peace.
O bless our God and Saviour,
    with songs that never cease!

Michael Perry (1942–96) altd.
based on the Canticle 'Song of Zechariah' (Benedictus)
(Luke 2: 68–79)

707

Nunc dimittis 667 667

Melody composed or adapted by
Louis Bourgeois (*c.*1510–61)
for *Nunc Dimittis* in *Genevan Psalter* (1549)

Φῶς ἱλαρὸν ἁγίας δόξης

1 O gladsome light, O grace
   of God the Father's face,
   the eternal splendour wearing;
   celestial, holy, blessed,
   our Saviour Jesus Christ,
   joyful in your appearing.

2 As day fades into night,
   we see the evening light,
   our hymn of praise outpouring:
   Father of might unknown,
   Christ, his incarnate Son,
   and Holy Spir't, adoring.

3 To you of right belongs
   all praise of holy songs,
   O Son of God, Lifegiver;
   you, therefore, O Most High,
   the world will glorify,
   and shall exalt for ever.

Greek Canticle 'Phos hilaron'
(3rd century or earlier)
tr. *Robert Bridges* (1844–1930) altd.

708

Laudate Dominum   10 10 11 11

From the anthem 'Hear my words, ye people'
by C. Hubert H. Parry (1848–1918)

Composed fot these words.

1 O praise ye the Lord! Praise him in the height;
rejoice in his word, ye angels of light;
ye heavens, adore him by whom ye were made,
and worship before him, in brightness arrayed.

2 O praise ye the Lord! Praise him upon earth,
in tuneful accord, ye sons of new birth;
praise him who hath brought you his grace from above,
praise him who hath taught you to sing of his love.

3 O praise ye the Lord, all things that give sound;
each jubilant chord, re-echo around;
loud organs, his glory forth tell in deep tone,
and sweet harp, the story of what he hath done.

4 O praise ye the Lord! thanksgiving and song
to him be outpoured all ages along:
for love in creation, for heaven restored,
for grace of salvation, O praise ye the Lord.

[Amen, Amen.]

Henry Williams Baker (1821–77)
based on Psalms 150; 148

709

Austria 87 87 D

Franz Joseph Haydn (1732–1809)

1 Praise the Lord! You heavens, adore him;
   praise him, angels, in the height;
sun and moon, rejoice before him,
   praise him, all you stars and light.
Praise the Lord, for he has spoken;
   worlds his mighty voice obeyed;
laws, which never shall be broken,
   for their guidance he has made.

2 Praise the Lord, for he is glorious;
   never shall his promise fail:
God has made his saints victorious;
   sin and death shall not prevail.
Praise the God of our salvation;
   hosts on high, his power proclaim;
heaven and earth and all creation,
   laud and magnify his name!

*3 Worship, honour, glory, blessing,
   Lord, we offer to your name;
young and old, your praise expressing,
   join their Saviour to proclaim.
As the saints in heaven adore you,
   we would bow before your throne;
as your angels serve before you,
   so on earth your will be done.

vv. 1 & 2 Foundling Hospital Collection (1796) altd.
v. 3 *Edward Osler* (1798–1863) altd.
based on the Canticle 'Laudate Dominum' (Psalm 148)

710

Ode to Joy   87 87 D

Ludwig van Beethoven (1770–1827)
from the 9th Symphony

1 Sing to God new songs of worship—
all his deeds are marvellous;
he has brought salvation to us
with his hand and holy arm:
he has shown to all the nations
righteousness and saving power;
he recalled his truth and mercy
to his people Israël.

2 Sing to God new songs of worship—
earth has seen his victory;
let the lands of earth be joyful,
praising him with thankfulness:
sound upon the harp his praises,
play to him with melody;
let the trumpets sound his triumph,
show your joy to God the king!

3 Sing to God new songs of worship—
let the sea now make a noise;
all on earth and in the waters
sound your praises to the Lord:
let the hills rejoice together,
let the rivers clap their hands,
for with righteousness and justice
he will come to judge the earth.

Michael Baughen (b. 1930)
based on the Canticle 'Cantate Domino' (Psalm 98)

711

Surrexit Christus

Jacques Berthier (1923–94)
for the Taizé Community

(hum)   Sur - re - xit Chris-tus, al - le - lu - ia!

(hum)   Can - ta - te Do - mi - no, al - le - lu - ia!

VERSES (Cantor)

1. All you hea-vens, bless the Lord.   Stars of the hea-vens,

bless the Lord.   2. Sun and moon, bless the Lord.

And you, night and day, bless the Lord.

3. Frost and cold, bless the Lord.   Ice and snow,

bless the Lord.   4. Fire and heat, bless the Lord.

* Choose either part.

The refrain is sung repeatedly by all, while a cantor sings the verses over the hummed phrases.
For other verses to this chant, see no. 282.

And you, light and dark-ness, bless the Lord.

5. Spi-rits and souls of the just, bless the Lord.

Saints and the hum-ble-heart-ed, bless the Lord.

Surrexit Christus, alleluia!
Cantate Domino, alleluia![1]

1 All you heavens, bless the Lord.
  Stars of the heavens, bless the Lord.

2 Sun and moon, bless the Lord.
  And you, night and day, bless the Lord.

3 Frost and cold, bless the Lord.
  Ice and snow, bless the Lord.

4 Fire and heat, bless the Lord.
  And you, light and darkness, bless the Lord.

5 Spirits and souls of the just, bless the Lord.
  Saints and the humble-hearted, bless the Lord.

Taizé Community
based on the Canticle 'Benedicite'
(Song of the Three: 35–65)

[1] Translation: Christ is risen, alleluia! Sing to the Lord, alleluia!

This version of the Benedicite is particularly suitable for use during the Easter season.

712

Woodlands   10 10 10 10   Walter Greatorex (1877–1949)

1 Tell out, my soul, the greatness of the Lord:
    unnumbered blessings, give my spirit voice;
  tender to me the promise of his word;
    in God my Saviour shall my heart rejoice.

2 Tell out, my soul, the greatness of his name:
    make known his might, the deeds his arm has done;
  his mercy sure, from age to age the same;
    his holy name, the Lord, the Mighty One.

3 Tell out, my soul, the greatness of his might:
    powers and dominions lay their glory by;
  proud hearts and stubborn wills are put to flight,
    the hungry fed, the humble lifted high.

4 Tell out, my soul, the glories of his word:
    firm is his promise, and his mercy sure.
  Tell out, my soul, the greatness of the Lord
    to children's children and for evermore.

Timothy Dudley-Smith (b. 1926)
based on the Canticle 'Magnificat' (Luke 1: 46–55)

713

Alleluia I

Plainsong, from Missa de Angelis

Al - le - lu - ia, al - le - lu - ia,___ al - le - lu - ia!

1st time: Cantor
2nd time: Full

Alleluia II

French Chant

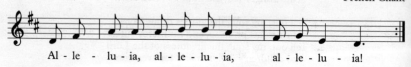

Al - le - lu - ia, al - le - lu - ia, al - le - lu - ia!

1st time: Cantor
2nd time: Full

Alleluia III

Fintan P. O'Carroll

Al - le - lu - ia, al - le - lu - ia!

Al - le - lu - ia, al - le - lu - ia!___

Alleluia IV

Donald Davison (b. 1937)

Al - le - lu - ia, al - le - lu - ia,

al - le - lu - ia, al - le - lu - ia!

Alleluia V

(Taizé Alleluia no. 7)

Jacques Berthier (1923–94)
for the Taizé Community

Al - le - lu - ia, al - le - lu - ia, al - le - lu -

- ia! Al - le - lu - ia, al - le - lu - ia, al - le - lu - ia!

Alleluia VI

South African Alleluia
transcribed from singing led by George Mxadana

Al - le - lu - ia, al - le - lu - ia! Al - le - lu -

- ia, al - le - lu - ia! Al - le - lu - ia, al -

- le - lu - ia! Al - le - lu - ia, al - le - lu - ia!

714

Sanctus

Franz Schubert (1797–1828)
from *Deutsche Messe* (1826)

Ho - ly, ho - ly, ho - ly Lord, God of power and might,____ ho - ly, ho - ly, ho - ly Lord, God of power and might,____ heav'n and earth are full,____ full____ of your glo - ry. Ho - san - na in the high - est! Ho - san - na in the high - est! *Bless - ed is he who comes____ in the name of the Lord.____

D.S. al Fine

English Language Liturgical Consultation
from the Liturgy of the Holy Communion

* The Benedictus qui venit (Blessed is he . . .) is optional.

715

Santo, Santo, Santo

Argentinian traditional melody

4. Blessed is he who comes, who comes in the name of the Lord!

Ho - san - na in ex - cel - sis, in ex - cel - sis!

1 Holy, holy, holy,
Lord God, the Lord almighty!
Angelic songs of praise we sing:
'You are holy, Lord!'

2 Holy, holy, holy,
we worship you, most mighty;
we join in never-ending praise:
'Holy is your name!'

3 Holy, holy, holy,
Lord God, the Lord almighty!
Hosannas ring in heaven and earth:
'You are holy, Lord!'

*4 Blessed is he who comes,
who comes in the name of the Lord!
Hosanna in excelsis,
in excelsis![1]

Edward F. Darling (b. 1933)
based on Ter Sanctus (verses 1–3)
& Benedictus qui venit (verse 4)

[1] Latin: Hosanna in the highest, in the highest.
('Hosanna' is a shout of adoration)

943

716

KYRIE ELEISON
(for use in Litanies and other prayers)

Jacques Berthier (1923–94)
for the Taizé Community

Kyrie 1

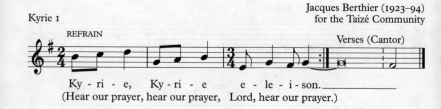

Ky - ri - e, Ky - ri - e e - le - i - son._____
(Hear our prayer, hear our prayer, Lord, hear our prayer.)

Kyrie 2 (Taizé no. 7)

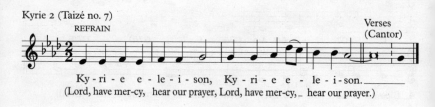

Ky - ri - e e - le - i - son, Ky - ri - e e - le - i - son._____
(Lord, have mer-cy, hear our prayer, Lord, have mer-cy,_ hear our prayer.)

Kyrie 3 (Taizé no. 3)

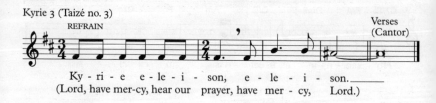

Ky - ri - e e - le - i - son, e - le - i - son._____
(Lord, have mer-cy, hear our prayer, have mer - cy, Lord.)

The refrain Kyrie eleison (*Lord, have mercy*) is sung by all, the final syllable changing to a hum after the double bar. Over this hummed chord (sustained by random breathing), the Cantor sings each petition (or other text) in free style, using a simple melodic formula to indicate when the change to the final chord is to occur (not required in Kyrie 3). Alternatively, the hummed chords may be omitted, in which case the English words may be sung if desired.

717

May the Lord bless you

Susie Hare

May the Lord bless you and keep you,
make his face to shine upon you
and be gracious unto you.
May the Lord lift up the light of his countenance upon you
and give you peace.

The Aaronic Blessing
(Numbers 6: 24–26) adpt.

718

Old 124th   10 10 10 10 10   Melody from *Genevan Psalter* (1551)

1 O praise the Lord, ye servants of the Lord,
    into his courts your joyful homage bring,
ye that within his holy temple stand,
     lift up your hands, lift up your voice and sing:
     so shall ye have the blessing from your King.

2 He that hath made all heav'n and all the worlds,
    shall from that Zion where his saints adore
look down with favour, sanctify his Church,
     bless them that tread his sanctuary floor,
     and keep them in his ways for evermore.

3 All glory now to God the Father's name;
    Son everlasting, glory unto thee;
and, Holy Spirit, glory thine the same;
     One God eternal, blessèd Trinity,
     as ever was, and evermore shall be.

From a 19th-century pamphlet
at St. Oswald's, Durham
based on Psalm 134
suitable at 'A Late Evening Office'

719

Praise the Lord, all you servants

Ian White

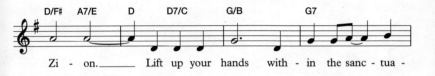

Zi - on.____ Lift up your hands with - in the sanc - tua -

\- ry,_____ and__ praise,_____ the

Lord.____ We praise you, Lord;____ we praise you, Lord.__

__ Al - le - lu - ia!____ We praise you, Lord.____

1 Praise the Lord, all you servants of the Lord,
who minister by night within his house.
Lift up your hands within the sanctuary,
and praise the Lord.

2 May the Lord, the maker of heaven and earth,
may this Lord bless you from Zion.
Lift up your hands within the sanctuary,
and praise the Lord.
We praise you, Lord; we praise you, Lord.
Alleluia! We praise you, Lord.

Psalm 134
Suitable at 'A Late Evening Office'

949

COPYRIGHT ACKNOWLEDGEMENTS

173 © Breitkopf & Härtel, Wiesbaden – Leipzig.

174 Melody: (i) Oxford University Press from the *English Hymnal*.

176 Words & Melody: © 1919 Stainer & Bell Ltd.

178 Words: © E. Cosnett.

180 Words: © The United Reformed Church.

181 Words & Melody: Copyright untraced.

184 Words: Translation Oxford University Press.

186 Words: © 1978 Stainer & Bell Ltd.

191 Melody: (i) © 1962 Josef Weinberger Ltd.

195 Copyright © 1987 Make Way Music.

200 Words: Oxford University Press from *English Praise*.

203 Words: © E. Cosnett.

204 Words: © 1980 Stainer & Bell Ltd.

205 Words: © 1977, 1995 Stainer & Bell Ltd. Text includes variants agreed with author; not to be further reproduced. Music: (i) © Hymns Ancient & Modern Ltd.

208 Words: Translation © Hymns Ancient & Modern Ltd.: Harmony Oxford University Press.

209 Words: © Kevin Mayhew Ltd. Melody: © Burns & Oates.

210 Words: © Kevin Mayhew Ltd.

213 Words: © Stainer & Bell Ltd.

215 Words: Oxford University Press from the *Yattendon Hymnal*.

216 Copyright ©1975 Celebration/Kingsway's Thankyou Music.

219 Copyright ©1983 Kingsway's Thankyou Music.

221 Words: © in this version Jubilate hymns.

223 Copyright © 1985 Mercy/Vineyard Publishing/CopyCare.

224 Copyright © 1995 Kingsway's Thankyou Music.

226 Melody: Oxford University Press from the *English Hymnal*.

228 Copyright © 1986 Kingsway's Thankyou Music.

230 Copyright © 1989 Make Way Music.

231 Melody: © The John Ireland Trust.

232 Melody: (i) Adaptation Oxford University Press.

233 Words: © Mowbray, an imprint of Continuum. Melody: (ii) Broomhill Church, Glasgow.

236 Copyright © 1941 The Rodeheaver Co/Word Music/CopyCare. music@copycare.com

239 Words: © 1971 Faber Music Ltd. From the *NewCatholic Hymnal*. Melody: Cambridge University Press.

243 Melody: (ii) Oxford University Press.

245 Words: © 1973 Stainer & Bell Ltd.

248 Melody: © Hymns Ancient & Modern Ltd.

252 Copyright © 1973 Word of God Music/CopyCare.

253 Words: © 1988 WGRG, Iona Community from *Enemy of apathy*.

256 Words: © Timothy Dudley-Smith. Melody: © J. Carter.

259 Words: © M Saward/Jubilate Hymns. Melody: © J Barnard/Jubilate Hymns.

260 Words: © 1969, 1995 Stainer & Bell Ltd.

264 Melody: © the Trustees of Downside Abbey.

265 Words: © National Society (Church of England) for Promoting Religious Education.

267 Words: © Kevin Mayhew Ltd.

273 Copyright ©1983 Kingsway's Thankyou Music.

274 Music: Oxford University Press from the *English Hymnal*.

276 Copyright: © 1981 Rocksmith Music/Leosong Copyright Service Ltd.

278 Words: Oxford University Press.

280 Melody: (ii) J. Kelly.

282 Copyright © Ateliers et Presses de Taizé.

284 Melody: © APCK.

287 Words: Oxford University Press from the *Oxford Book of Carols*. Melody: Oxford University Press from the *English Hymnal*.

289 Words: © Mowbray, an imprint of Continuum.

290 Words: © the Society of the Sacred Mission. Melody: Oxford University Press.

293 Melody: (ii) Oxford University Press.

294 Melody: Oxford University Press from the *English Hymnal*.

298 Words: © the Revd M J Hancock. Melody: (ii) Oxford University Press.

299 Words: © 1971 by Faber Music Ltd from the *New Catholic Hymnal*.

301 Words: © 1971 Stainer & Bell Ltd. Melody: © Royal School of Church Music.

303 Words: © Timothy Dudley-Smith.

304 Words: © 1987 by The Hymn Society/Hope Publishing Co./CopyCare.

305 Words: Copyright revived: owner untraced. Melody: Copyright: owner untraced.

308 Melody: © J Barnard/Jubilate Hymns.

309 Words: © Timothy Dudley-Smith. Melody: (i) Oxford University Press. (ii) Oxford University Press.

COPYRIGHT ACKNOWLEDGEMENTS

COPYRIGHT ACKNOWLEDGEMENTS

715 Words: Oxford University Press.
716 Melody: Ateliers et Presses de Taizé.
719 Copyright © 1985 Little Misty Music/
     Kingsway's Thankyou Music.

Addresses of main copyright holders

Cambridge University Press
The Edinburgh Building
Shaftesbury Road
Cambridge CB2 2RU

Hymns Ancient & Modern Ltd
SCM-Canterbury Press
St Mary's Works
St Mary's Plain
Norwich NR3 3BH

**The Continuum International Publishing
Group Ltd**
Wellington House
125 Strand
London WC2R OBB

CopyCare Limited
PO Box 77
Hailsham
East Sussex BN27 3EF

Bishop T Dudley-Smith
9 Ashlands
Ford
Salisbury
Wiltshire SP4 6DY

Faber Music
3 Queen Square
London WC1N 3AU

International Music Publications Limited
Griffin House
161 Hammersmith Road
London W6 8BS

Jubilate Hymns
4 Thorpe Park Road
Chelston
Torquay TQ2 6RX

Kingsway's Thankyou Music
Lottbridge Drove
Eastbourne
East Sussex BN23 6NT

Make Way Music
PO Box 263
Croydon CR9 5AP

Kevin Mayhew Limited
Buxhall
Stowmarket
Suffolk IP14 3BW

McCrimmon Publishing Co Ltd
10–12 High Street
Great Wakering
Essex SS3 OEQ

Music Sales
8/9 Frith Street
London
W1V 5TZ

OCP Publications & New Dawn Music
5536 N E Hassalo
Portland OR 97213
USA

Oxford University Press
Music Copyright
Great Clarendon Street
Oxford OX2 6DP

The Royal School of Church Music
Cleveland Lodge
Westhumble Street
Westhumble, Dorking
Surrey RH5 6BW

**Sovereign Music UK and Restoration
Music**
PO Box 356
Leighton Buzzard
Bedfordshire LU7 8WP

Stainer & Bell Ltd
PO Box 110, Victoria House
23 Gruneisen Road
London N3 1DZ

Ateliers et Presses de Taizé
F-71250 Taizé-Community
France

Josef Weinberger Ltd
12 Mortimer Street
London W1N 7RD

WGRG (Wild Goose Resource Group)
Iona Community
Pearce Institute
840 Govan Road
Glasgow G51 3UU

INDEX OF FIRST LINES AND
CORRESPONDING TUNES

INDEX OF FIRST LINES AND CORRESPONDING TUNES

INDEX OF FIRST LINES AND CORRESPONDING TUNES

INDEX OF FIRST LINES AND CORRESPONDING TUNES

INDEX OF FIRST LINES AND CORRESPONDING TUNES

INDEX OF FIRST LINES AND CORRESPONDING TUNES

INDEX OF FIRST LINES AND CORRESPONDING TUNES

INDEX OF FIRST LINES AND CORRESPONDING TUNES

INDEX OF FIRST LINES AND CORRESPONDING TUNES

INDEX OF FIRST LINES AND CORRESPONDING TUNES

INDEX OF FIRST LINES AND CORRESPONDING TUNES

INDEX OF FIRST LINES AND CORRESPONDING TUNES

INDEX OF FIRST LINES AND CORRESPONDING TUNES